Edward Samuel Hamilton
1102 La Rosa Terrace
Atlanta Ga
Jan 9/1927

STANDARD ARITHMETIC

EMBRACING A COMPLETE COURSE FOR SCHOOLS AND ACADEMIES

BY

WILLIAM J. MILNE, Ph.D., LL.D.

PRESIDENT OF NEW YORK STATE NORMAL COLLEGE, ALBANY N.Y.

———•○:◦:○•———

NEW YORK ·:· CINCINNATI ·:· CHICAGO

AMERICAN BOOK COMPANY

MILNE'S MATHEMATICS

MILNE'S ELEMENTS OF ARITHMETIC

MILNE'S STANDARD ARITHMETIC

MILNE'S MENTAL ARITHMETIC

MILNE'S ELEMENTS OF ALGEBRA

MILNE'S GRAMMAR SCHOOL ALGEBRA

MILNE'S HIGH SCHOOL ALGEBRA

MILNE'S PLANE AND SOLID GEOMETRY

MILNE'S PLANE GEOMETRY—SEPARATE

Stand. Ar.

E-P 93

PREFACE.

In the preparation of this work the author has aimed to secure two results; namely, skill in numerical computations, and a proper understanding of the reasons for the steps in the explanation of processes and the solution of problems. Skill in computing may be acquired without any intelligent apprehension of arithmetical science, and a profound insight into the truths and principles of arithmetic may be attained without much facility in using numbers. Very many people will prefer to have the student trained to be rapid and accurate in computations, and they will esteem a rapid accountant more competent in mathematics than the learned astronomers of our time; while others will prefer that training which cultivates the reasoning powers, even at the expense of practical expertness in the use of numbers. The author has endeavored to secure both these ends by embodying in the book a large number of examples upon which the pupil may be trained to accuracy and rapidity, while at the same time he has not failed to incorporate in it a large number of problems that are designed to train the analytical powers and to develop the reasoning faculties. In practical business life, the processes learned in schools are often of very little value, because they are not the natural processes of the business man. Students who learn to work examples in a mechanical way find themselves unable to solve with certainty very simple problems, after they have left school a few weeks, because they have been taught a school method rather than a natural method. The author has, therefore, adopted business methods of computation wherever they could be wisely substituted for the processes of the schools: he has preceded them with exercises which lead the student directly and easily to a clear apprehension of the steps in the solution and the necessity for them; and he has accompanied the solutions with explanations which enable the pupil to comprehend all that he needs to know about the operations. By these means the student is led to employ business methods of solution because they are generally natural methods, and to understand and explain every step in the process. A student who has been trained in this manner will never forget a process or a rule, because he can devise the process and frame the rule at will.

The work is of sufficiently comprehensive scope to meet the demands of even the most advanced schools. The unusually practical character of the problems will be discerned by a very cursory examination; oral and written exercises are given in connection with each subject, and frequent and thorough reviews serve to test the pupil's proficiency, to fix the principles of the science in his mind, and to train and develop his power of reasoning.

The method exemplified in presenting the various subjects is in accord with what is deemed best in modern methods of teaching; the order and arrangement of the subjects, though they are in some respects a departure from that usually given, will hasten the pupil's progress by removing to the latter part of the book subjects too difficult for the average pupil when he reaches them, and of little practical value to any student; the explanations are thought to be conspicuously lucid, the steps logical, the definitions, principles, and rules brief and accurate.

The author desires to express his indebtedness to many educators of prominence for valuable suggestions regarding the scope of the work and its educational character. The cordiality with which his former works have been received gives him the hope that this book also may meet with general favor.

WILLIAM J. MILNE.

CONTENTS.

CONTENTS.

8 CONTENTS.

STANDARD ARITHMETIC.

———∘∘✿∘∘———

NOTATION AND NUMERATION.

———∘✦∘———

1. A single thing is called a **Unit**.

2. A unit or a collection of units is a **Number**.

A number answers the question " how many ? "

A number may be expressed by *words* or other *characters,* viz. *figures* and *letters.*

3. The method of expressing numbers by figures or letters is called **Notation**.

The method of expressing numbers by *figures* is called the **Arabic Notation,** from the Arabs who first introduced it into Europe.

The method of expressing numbers by *letters* is called the **Roman Notation,** because it was used by the ancient Romans.

4. The method of reading numbers expressed by figures or letters is called **Numeration**.

THE ARABIC SYSTEM.

5. In counting a large number of objects, it is natural to arrange them in equal groups. When the number of the first groups becomes large they may be gathered into larger groups, and these again into larger groups, and so on. By general agreement the system of grouping *by tens*, called the *decimal* system, has been adopted.

9

6. The Arabic system of notation, which is a decimal system, employs ten figures to express numbers, viz.:

O 1 2 3 4 5 6 7 8 9
Naught One Two Three Four Five Six Seven Eight Nine

Naught is also called *zero* and *cipher.*

By combining these figures in accordance with certain principles, any number can be expressed.

7. PRINCIPLE. — *When figures are written side by side, the one at the right expresses units, the next tens, and the next hundreds.*

EXERCISES.

8. Tell what each figure in the following expresses:

43	37	57	186	453	304
36	86	48	371	416	215
81	29	73	218	830	507
32	51	63	134	591	290

9. Figures in *units'* place express *units of the first order;* those in *tens'* place, *units of the second order;* those in *hundreds'* place, *units of the third order;* etc.

10. The *units of the second order,* or *tens,* are named *ten, twenty, thirty, forty, fifty, sixty, seventy, eighty, ninety.*

The suffix *ty* means *ten.* Thus *forty* means *four tens.*

11. The numbers between 1 ten and 2 tens are named *eleven, twelve, thirteen, fourteen, fifteen, sixteen, seventeen, eighteen, nineteen.*

Thirteen means *three* and *ten; fourteen, four* and *ten,* etc.

12. The other numbers between 20 and 100 are read *without* the word *and* between the tens and the units.

Thus, 35 is read thirty-five, not thirty *and* five.

13. Read the following:

18	46	54	49	35	98	39
15	14	38	93	17	85	27
34	72	23	69	24	65	40
22	20	50	66	79	30	77
25	43	61	83	16	28	99
33	12	21	45	31	44	80

Express by figures the following:

Seventy-five.	Forty-five.	Eighty.
Eighty-six.	Fifty-eight.	Eighteen.
Thirty-nine.	Eighty-one.	Seventy-eight.
Ninety-eight.	Twenty-four.	Thirty-three.
Seventy-seven.	Fifty-nine.	Ninety-nine.
Twenty-one.	Ninety-one.	Sixty-four.

Three units of the second order, five of the first order.
Five units of the second order, seven of the first order.
Seven units of the first order, nine of the second order.
Write all numbers below twenty.
Write all numbers between twenty and forty.
Write all numbers between fifty and seventy.

14. In reading numbers expressed by three figures, the tens are read after the hundreds, and the units after the tens, without the word *and*.

Thus, 346 is read three hundred forty-six.

15. Read the following:

442	815	844	600	765
378	763	419	408	811
426	341	906	391	501

Read the following:

927	594	836	903	700
538	318	379	830	555
421	423	221	712	279
376	873	718	127	380
673	465	178	104	308
894	347	187	199	300

Express by figures the following:

Seven hundred forty-five. One hundred three.
Eight hundred eighty-four. Two hundred ninety-five.
Six hundred forty-eight. Seven hundred.
Nine hundred fifty-nine. Nine hundred ninety-nine.
Five hundred eighty-one. Four hundred five.
Six hundred four. Two hundred eighteen.
One hundred eighty-one. Six hundred nine.
Eight hundred fifty. Eight hundred eighty.
Two hundred fifteen. Nine hundred.

Three hundreds, six tens, eight units.

Eight hundreds, four units.

Seven hundreds, eight tens.

Five units of the third order, two of the second, three of the first.

Two units of the third order, two of the second, two of the first.

Four units of the third order, four of the second, four of the first.

16. From the previous examples the following general principle is deduced:

PRINCIPLE. — *The representative value of a figure is increased ten-fold by each removal one place to the left, and decreased ten-fold by each removal one place to the right.*

17. In writing and reading numbers, the figures are separated into groups of three figures each, called *periods*. These periods contain the hundreds, tens, and units of each denomination.

18. The following table illustrates the system of notation:

PERIODS.	6th.	5th.	4th.	3d.	2d.	1st.
NAMES OF PERIODS.	QUADRILLIONS.	TRILLIONS.	BILLIONS.	MILLIONS.	THOUSANDS.	UNITS.
ORDERS.	HUNDREDS TENS UNITS	HUNDREDS TENS UNITS	HUNDREDS TENS UNITS	HUNDREDS TENS UNITS	HUNDREDS TENS UNITS	HUNDREDS TENS UNITS
	25,	673,	210,	040,	385,	861

The number is read *twenty-five* quadrillion, *six hundred seventy-three* trillion, *two hundred ten* billion, *forty* million, *three hundred eighty-five* thousand, *eight hundred sixty-one.*

1. Each period, except the one at the left, must contain three figures.
2. The periods are separated from each other by commas.
3. In reading numbers the name of units' period is omitted.
4. The periods above quadrillions in their order are quintillions, sextillions, septillions, octillions, nonillions, decillions, etc.

RULE FOR NUMERATION. *Beginning at the right, separate the numbers into periods of three figures each.*

Beginning at the left, read each period as if it stood alone, adding its name.

EXERCISES.

19. Copy, point off into periods, and read:

1.	3825,	42865,	346812,	18573912.
2.	1713,	31793,	386045,	43056784.

3.	4651,	84275,	713204,	36700431.
4.	3042,	80163,	504216,	45320406.
5.	2104,	25068,	800437,	781003042.
6.	3640,	40016,	504036,	451320645.
7.	5812,	32004,	240040,	800400300.
8.	7346,	41500,	213045,	729009001.
9.	7604,	68314,	508023,	738040000.
10.	6150,	65036,	700016,	1245679316.
11.	2738,	42050,	910006,	4506780259.
12.	3807,	71685,	380460,	37009854629.
13.	3943,	91804,	402040,	870053126945.
14.	5008,	87005,	180247,	650030012503.
15.	6900,	34506,	707365,	19876005012036.
16.	7165,	71346,	205006,	47020100316042.

EXERCISES.

20. Write in figures:

1. Twenty-nine billion, ninety-five thousand, forty-five.

EXPLANATION. — We first write the numbers of the highest denomination, following them with a comma. After that we write the numbers of the next lower denomination, or millions, but since there are none, we fill the period with ciphers, and write a comma after them. This is followed by 095 in the next lower period, and 045 in the last, the figure 0 being placed *before* the significant figures to make the periods complete.

29,000,095,045.

RULE FOR NOTATION. — *Begin at the left and write the hundreds, tens, and units of each period in their proper order, putting ciphers in all vacant places and periods.*

While writing, separate each period by a comma from the one that follows it.

Write in figures :

2. Twenty-five thousand, eight hundred fourteen.

3. Thirty-nine thousand, seven hundred twenty-four.

4. Ninety-four thousand, six hundred fifty-five.

5. Twenty-nine thousand, five hundred eighty-five. Eight thousand, six hundred five.

6. Forty-six thousand, eight hundred twenty. Forty thousand, eight hundred nineteen.

7. Eighty-four thousand, nine hundred four. Fifteen thousand, nine. Eight thousand, four hundred.

8. Nineteen thousand, nine hundred nine. Four thousand, eight. Eighteen thousand, seven hundred.

9. Twenty-four thousand, two hundred eight. Twenty thousand. Thirty thousand, seven hundred.

10. Fifteen thousand, four hundred seven. Four thousand, seven. Twenty thousand, two hundred.

11. Thirty-seven thousand, nine hundred. Thirty thousand, thirty. One hundred thousand, eight hundred five.

12. Fifty-five thousand, five hundred five. Five thousand, five. Thirty thousand, nine hundred nine.

13. Forty-eight thousand, fifty-five. Forty thousand, eight. Seventeen thousand, seven hundred three.

14. Sixty-six thousand, eighty. Fifty-five thousand, nine. Fifty thousand, three hundred eighty-five.

15. Eighty-five thousand, eight hundred eight. Eighty-eight thousand. Eight thousand, eight hundred eight.

16. Thirty thousand, three hundred thirty-five. Twenty thousand, nine. Ninety thousand, two hundred eight.

17. Two hundred eighteen thousand, five hundred sixty-seven. Eighty thousand, seven hundred twenty.

18. Four hundred thirty-three thousand, six hundred fifty-five. Fifty-five thousand, eight hundred nine.

19. Five hundred forty-three thousand, eight hundred seventy-six. Three hundred ten thousand.

20. Nine hundred ninety thousand, two hundred nine.

21. Five hundred fifty thousand, eight hundred four.

22. Six hundred sixty thousand, two hundred fifteen.

23. Seven hundred thousand, eighty. Two hundred thousand, five. Six hundred forty thousand.

24. Eight hundred twenty-five thousand, seven hundred eight. Fifty thousand, five hundred five.

25. Two hundred forty thousand, six hundred eighty-five.

26. Nine hundred ninety-seven thousand, four hundred.

27. Six hundred thousand, eight hundred eighty-nine.

28. Nine hundred thousand, nine hundred. Seven hundred thousand. Ninety-five thousand, five.

29. Four hundred sixteen thousand, two hundred twenty.

30. Three hundred eighty thousand, five hundred fifty.

31. Four hundred fifty thousand, three hundred eighty.

32. Three hundred eighty-six thousand, forty-seven.

33. One hundred twenty-eight million, three hundred twenty-eight thousand, six hundred fifty-seven.

34. Five hundred twenty-seven million, six hundred eighteen thousand, two hundred sixty-four.

35. Two hundred forty-three million, four hundred sixty-seven thousand, eight hundred sixty-nine.

36. Forty-five million, two hundred thirty-four thousand, six hundred ninety-four.

37. Two hundred eighteen million, eighty-four thousand, eight hundred fifteen.

38. 39 million, 46 thousand, 90; 24 million, 180 thousand, 340; 49 million, 18 thousand, 20.

39. 212 million, 206 thousand, 8; 91 million, 87 thousand, 65; 37 million, 8 thousand, 206.

40. 526 million, 300 thousand, 80; 418 million, 40 thousand, 210; 408 million, 48 thousand, 48.

41. 312 million, 115 thousand, 116; 40 million, 80 thousand, 80; 250 million, 105 thousand, 37.

42. 206 million, 6 thousand, 6; 505 million, 40 thousand, 40; 315 million, 75 thousand, 75.

43. 400 million, 40 thousand, 40; 60 million, 60 thousand, 60; 360 million, 265.

44. 50 million; 200 million, 200; 300 million, 3.

45. 215 billion, 618 million, 415 thousand, 816.

46. 236 billion, 212 million, 836 thousand, 309.

47. 454 billion, 369 million, 800 thousand, 80.

48. 500 billion, 41 million, 41 thousand, 45.

49. 613 billion, 40 million, 40 thousand, 40.

50. Forty billion, eighty million, nine thousand, eighty.

51. Twenty billion, two hundred million, ten thousand, ten.

52. One hundred billion, one million, one thousand, one.

53. Four trillion, three hundred six billion, four hundred eight million, two hundred twenty thousand, forty.

54. Twenty-eight trillion, two hundred billion, forty-six million, eight hundred forty thousand, two hundred fifty.

55. Seventy-five trillion, two hundred billion, two hundred million, two hundred thousand, two hundred.

56. Eight hundred trillion, eight billion, eight million, eight hundred thousand, eighty.

NOTATION AND NUMERATION OF UNITED STATES MONEY.

21. The currency of the United States has a decimal system of notation, dollars being written as whole numbers and cents as decimal parts of a dollar.

22. The **dollar sign** is $. It is written before the number.

Thus, $25 is read twenty-five dollars.

23. In notation of United States currency a period, called the *decimal point*, is placed before the cents.

The dollars are written at the left of the decimal point. The *first two places* at the right of the decimal point express *cents*, and the *third*, tenths of a cent or *mills*.

Thus, $10.485 is read ten dollars, forty-eight cents, five mills.

24. When the number of cents is *less* than *ten*, a cipher must be written in the first place at the right of the decimal point.

Thus, Five dollars five cents is written $5.05.

EXERCISES.

25. Read the following:

1. $52.28,	$212.84,	$200.855,	$7004.275.
2. $13.71,	$358.16,	$196.327,	$3648.032.
3. $16.04,	$427.24,	$518.043,	$36845.92.
4. $15.90,	$600.85,	$508.405,	$29043.06.
5. $43.09,	$693.05,	$700.049,	$3104.066.
6. $37.86,	$410.30,	$326.416,	$21040.30.

26. Write the following:

1. Fifteen dollars, twelve cents. Eighteen dollars, eight cents. Twenty-four dollars, eight cents.

2. Thirty-four dollars, thirty cents. Fifty-five dollars, twenty cents. Nineteen dollars, thirty-eight cents.

3. Forty dollars, four cents. Ninety-nine dollars, nine cents. Sixty-four dollars, eleven cents.

4. Four hundred dollars, eight cents. Seven hundred dollars. Seventeen dollars, eight cents, eight mills.

5. Two hundred thirty-eight dollars, twenty cents, five mills. Ninety-three dollars, forty cents, eight mills.

6. Three hundred ninety-one dollars, forty-eight cents, three mills. Sixty-seven dollars, sixty-seven cents, three mills.

7. Four thousand three hundred twenty dollars, eight cents. Fifty-nine dollars, twenty cents, seven mills.

8. One thousand two hundred forty-nine dollars, nine cents, five mills. Forty-seven dollars, ninety cents, five mills.

9. Eighty-four thousand three hundred dollars, nine cents. Thirty dollars, nine cents, nine mills.

10. Fifty-five thousand eight hundred sixteen dollars, five cents. One thousand dollars, ten cents, five mills.

THE ROMAN SYSTEM.

27. This system uses seven capital letters to express numbers, viz.:

Letters,	I,	V,	X,	L,	C,	D,	M.
Values,	1,	5,	10,	50,	100,	500,	1000.

23. The following principles are followed in combining the letters :

PRINCIPLES. — 1. *Repeating a letter repeats its value.*

Thus, I represents one ; II, two ; III, three ; X, ten ; XX, twenty.

2. *When a letter is placed before another of greater value, its value is to be taken from that of the greater.*

Thus, IV represents four ; IX, nine ; XIX, nineteen ; XL, forty.

3. *When a letter is placed after another of greater value, their values are to be united.*

Thus, VII represents seven ; XV, fifteen ; LXXX, eighty.

4. *A bar placed over a letter increases its value a thousand-fold.*

Thus, $\overline{V}$ represents five thousand ; $\overline{L}$, fifty thousand ; $\overline{M}$, one million.

The following table illustrates the method of combination.

I . . 1	X . . 10	XXIV . . 24	C . . 100
II . . 2	XI . . 11	XXIX . . 29	CC . . 200
III . . 3	XIV . . 14	XXX . . 30	CCCC . . 400
IV . . 4	XV . . 15	XL . . 40	CD . . 400
V . . 5	XVI . . 16	L . . 50	D . . 500
VI . . 6	XIX . . 19	LX . . 60	DCCC . . 800
VII . . 7	XX . . 20	LXX . . 70	M . . 1000
IX . . 9	XXI . . 21	XC . . 90	MMM . . 3000

EXERCISES.

29. Read the following numbers :

XVII; XXV; LXXX; XIX; XXIX; XLV; CXV; XCV; LXXIX; CXIX; XCIX; XLIV; CCCIV; CCXLIV; CCCCXC; DCCLXXXIX; $\overline{X}$DCCCLXXII.

Express the following numbers by the Roman notation :
13, 24, 71, 68, 132, 514, 244, 555, 617, 1040, 7216, 2899.

ADDITION.

30. 1. How many apples are 3 apples and 2 apples?

2. How many books are 3 books and 4 books?

3. How many leaves are 2 leaves and 3 leaves?

4. How many oranges are 4 oranges and 2 oranges?

5. What have you been doing with the numbers given above?

6. Why can you not tell how many 5 cents and 4 rabbits are?

7. What kind of numbers only can be united?

31. The process of finding a number which is equal to two or more given numbers is called **Addition**.

32. The result obtained by adding is called the **Sum**, or **Amount**.

33. The numbers added are called **Addends**.

34. The **Sign of Addition** is an upright cross $+$. It is called plus, and is placed between the numbers to be added.

Thus, $3 + 7$ is read 3 plus 7, and it means that 3 and 7 are to be added.

35. The **Sign of Equality** is two equal short horizontal lines: $=$. It is read *equals* or *is equal to*.

Thus, $3 + 7 = 10$ is read 3 plus 7 equals 10.

36. Any expression of equality is called an **Equation.**

Thus, $3 + 7 = 10$ and $5 + 4 = 9$ are equations.

37. Numbers that have the same unit are called **Like Numbers.**

Thus, $7 and $5 are like numbers; so also are 15 pounds and 8 pounds.

38. PRINCIPLES. — 1. *Only like numbers can be added.*

2. *The sum and the addends must be like numbers.*

DRILL EXERCISES.

39. The student should practice adding the following numbers daily until he can tell the sums at a glance.

The list contains all the combinations of two numbers from 1 to 9.

3	4	2	6	8	2	6	2	5
7	5	6	3	1	9	1	2	7
—	—	—	—	—	—	—	—	—

6	2	3	3	1	4	7	8	6
4	7	3	8	2	9	1	5	7
—	—	—	—	—	—	—	—	—

3	1	2	7	6	9	8	6	7
5	1	8	4	6	5	8	5	7
—	—	—	—	—	—	—	—	—

6	5	4	3	2	4	3	4	1
8	5	8	1	5	4	2	3	4
—	—	—	—	—	—	—	—	—

5	8	4	9	3	7	9	9	7
1	9	2	1	9	8	9	6	9
—	—	—	—	—	—	—	—	—

ORAL EXERCISES.

40. **1.** Harry paid 5 cents for a pencil and 10 cents for a writing book. How much did he pay for both? $5 + 10 = ?$

2. Mary learned 8 new words on Monday and 9 on Tuesday. How many did she learn on both days? $8 + 9 = ?$

3. James earned \$3 in May, \$4 in June, and \$6 in July. How much did he earn in the three months? $3 + 4 + 6 = ?$

4. I gave 5 apples to my sister, 6 to my brother, and then had 7 for myself. How many had I at first? $5 + 6 + 7 = ?$

5. A teacher gave for a lesson on Monday 6 problems, on Tuesday 7, and on Wednesday 8. How many did she give in the three days? $6 + 7 + 8 = ?$

6. Mary put into her bank 5 cents at one time, 8 cents at another, and 10 at another. How much did she put in altogether?

7. A lad saw three flocks of wild geese. In the first there were 9, in the second 7, and in the third 10. How many were there in all?

8. Sarah's locket cost \$8, the chain \$6, and her ring \$10. How much did they all cost? $8 + 6 + 10 = ?$

9. A gentleman owned 9 gray horses, 7 black ones, and 10 bay ones. How many horses did he own? $9 + 7 + 10 = ?$

10. A bookseller one day sold 8 first readers, 4 second readers, and 5 third readers. How many readers did he sell?

11. A boy rode 5 miles and back on his bicycle, and then walked 3 miles. How far did he travel? $5 + 5 + 3 = ?$

12. A farmer planted three fields with corn, the first

containing 9 acres, the second 5 acres, and the third 7 acres.
How many acres of corn did he plant? $9 + 5 + 7 = ?$

13. Samuel caught 8 rats with one trap, 5 with another,
and 6 with another.   How many rats did he catch?
$8 + 5 + 6 = ?$

41. Count or add by 2's from 0 to 30, thus: 0, 2, 4, 6, etc.

Add by 2's from 1 to 31, thus; 1, 3, 5, 7, etc.
Add by 3's from 0 to   36.   From 1 to 43.
Add by 3's from 2 to   47.   From 3 to 45.
Add by 4's from 0 to   48.   From 1 to 61.
Add by 4's from 2 to   50.   From 3 to 63.
Add by 5's from 0 to   60.   From 1 to 61.
Add by 5's from 2 to   52.   From 3 to 63.
Add by 5's from 4 to   54.   From 7 to 82.
Add by 6's from 0 to   60.   From 1 to 55.
Add by 6's from 2 to   56.   From 3 to 63.
Add by 6's from 4 to   58.   From 5 to 59.
Add by 7's from 0 to   70.   From 1 to 78.
Add by 7's from 2 to   79.   From 3 to 87.
Add by 7's from 4 to   88.   From 5 to 96.
Add by 7's from 6 to   97.   From 9 to 100.
Add by 8's from 0 to   80.   From 1 to 81.
Add by 8's from 2 to   90.   From 3 to 91.
Add by 8's from 4 to   92.   From 5 to 101.
Add by 8's from 6 to 102.   From 7 to 103.
Add by 9's from 0 to   90.   From 1 to 100.
Add by 9's from 2 to 101.   From 3 to 111.
Add by 9's from 4 to 103.   From 5 to 113.
Add by 9's from 6 to 114.   From 7 to 106.
Add by 9's from 8 to 116.   From 9 to 126.
Add 6 to 35, 45, 55, 65, 75, 85, 95.
Add 7 to 38, 48, 58, 68, 78, 88, 98.

Add 8 to 36, 46, 56, 66, 76, 86, 96.
Add 5 to 33, 43, 53, 63, 73, 83, 93.
Add 9 to 39, 49, 59, 69, 79, 89, 99.
Add 4 to 37, 47, 57, 67, 77, 87, 97.

WRITTEN EXERCISES.

42. Copy and add from the bottom upwards, and then from the top downwards, each of the following:

In adding, name results only. Thus in example 1 add as follows: 2, 6, 15, 22, 25 instead of 2 and 4 are 6, 6 and 9 are 15, etc.

1.	2.	3.	4.	5.	6.	7.	8.	9.	10.	11.	12.
3	5	4	6	8	6	5	6	4	6	5	7
7	6	5	2	2	6	8	8	3	4	8	9
9	2	3	7	9	3	4	3	3	8	7	3
4	7	8	5	5	8	7	9	8	2	6	1
2	9	1	3	7	6	2	4	7	5	4	5

13.	14.	15.	16.	17.	18.	19.	20.	21.	22.	23.	24.
5	6	3	5	8	5	8	8	3	5	4	8
6	8	9	4	3	7	3	8	9	4	3	8
8	4	7	6	9	6	2	7	2	3	8	9
7	9	6	8	2	9	9	7	1	7	5	9
9	3	8	7	1	8	5	6	8	6	7	4
2	5	4	3	9	4	1	6	2	8	9	4
3	8	9	4	5	7	6	6	9	5	6	3

25.	26.	27.	28.	29.	30.	31.	32.	33.	34.	35.	36.
7	4	3	4	9	1	5	9	8	5	4	4
4	5	2	3	2	2	5	8	1	6	4	9
9	3	3	4	3	3	5	4	4	8	5	1
3	4	5	3	7	4	6	5	6	4	3	8
8	6	4	7	1	5	6	3	5	3	8	2
6	8	7	6	5	6	6	1	7	9	7	9
5	3	6	1	4	7	7	2	3	6	6	3

ADDITION.

Find the sum of the following:

	(a)	(b)	(c)	(d)	(e)	(f)	(g)	(h)	(i)	(j)	(k)	(l)
37.	7,	8,	3,	6,	4,	5,	1,	2,	9,	8,	4,	6.
38.	6,	5,	4,	6,	3,	8,	7,	5,	4,	7,	3,	5.
39.	3,	9,	6,	5,	4,	1,	9,	3,	2,	3,	5,	4.
40.	8,	1,	6,	3,	4,	3,	6,	7,	8,	2,	8,	8.
41.	5,	4,	9,	3,	8,	9,	6,	1,	7,	1,	7,	4.
42.	8,	3,	1,	9,	4,	2,	2,	6,	4,	4,	1,	3.
43.	4,	1,	3,	2,	6,	8,	8,	3,	5,	6,	6,	7.
44.	2,	7,	9,	1,	8,	5,	7,	3,	6,	3,	4,	9.
45.	9,	1,	6,	8,	4,	9,	3,	2,	1,	8,	3,	6.
46.	8,	3,	4,	2,	6,	8,	5,	6,	9,	7,	7,	4.
47.	1,	3,	8,	4,	3,	2,	5,	4,	8,	2,	8,	7.
48.	5,	9,	8,	4,	2,	7,	6,	8,	3,	6,	2,	5.
49.	3,	7,	8,	4,	5,	3,	6,	9,	5,	5,	7,	4.
50.	9,	5,	9,	8,	7,	6,	5,	4,	2,	5,	3,	2.

	(m)	(n)	(o)	(p)	(q)	(r)	(s)	(t)	(u)	(v)	(w)	(x)
51.	3,	5,	4,	3,	3,	8,	4,	6,	5,	7,	3,	5.
52.	4,	2,	2,	9,	6,	5,	2,	9,	7,	8,	5,	8.
53.	2,	9,	5,	5,	4,	3,	8,	4,	2,	9,	6,	3.
54.	8,	8,	8,	7,	5,	7,	2,	6,	3,	9,	1,	7.
55.	7,	3,	2,	5,	1,	8,	9,	2,	4,	5,	7,	6.
56.	6,	4,	6,	8,	2,	8,	3,	6,	5,	7,	6,	9.
57.	9,	5,	3,	1,	5,	2,	4,	5,	8,	2,	7,	5.
58.	5,	3,	9,	7,	7,	8,	3,	4,	2,	6,	5,	8.
59.	2,	8,	4,	4,	1,	8,	5,	4,	3,	1,	4,	4.
60.	3,	1,	8,	2,	7,	9,	2,	6,	5,	4,	2,	2.
61.	1,	7,	2,	3,	5,	4,	3,	9,	8,	7,	8,	3.
62.	8,	9,	9,	8,	2,	6,	3,	1,	8,	4,	7,	9.
63.	7,	2,	3,	4,	5,	2,	6,	8,	5,	4,	1,	1.
64.	6,	5,	5,	2,	5,	4,	3,	9,	2,	7,	6,	5.

Add the columns as follows:

65. (*a*).	71. (*g*).	77. (*m*).	83. (*s*).
66. (*b*).	72. (*h*).	78. (*n*).	84. (*t*).
67. (*c*).	73. (*i*).	79. (*o*).	85. (*u*).
68. (*d*).	74. (*j*).	80. (*p*).	86. (*v*).
69. (*e*).	75. (*k*).	81. (*q*).	87. (*w*).
70. (*f*).	76. (*l*).	82. (*r*).	88. (*x*).

ORAL EXERCISES.

43. 1. A certain school had 30 boys and 40 girls in attendance. How many pupils were there in the school?

2. A boy paid 25 cents for a reading book and 55 cents for an arithmetic. How much did he pay for both?

3. January has 31 days and February usually 28. How many days are there from January 1 to March 1?

SUGGESTION. — Add by uniting the *tens* and *units* separately. Thus, $31 + 20 = 51$; $51 + 8 = 59$. Or $30 + 20 = 50$, $8 + 1 = 9$, and $50 + 9 = 59$.

4. A boy who is now 12 years of age is 35 years younger than his father. How old is his father?

5. A railway train ran 35 miles the first hour and 33 miles the second hour. How far did it run in the two hours?

6. I bought a pound of tea for 45 cents and some raisins for 32 cents. How much did I pay for both?

7. A farmer sold three loads of potatoes, the first containing 25 bushels, the second 25 bushels, and the third 20 bushels. How many bushels did he sell? $25 + 25 + 20 = ?$

8. A lady paid $25 for a cloak, $15 for a dress, and $20 for blankets. How much did she pay for all?

9. I traveled 35 miles by railroad, 25 miles on a steamboat, and 15 miles by stage. How many miles did I travel?

SUGGESTION. — Add thus: $35 + 20 = 55$; $55 + 5 = 60$; $60 + 15 = 75$.

10. Henry owned 22 Leghorn chickens, 30 Plymouth Rocks, and 12 bantams. How many chickens did he own?

11. A cotton merchant bought 30 bales on Monday, 25 on Tuesday, and 33 on Wednesday. How many did he buy in all?

12. A lad sold 30 morning papers, 40 evening papers, and 21 illustrated papers. How many papers did he sell?

13. The distance from Brent to Afton is 15 miles; from Afton to Sandley, 30 miles; from Sandley to Darmel, 40 miles. How far is it from Brent to Darmel?

14. In an intermediate school I counted 25 pupils who read in the third reader, 35 who read in the fourth reader, and 36 who read in the fifth reader. If these were all the pupils, how many were there in the school?

15. Three girls made paper dolls for a fair; the first made 15, the second made 22, the third made 20. How many did they all make?

16. When I arose the temperature was 47 degrees; an hour later it was 13 degrees higher; and at noon it was 17 degrees higher still. What was the temperature at noon?

17. A grocer had three barrels of molasses, the first containing 51 gallons, the second 44, and the third 50. How many gallons did they all contain?

18. A merchant sold three webs of cloth, the first containing 37 yards, the second 43 yards, and the third 30 yards. How many yards did he sell?

19. A student misspelled 45 words the first term of the year, 30 the second term, and 25 the third. How many were misspelled by him during the year?

20. The Empire State express train ran 52 miles in one hour, 61 miles the next hour, and 53 miles the next hour. How far did it travel in the three hours?

WRITTEN EXERCISES.

44. 1. What is the sum of $394, $476, and $549?

EXPLANATION. — For convenience in adding, the numbers are arranged so that units of the same order stand in the same vertical column.

$394
476
549
———
$1419

Each column is then added separately, beginning with the right hand column, or units. Thus, $9 + 6 + 4 = 19$, the sum of the units. 19 units are equal to 1 ten and 9 units. The 9 is therefore written under the units' column, and the 1 is reserved to add with the tens.

1 reserved $+ 4 + 7 + 9 = 21$, the sum of the tens. 21 tens are equal to 2 hundreds and 1 ten. The 1 is therefore written under the tens' column, and the 2 is reserved to add with the hundreds.

2 reserved $+ 5 + 4 + 3 = 14$, the number of hundreds. 14 hundreds are equal to 1 thousand and 4 hundreds, and are written in thousands' and hundreds' places in the sum.

Hence the sum is $1419.

1. In adding, only the results should be named. Thus, instead of saying 9 and 6 are 15 and 4 are 19, add in the following manner: 9, 15, 19.

2. When the sum of any column is 10, 20, or some exact number of tens, a cipher is written under the column added, and the 1, 2, or 3, etc., is reserved to add with the next column.

RULE. — *Arrange the numbers so that the units of the same order stand in the same column.*

Beginning at the right, add each column separately and write the sum, if it is less than ten, under the column added.

If the sum of any column is ten or more, write the unit figure only under that column, and add the tens with the next column.

Write the entire sum of the last column.

PROOF. — *Add each column in the reverse order. **If the results agree, the work is probably correct.***

Copy, add, and prove:

2.	3.	4.	5.	6.	7.
416	328	265	796	834	$ 4.37
325	419	783	843	912	9.28
843	327	248	685	897	7.36
794	818	415	792	685	8.94

8.	9.	10.	11.	12.	13.
487	384	$ 3.85	$ 4.37	$ 2.38	6.66
95	296	4.16	2.16	4.51	5.84
385	818	5.86	5.05	2.18	.73
486	47	.79	7.26	3.09	.81
793	93	3.24	.83	.92	.92
43	786	5.87	.87	.85	1.69
861	695	4.83	.91	4.65	9.99
459	888	5.12	4.55	5.93	4.00

14.	15.	16.	17.	18.
3297	8568	3972	4184	$ 24.36
2935	3864	4136	3879	12.48
4683	3979	5864	4987	63.23
5987	6846	4839	5998	47.84
3869	5976	8645	7986	84.38
6984	7143	9256	8438	34.24

19.	20.	21.	22.	23.
4837	4896	6868	$ 38.16	$ 58.79
5192	1543	4739	24.34	21.83
7185	9834	8314	73.58	56.91
3925	8567	7934	48.15	63.82
3987	8919	9256	41.93	84.68
7981	9124	8567	98.34	91.94
8426	9395	8394	90.09	87.58
5155	8304	8040	39.90	16.85

24.	25.	26.	27.	28.
3857	4168	$ 53.87	$ 32.54	$ 15.92
5879	3925	4.83	16.87	4.86
389	4095	15.00	8.34	.76
1089	5683	3.64	.58	43.41
83	7925	.98	13.24	6.88
1396	84	42.79	24.48	15.62
3859	8	.09	72.16	9.24
518	385	4.79	8.43	.89

29.	30.	31.	32.	33.
$ 3.965	$ 23.14	$ 9.875	$ 11.18	$ 45.83
4.18	51.07	3.186	24.16	2.155
5.465	18.05	7.24	5.865	.875
9.235	31.94	8.39	3.19	4.18
8.015	41.06	9.157	24.54	24.35
7.07	38.94	8.386	9.573	21.375
6.155	48.358	4.58	18.46	18.469

34. Add 3985, 4168, 3975, 4189, 2853, 9168.

35. Add 3854, 2198, 3864, 593, 786, 4153, 841.

36. Add 5841, 2976, 9183, 24, 863, 719, 818.

37. Add 3985, 268, 39403, 218, 36, 3965, 824.

38. Add 453, 2795, 68, 3920, 7, 8596, 873, 91.

39. Add 2168, 421, 3973, 263, 114, 3846, 200, 392.

40. Add 385, 2964, 372, 916, 84, 849, 9327, 56, 294.

41. Add 936, 1728, 494, 1672, 18, 5148, 614, 792, 371.

42. Add 7342, 8165, 294, 38, 297, 1986, 24, 386, 48, 24.

43. Add 3759, 2836, 384, 2795, 73, 295, 3865, 362, 51.

44. Add 415, 38, 2068, 504, 37, 3958, 26, 394, 283, 64.

45. Add 5168, 3796, 584, 317, 29, 38, 47, 6847, 365, 84.

46. Add 342, 81, 8, 9164, 395, 19, 8, 4865, 96, 26, 813.
47. Add 49, 3812, 468, 9834, 275, 86, 391, 19, 35, 696.
48. Add 581, 27, 3986, 423, 4917, 2846, 9, 18, 48, 297.
49. Add 5396, 84, 4193, 875, 431, 97, 86, 8436, 938, 19.
50. Add 35, 2965, 47, 3894, 483, 769, 85, 94, 46, 324, 8.

Copy, add, and prove:

51.	52.	53.	54.
298576	2795843	38467589	241693798
382453	3865487	21438758	473185429
321294	4975836	47368975	391583768
514685	9843725	86123874	427936857
687349	7659814	98375692	819348673
593426	8537685	85399137	473925165
583724	9132586	92468546	274639827
417938	8149375	76856789	315987352
526867	4396854	39845926	675431298
493256	9198374	94398765	897316984
684325	8168937	85673423	931258469
796853	9857694	41798659	687316984
467397	8123586	98376954	931258469
685486	3712584	39257697	716874912
567834	4865392	82512763	843978517

55. Add 236 thousand, 8 hundred 85; 118 thousand, 9 hundred 27; 46 thousand, 8 hundred 95; 246 thousand, 7 hundred 17.

56. Add 8 million, 324 thousand, 7 hundred 96; 15 million, 289 thousand, 4 hundred 85; 91 million, 825 thousand, 4 hundred 12; 15 million, 116 thousand, 8 hundred 96.

57. Add 28 million, 16 thousand, 875; 46 million, 324 thousand, 536; 39 million, 413 thousand, 39; 24 million, 8 thousand, 18; 8 million, 8 thousand, 8.

58. Add 5 million, 816 thousand, 4; 291 million, 215 thousand, 86; 87 million, 16 thousand, 214; 93 million, 18 thousand, 57; 246 million, 9 thousand, 456.

59. Find the sum of three million, eight hundred twenty-four thousand, five hundred twenty-six; forty million, nineteen thousand, eight hundred twenty-five; eighty-six million, two hundred fifty-four thousand, two hundred; five million, five thousand, five.

60. What is the sum of eighteen million, eighteen thousand, eighteen; thirty-five million, fifty-eight thousand, two hundred seventy-eight; fifty-four million, seven hundred forty-seven thousand, five hundred eighty-six?

61. What is the sum of six hundred seven thousand, two hundred eight; eight hundred twenty-eight thousand, nine hundred; five hundred thousand, fifteen?

62. Find the sum of twenty-eight million, one hundred fifteen thousand, two hundred; thirteen million, two hundred twenty-eight thousand, four; nine million, eight thousand, eight; ninety-nine thousand, nine hundred nine.

63. Add twenty-five million, twenty-five thousand, twenty-five; forty million, four hundred thousand, four hundred; eighty million, eighty thousand, eighty; eight hundred thousand.

64. A rolling mill in Buffalo turned out on Monday 1760 steel rails; on Tuesday, 1775; on Wednesday, 1809; on Thursday, 1826; and on Friday, 1919. What was the total number made in the five days?

65. A fruit-dealer in Pensacola shipped for New York in one week 2464 boxes of oranges, 1632 boxes of pine-apples, 1918 boxes of lemons, and 850 boxes of cocoanuts. What was the entire number of boxes of fruit shipped?

66. In the month of October there were shipped from New Orleans for Philadelphia during the first week 14,573 bales of cotton; the second week, 17,849; the third week, 19,387; and during the last week of the month 23,879 bales. What was the total number of bales sent to Philadelphia during the month?

67. Lake Superior covers a surface of 32,290 square miles; Lake Michigan, 23,903 square miles; Lake Huron, 23,684; Lake Erie, 9493; Lake Ontario, 7654. What is the entire area covered by these lakes?

68. A man owns five horses. The first is worth $250, the second $425, the third $475, the fourth as much as the second and third, and the fifth as much as the first and fourth. What is the value of the five horses?

69. An orchard contains 278 apple trees, and an equal number of pear trees; 354 peach trees, and an equal number of plum trees; and 117 cherry trees. How many trees are there in the orchard?

70. On June 1, a lumber firm in Portland shipped for Boston 73,452 shingles; on June 2, 56,280; on June 3, 4700; on June 4, 87,950; on June 5, 4000 shingles and 38,400 laths; and on the 6th of June, 68,000 laths. How many of each were shipped in the six days?

71. Mr. George Peabody gave to the poor of London $2,250,000; to the town of Danvers, $60,000; to the Grinnell Arctic Expedition, $10,000; to the city of Baltimore, $1,000,000; to Phillips Academy, $25,000; to the Massachusetts Historical Society, $20,000; to Harvard University, $150,000; to Yale University, $150,000; to the Southwest, $1,500,000. How much did he give away?

72. A drover bought horses for $3750, and cows for $2875. On his horses he gained $976, and on his cows

$ 673. What would he have received for both if he had gained $ 500 more than he did ?

73. The Missouri River, to its junction with the Mississippi, is 2908 miles long; the Mississippi proper is 2616 miles long; the St. Lawrence is 2120 miles long; the Amazon 3596 miles long. What is the combined length of these rivers ?

74. New York is 1405 miles east of Omaha, and San Francisco is 1864 miles west of Omaha. How far is it from New York to San Francisco ?

75. A gentleman willed his property to his wife, three sons, and four daughters; to each of his daughters he willed $ 3869; to his sons each $ 4781; and to his wife $ 12,000. How much was his property ?

76. From the nail works at Pittsburg there were shipped 7650 kegs of nails on Monday, 8640 kegs on Tuesday, 300 kegs more on Wednesday than on Tuesday, 9850 kegs on Thursday, and 10,000 kegs on each of the remaining two days of the week. How many kegs were shipped during the week ?

77. A train left Rutland with seven cars loaded with marble, as follows : The first car had on it 36,725 pounds; the second, 36,850; the third, 37,200; the fourth, 37,650; the fifth, 37,150; the sixth, 38,090; and the seventh, 27,360 pounds. How many pounds of marble were there on the train ?

78. If a button manufactory at Lowell made in one day 17,200 buttons, in another 18,560, in another 18,569, in another 16,502, and in another 18,250, how many buttons were made in those five days ?

79. The area of Maine in square miles is 33,040; of New Hampshire, 9305; of Vermont, 9565; of Massachusetts, 8315; of Rhode Island, 1250; of Connecticut, 4990. What is the area of New England in square miles?

80. Mr. A deposited in the First National Bank of Albany, N.Y., on June 5, 1892, $469.50; on June 10, $764.35; on June 12, $320; on June 16, $125.75; on June 18, $673.85. He also deposited in the National Park Bank of New York City, on June 22, 1892, $3450.27; and on June 24, $1250. How much did he deposit in each of the banks? How much in both banks?

81. A glass factory in Newark made in one day 1760 tumblers, 860 goblets, 2125 ounce bottles, 1240 two-ounce bottles, 375 fruit jars, 3600 glass tubes, and 1200 other articles for laboratory purposes. How many articles were made in all?

82. A grain dealer in Chicago shipped 3750 bushels of wheat and 4560 bushels of corn to Baltimore one week; the next week 4675 bushels of wheat and 5000 bushels of corn; and the week following 6000 bushels of wheat and 7180 bushels of corn. How many bushels of each kind did he ship? How many bushels of grain?

83. If it takes 16,718 bricks to build a dwelling house, 39,900 for a school building, and 50,000 for a church, how many bricks will be required for the three buildings?

84. A business firm sold in the month of December $6575 worth of goods; a second firm sold $7480 worth; a third, $7850; a fourth, $8175; a fifth, $8262; and a sixth firm sold $9150 worth. What was the value of the goods sold?

85. If in Hartford there were made during the first week in September 3980 clocks, the second week 3986, the third week 4015, and the fourth week 4220, how many clocks were made there during those four weeks?

86. Virginia contains 42,450 square miles; Tennessee, 42,050 square miles; North Carolina, 10,200 square miles more than Tennessee; and Louisiana 6270 square miles more than Virginia; Maryland contains 12,210 square miles. How many square miles do all these states contain?

87. In a certain town there were manufactured in one week 5860 yards of broadcloth, 7970 yards of black cheviot, 9370 yards of muslin, 6250 yards of calico, 3600 yards of gingham, and 12,000 yards of various other woolen and cotton goods. How many yards were manufactured in the entire week?

88. A cork factory made 16,150 corks on Monday, 17,050 on Tuesday, 17,364 on Wednesday, 17,500 on Thursday, 18,008 on Friday, and 18,169 on Saturday. The week following 4000 more corks were made than during the preceding week. How many corks were made in the two weeks?

89. On October 23 a vessel arrived at Cincinnati from Mobile having on board 90 bales of cotton, weighing 27,600 pounds, in one part of the ship, and 17,900 pounds of cotton in another part; also 156 hogsheads of cane sugar, 5060 gallons of cane molasses, and 1260 gallons of sorghum molasses. On the same day a vessel arrived from New Orleans, with 45,760 pounds of cotton, 3600 gallons of cane molasses, 630 gallons of sorghum molasses, and 175 hogsheads of cane sugar. How many pounds of cotton, how many gallons of molasses, and how many hogsheads of sugar were there on both vessels?

SUBTRACTION.

45. **1.** How many books are left when 3 books are taken from 6 books?

2. How many horses are left when 3 horses are taken from 4 horses?

3. Henry drew 5 pictures, all but 2 of which were pictures of birds. How many pictures of birds did he make?

4. What is the difference between 4 cents and 2 cents?

5. What is the difference between 5 and 3? Between 4 and 2?

6. What have you been doing with the numbers given above?

7. Take 3 from 4, and what number remains? Add this remainder to the smaller number, and tell how the sum compares with the larger number.

8. Take 3 from 5, and what number remains? Add this remainder to the smaller number, and tell how the sum compares with the larger number?

9. When one number is subtracted from another, how does the sum of the remainder and the smaller compare with the larger?

10. Why can we not express the difference between 6 apples and 5 cents?

46. The process of finding what is left when a part of a number is taken away from it, or of finding the difference between two numbers is called **Subtraction.**

47. The number from which another is to be subtracted is called the **Minuend.**

48. The number to be subtracted is called the **Subtrahend.**

49. The result obtained by subtracting is called the **Remainder** or **Difference.**

50. The **Sign of Subtraction** is a short horizontal line —. It is called *minus.* When it is placed between two numbers, it shows that the one after it is to be subtracted from the one before it.

Thus, $9 - 5$ is read 9 *minus* 5, and means that 5 is to be subtracted from 9.

51. PRINCIPLES : — 1. *Only like numbers can be subtracted.*

2. *The sum of the subtrahend and the remainder is equal to the minuend.*

DRILL EXERCISES.

52. Students should practice these exercises daily until they can tell the results instantly.

1. $9 + ? = 15$	$15 - 9 = ?$	$8 + ? = 13$	$13 - 8 = ?$	
2. $7 + ? = 17$	$17 - 7 = ?$	$6 + ? = 15$	$15 - 6 = ?$	
3. $8 + ? = 19$	$19 - 8 = ?$	$5 + ? = 14$	$14 - 5 = ?$	
4. $4 + ? = 13$	$13 - 4 = ?$	$9 + ? = 17$	$17 - 9 = ?$	
5. $7 + ? = 15$	$15 - 7 = ?$	$8 + ? = 18$	$18 - 8 = ?$	
6. $13 - 3$	$10 - 4$	$9 - 6$	$8 - 4$	$11 - 3$
7. $9 - 9$	$12 - 3$	$11 - 2$	$8 - 6$	$7 - 4$
8. $11 - 6$	$12 - 9$	$10 - 3$	$10 - 2$	$12 - 2$

9.	$10-7$	$9-8$	$11-9$	$9-7$	$8-2$
10.	$9-3$	$8-7$	$9-2$	$7-6$	$10-9$
11.	$7-2$	$6-5$	$7-3$	$6-4$	$5-2$
12.	$6-3$	$8-3$	$7-5$	$5-3$	$8-5$
13.	$6-2$	$3-2$	$4-3$	$4-2$	$5-4$
14.	$17-4$	$18-6$	$18-5$	$15-8$	$14-4$
15.	$17-6$	$16-8$	$12-6$	$13-9$	$18-9$
16.	$11-5$	$16-4$	$19-9$	$13-6$	$12-7$
17.	$13-5$	$17-8$	$12-8$	$10-5$	$9-5$
18.	$10-8$	$16-6$	$12-5$	$14-6$	$12-4$
19.	$18-7$	$11-7$	$14-2$	$18-8$	$13-7$
20.	$17-5$	$14-9$	$11-8$	$15-4$	$19-7$
21.	$14-8$	$9-4$	$11-4$	$14-3$	$15-2$
22.	$15-5$	$16-7$	$16-9$	$15-3$	$13-2$
23.	$10-6$	$16-5$	$14-7$	$19-6$	$16-3$

24. Subtract by 2's from 24 to 0; thus, 24, 22, 20, 18, etc.

25. Subtract by 3's from 36 to 0. From 34 to 1.

26. Subtract by 4's from 40 to 0. From 43 to 3.

27. Subtract by 5's from 55 to 0. From 57 to 2.

ORAL EXERCISES.

53. 1. If I have 12 cents, and spend 5 cents for a pencil, how many cents will I have left? $12-5=$?

2. A man earns $15 per week, but spends $10. How much has he left at the end of the week? $15-10=$?

3. Our lesson contained 11 problems, of which I solved all but 3. How many did I solve? $11-3=$?

4. A hen hatched 13 chicks, but 5 of them died. How many lived? $13-5=$? $13-3=$? $13-4=$?

5. Henry found that his toy bank contained 14 cents, but 8 cents of the money belonged to his brother. How much belonged to Henry?

6. William and James together caught 15 fish. If William caught 7 of them, how many did James catch? $15 - 7 = ?$

7. Mary is 13 years old, and her brother is 8. How much older is Mary than her brother? $13 - 8 = ?$

8. Homer was away from home 2 weeks. He spent 5 days with his uncle, and the rest of the time with his grandfather. How many days was he with his grandfather?

9. I bought an orange for 3 cents, a banana for 2 cents, and candy for 5 cents. How much did I have left after paying for all, if I had 15 cents to begin with?

10. A boy earned during vacation $15. He spent $2 for books, $3 for clothing, and $5 for other things. How much had he left? $15 - 2 - 3 - 5 = ?$

11. By an accident a boy had 2 fingers cut from his right hand, and 3 from his left hand. How many fingers has he left? $10 - 3 - 2 = ?$

12. A gentleman who had 7 horses bought 6, and afterward sold at one time 4, and at another 3. How many had he left?

13. If a man earns $19 per week and spends $10, how much does he save?

14. James received 18 marbles at Christmas, of which 8 were glass and the rest clay. How many were clay?

15. How much will I have left if I have 15 cents and spend 8 cents?

16. A girl had to knit 15 rows to finish her work. After she had knit 6 rows how many had she still to do?

17. A park had 19 elm trees in it, of which 9 were small and the rest large. How many were large?

18. Alice has 18 pins, and Ella has 7. How many more than Ella has Alice?

19. A man earned $ 17 and spent $ 8. How many dollars had he left?

20. Harry had 14 cents given him by two boys. One gave him 6 cents. How much did the other give?

21. John earned $ 7, and his father gave him enough to make his money $ 16. How much did his father give him?

22. A newsboy bought papers for 9 cents, and sold them for 17 cents. How much did he gain?

23. If I have 13 cents and spend 6 cents for a ball and 3 cents for a pencil, how much will I have left?

24. There were 15 birds on a tree, and 4 of them flew away. How many remained on the tree?

25. James had 14 apples and ate 5 of them. How many had he left?

26. Charles is 17 years old, and his brother is 6 years younger. How old is his brother?

27. Joseph had 8 cents, and his father gave him 5 cents. He afterwards spent 7 cents. How much money had he left?

28. Ada picked 13 quarts of cherries, and Emma 7 quarts. How many more quarts must Emma pick so that the amount she picked will equal what Ada picked?

29. A man had 16 horses and sold 9 of them. How many horses did he keep?

30. From a pile of wood containing 17 cords, a farmer sold at one time 5 cords, and at another time 6 cords. How many cords remained unsold?

31. A watch cost $15, and was sold for $6 less than cost. For how much was it sold?

32. From a bin containing 19 bushels of wheat, 5 bushels were taken for seed and 7 bushels were sold. How many bushels remained in the bin?

33. A farmer having 9 cows, bought at one time 3, and at another time 5, and afterwards sold 10. How many cows had he then?

WRITTEN EXERCISES.

54. 1. From 796 subtract 343.

Minuend,   **796**   EXPLANATION. — For convenience the less num-
Subtrahend, **343**   ber is written under the greater, units under units,
                   tens under tens, etc.
Remainder, **453**   Each order of units of the subtrahend is then
                   subtracted separately from the same order in the
minuend, and the remainders are written beneath.

PROOF. — 453, the remainder, plus 343, the subtrahend, equals 796, the minuend. Hence the result is correct (Prin. 2).

Copy, subtract, and prove:

2.	3.	4.	5.	6.
734	685	767	584	295
412	541	634	420	173

7.	8.	9.	10.	11.
7596	8493	5694	6897	6843
3152	6271	4253	5385	4122

12.	13.	14.	15.	16.
$38.76	$67.58	$93.85	$65.86	$79.39
15.24	33.24	61.50	34.43	47.18

17.	18.	19.	20.	21.
$85.39	$76.83	$69.84	$63.73	$91.87
54.08	66.02	55.41	31.61	50.43

22.	23.	24.	25.	26.
95684	86431	81396	79265	51869
71271	73210	40285	41132	20714

27.	28.	29.	30.	31.
98316	83468	68793	88416	48319
71004	41215	54251	42304	24207

32. A house was bought for $1639, and sold for $1859. What was the gain?

33. A man bought a farm for $8768, and sold it for $6424. What was the loss?

34. Mr. A traveled 2168 miles, and Mr. B traveled 1145 miles. How much farther did Mr. A travel than Mr. B?

35. A drover having 1836 sheep sold 1220 of them. How many had he left?

36. I bought a house for $3425, and sold it for $4538. How much did I gain?

37. A farmer who raised 2560 bushels of corn sold all but 350 bushels. How much did he sell?

38. Two men together own 5656 acres of land. If the one owns 2535 acres, how many acres does the other own?

39. A man bought a horse, a buggy, and a harness for $278.75. The buggy and harness cost him $136.50. What did he pay for the horse?

40. A man's income for one year was $2568.48, and his expenses were $1445.23. How much did he save?

41. A builder contracted to build a house for $2885. The expenses for material and labor were $2552. How much were the profits?

42. A grain dealer bought in one week 38,547 bushels of wheat, and sold 25,336 bushels. How much more did he buy than he sold?

ORAL EXERCISES.

55. **1.** A jeweler bought a watch for $18, and sold it for $25. How much did he gain?

2. A man proposed to walk 30 miles, but after he had walked 19 miles he stopped. How many more miles must he travel to complete the distance?

3. A lady made purchases to the amount of $17, which she paid for with a twenty-dollar bill. How much change did she receive?

4. A grocer purchased tea for $32, and sold it for $40. How much was his gain?

5. Two trains left New Orleans at the same time, one running 31 miles per hour and the other 24 miles per hour. What was the difference in the rate of speed?

6. The Empire State express train runs about 53 miles per hour, and other fast express trains about 40 miles per hour. How much faster does the Empire State train run?

7. A boy earned 50 cents per day, but was obliged to pay 15 cents for a lunch and 10 cents for car fare. How much did he save daily?

8. The receipts of an entertainment were $35, and the expenses $26. What were the profits?

9. A lady purchased a table for $7 and a chair for $13. How much change should she receive if she gave the merchant a fifty-dollar bill?

10. A three-story house was 42 feet high. The first story was 15 feet, and the second 14 feet. How high was the third story?

11. A boy read 47 books during the year, of which 20 were books of travel, 12 histories, and the rest stories. How many stories did he read?

12. $9 + 7 - 3 + 2 - 5 + 4 - 5 + 7 - 4 - 2 - 5 = ?$

13. $8 + 3 + 2 - 5 + 2 - 4 + 7 - 3 + 5 - 6 + 2 = ?$

14. $8 + 2 - 5 + 9 - 3 + 4 - 5 + 7 + 3 - 5 - 4 = ?$

15. $5 + 6 + 2 - 5 + 4 - 6 + 9 - 3 - 2 + 4 - 2 = ?$

16. $3 + 9 - 3 + 4 - 2 - 4 + 8 + 2 - 6 + 3 - 5 = ?$

17. $4 + 6 - 5 + 8 - 3 + 7 - 6 - 2 + 9 + 1 - 4 = ?$

18. $7 - 3 + 7 + 3 + 5 - 6 + 9 - 3 + 5 - 6 - 4 = ?$

19. $6 + 5 - 4 + 4 - 2 + 5 - 7 + 4 + 2 - 5 - 2 = ?$

20. $8 - 2 + 9 - 7 + 6 + 3 - 5 + 2 - 7 + 5 + 6 = ?$

21. $5 + 4 - 3 + 7 - 2 - 5 + 6 + 8 - 3 - 5 + 4 = ?$

22. Subtract by 6's from 66 to 0.   From 61 to 1.

23. Subtract by 7's from 63 to 0.   From 65 to 2.

24. Subtract by 8's from 56 to 0.   From 74 to 2.

25. Subtract by 9's from 72 to 0.   From 75 to 3.

26. Subtract by 10's from 95 to 5.   From 87 to 7.

27. Subtract by 20's from 106 to 6.   From 145 to 5.

28. Subtract 6 from 34, 44, 54, 64, 74, 84.

29. Subtract 7 from 32, 42, 52, 62, 72, 82.

30. Subtract 8 from 35, 45, 55, 65, 75, 85.

WRITTEN EXERCISES.

56. **1**. From 925 subtract 476.

EXPLANATION. — The subtrahend is written under the minuend, and we begin at the right to subtract.

925
476
———
449

Since 6 units cannot be subtracted from 5 units, one of the tens, which is equal to 10 units, is united with the 5 units, making 15 units. 6 units from 15 units leave 9 units, which are written under the units.

Since *one* of the tens was united with the units, there is but 1 ten left. Because 7 tens cannot be subtracted from 1 ten, 1 hundred, which is equal to 10 tens, is united with the 1 ten, making 11 tens. 7 tens from 11 tens leave 4 tens, which are written under the tens.

Since *one* of the hundreds was written with the tens, there are but 8 hundreds left. 4 hundreds from 8 hundreds leave 4 hundreds, which are written under the hundreds. Hence the remainder is 449.

PROOF. — 449, the remainder, plus 476, the subtrahend, equals 925, the minuend. Hence the result is correct (Prin. 2).

RULE. — *Write the subtrahend under the minuend, units under units, tens under tens, etc.*

Begin at the right and subtract each figure of the subtrahend from the corresponding figure of the minuend, writing the result beneath.

If a figure in the minuend has a less value than the corresponding figure in the subtrahend, increase the former by ten, and subtract; then diminish by one the units of the next higher order in the minuend, and subtract as before.

PROOF. — *Add together the remainder and subtrahend. If the result is equal to the minuend, the work is correct.*

Subtract and prove :

2. $913 - 426.$	**5.** $913 - 746.$	**8.** $592 - 176.$
3. $835 - 341.$	**6.** $583 - 279.$	**9.** $735 - 444.$
4. $736 - 453.$	**7.** $468 - 349.$	**10.** $596 - 288.$

11. 732 — 456.	18. 782 — 458.	25. 931 — 588.
12. 594 — 427.	19. 854 — 527.	26. 714 — 329.
13. 635 — 387.	20. 834 — 456.	27. 531 — 423.
14. 925 — 443.	21. 318 — 129.	28. 685 — 395.
15. 876 — 687.	22. 893 — 467.	29. 419 — 199.
16. 319 — 127.	23. 752 — 556.	30. 327 — 159.
17. 486 — 349.	24. 816 — 724.	31. 743 — 358.

32. 39456 — 31567.	41. 49836 — 31849.
33. 48317 — 27592.	42. 84391 — 43875.
34. 87593 — 52869.	43. 73186 — 38592.
35. 81364 — 68537.	44. 49315 — 18674.
36. 73586 — 49288.	45. 37926 — 18395.
37. 39271 — 14683.	46. 72853 — 41687.
38. 98375 — 45792.	47. 91835 — 84635.
39. 83125 — 72165.	48. 42931 — 28724.
40. 63259 — 42199.	49. 52361 — 23854.

50. $ 615.29 — $ 492.36.	58. $ 392.18 — $ 237.43.
51. $ 732.84 — $ 537.39.	59. $ 576.88 — $ 499.90.
52. $ 459.97 — $ 263.18.	60. $ 813.95 — $ 358.16.
53. $ 159.13 — $ 137.29.	61. $ 927.86 — $ 423.58.
54. $ 843.25 — $ 391.65.	62. $ 593.70 — $ 345.96.
55. $ 917.36 — $ 427.58.	63. $ 315.91 — $ 256.19.
56. $ 593.18 — $ 505.09.	64. $ 296.30 — $ 235.84.
57. $ 691.23 — $ 319.47.	65. $ 483.35 — $ 219.35.

66. From 9000 subtract 7685.

8 9 9 10
9000
7685
——
1315

EXPLANATION. — Since 5 units cannot be subtracted from 0 units, and since there are no tens nor hundreds, 1 thousand must be changed into hundreds, leaving 8 thousand; 1 of the hundreds must be changed into tens, leaving 9 hundreds and 1 of the tens into units, leaving 9 tens. The expression 8 thousands, 9 hundreds, 9 tens, and 10 units is thus equivalent to the minuend, from which the units of the subtrahend can be readily subtracted.

Subtract and prove:

67. 50000 — 38517.	**80.** $ 39600.85 — $ 1915.68.
68. 60000 — 29365.	**81.** $ 58400.00 — $ 29318.54.
69. 55000 — 51093.	**82.** $ 38600.05 — $ 3743.08.
70. 39000 — 28739.	**83.** $ 50000.00 — $ 1830.05.
71. 80000 — 65004.	**84.** $ 39000.65 — $ 937.97.
72. 30040 — 18391.	**85.** $ 30040.08 — $ 19275.09.
73. 70101 — 43217.	**86.** $ 70410.00 — $ 45200.18.
74. 99003 — 45009.	**87.** $ 60060.60 — $ 39123.54.
75. 834760 — 83290.	**88.** 9138700 — 23047.
76. 410506 — 23837.	**89.** 8004040 — 183079.
77. 175004 — 23516.	**90.** 6700880 — 58369.
78. 393400 — 16042.	**91.** 5970008 — 4999.
79. 913043 — 4009.	**92.** 3002250 — 210590.

93. A borrowed of B $ 6450, and paid back $ 3740. How much does he still owe?

94. A merchant bought a quantity of goods for $ 15,125, and sold them for $ 17,015. What was the gain?

95. The sum of two numbers is 9416, and the greater is 6809. What is the less number?

96. The year 1891 was 399 years after the discovery of America by Columbus. In what year did that event take place?

97. B bought some goods which he sold for $ 11,325, and thereby gained $ 2150. How much did they cost him?

98. I bought a horse for $325 and a cow for $150. I sold the horse for $410, and the cow for $216. How much did I gain by the sale?

99. A merchant deposited in a bank on Monday $584; on Tuesday, $759; and on Wednesday, $327. During this time he drew out $987. How much did his deposits exceed what he drew out?

100. A man bought 16,750 bricks, and then sold B and C each 4926. How many had he left?

101. In an army of 7569 men, 388 were killed, 432 were wounded, and 273 deserted. How many remained for duty?

102. A man bought a farm for $7850. He expended $2169 for improvements, paid $97 for taxes, and then sold it for $10,650. Did he gain or lose, and how much?

103. A man left $3450 to his son, $2765 to his daughter, and the remainder to his wife. How much did his wife receive if the fortune was $20,000?

104. If the distance of the moon from the earth is 240,000 miles, and that of the sun 95,000,000, how much farther is it to the sun than to the moon?

105. On Monday morning a bank had on hand $2862. During the day $1831 were deposited, and $2172 drawn out; on Tuesday, $3126 were deposited, and $1954 drawn out. How many dollars were on hand Wednesday morning?

106. B had $12,000; but after paying his debts and giving away $3105, he had remaining only $7000. What was the amount of his debts?

107. A had $425, B had $160 more than A, and C had as much as A and B together. How much had C?

108. A merchant bought 500 yards of silk for $375, 3500 yards of muslin for $175, and 600 yards of linen for $235; he sold the whole for $1000. How much did he gain?

109. An estate of $12,350 was divided among a widow and two children. The widow's share was $6175, the son's, $2390 less than the widow's, and the rest fell to the daughter. What was the daughter's share?

110. A drover bought 300 horses for $32,150, and 150 cows for $4265, and sold them all for $37,000. What was the gain?

111. Mr. E bought two farms. For one he paid $4560, and for the other $6000. He spent on each $537 for improvements, and paid taxes which amounted to $78. He sold both farms for $12,450. Did he gain or lose on the sale, and how much?

112. If a ship was bought for $43,650, and sold for $45,000, what was the gain?

113. A gentleman gave $13,465 for a house and some land. The house alone was worth $8978. What was the value of the land?

114. If two candidates for office received in the aggregate 93,565 votes, and the successful one had 47,659 votes, how many did the other have?

115. A lumberman, having 632,000 feet of boards, sold 328,582 feet of them. How many feet remained unsold?

116. A man is worth $16,425, of which $3750 is invested in bank stock, $2746 in mortgages, and the rest in land. How much has he invested in land?

MULTIPLICATION.

57. **1.** How many cents are there in 3 two-cent pieces ?

2. How many blocks are there in 3 piles containing 3 blocks each ?

3. How many are two 4's ? Two 3's ? Three 3's ?

4. What have you been doing with the numbers given above ?

5. When numbers are used without reference to any particular thing, what name is given to them ? *Abstract Numbers.*

6. What name is given to numbers used in connection with some thing ? *Concrete Numbers.*

7. How many trees are 3 times 3 trees ? What is taken 3 times in this example ?

8. How many ponies are 4 times 3 ponies ? What is taken 4 times in this example ?

9. How many cents are 3 times 4 cents ? What is taken 3 times in this example ?

10. In each example, is the number in the answer like the *number taken* or like the number which tells how many *times* the number is taken ?

11. Is the number which tells how many times the other number is taken *concrete* or *abstract ?*

12. How does 3 times 2 compare with 2 times 3 ? 4 times 2 with 2 times 4 ? 3 times 4 with 4 times 3 ?

58. The process of taking one number as many times as there are units in another is called **Multiplication;** or,

Multiplication is a short process of adding equal numbers.

59. The number taken or multiplied is called the **Multiplicand.**

60. The number showing how many times the multiplicand is taken is called the **Multiplier.**

61. The result obtained by multiplying is called the **Product.**

62. The multiplicand and multiplier are called the **Factors of the Product.**

63. The **Sign of Multiplication** is an oblique cross ×. It is read *multiplied by* when the multiplicand precedes it and *times* when the multiplier precedes it.

Thus, 4×3 is read 4 multiplied by 3 when 4 is the multiplicand, but it is read 4 times 3 when 4 is the multiplier.

64. A number used without reference to any particular thing is called an **Abstract Number.**

Thus, 4, 7, 9, etc., are called abstract numbers.

65. A number used in connection with some thing is called a **Concrete Number.**

Thus, 4 books, 7 days, 9 dollars, are concrete numbers.

66. PRINCIPLES. — 1. *The multiplier must be regarded as an abstract number.*

2. *The multiplicand and product must be like numbers.*

3. *Either factor may be used as multiplier or multiplicand when both are abstract.*

In practice, for convenience, the smaller number is generally used as the multiplier.

MULTIPLICATION TABLE.

1	2	3	4	5	6	7	8	9	10	11	12
2	4	6	8	10	12	14	16	18	20	22	24
3	6	9	12	15	18	21	24	27	30	33	36
4	8	12	16	20	24	28	32	36	40	44	48
5	10	15	20	25	30	35	40	45	50	55	60
6	12	18	24	30	36	42	48	54	60	66	72
7	14	21	28	35	42	49	56	63	70	77	84
8	16	24	32	40	48	56	64	72	80	88	96
9	18	27	36	45	54	63	72	81	90	99	108
10	20	30	40	50	60	70	80	90	100	110	120
11	22	33	44	55	66	77	88	99	110	121	132
12	24	36	48	60	72	84	96	108	120	132	144

EXPLANATION. — The numbers in the left-hand column may be regarded as the multipliers, and the numbers across the top as the multiplicands. The products will be found in the *horizontal columns* opposite the multipliers.

Thus, 2 ones are 2 ; 2 twos are 4 ; 2 threes are 6 ; 2 fours are 8, etc.

The order may be changed so that the numbers in the upper horizontal line may be regarded as the multipliers, and the numbers on the left as the multiplicands. The products will then be found in columns *under* the multiplier.

DRILL EXERCISES.

67. Find the products of :

8×4.	5×11.	12×6.	7×5.	2×7.
5×3.	12×7.	11×5.	2×6.	3×4.
6×8.	9×9.	4×9.	3×5.	2×4.
7×2.	8×12.	5×5.	4×2.	12×3.
9×8.	3×3.	7×6.	5×2.	9×4.
8×7.	4×10.	9×7.	6×9.	10×12.
3×9.	5×7.	10×8.	7×11.	11×4.
4×6.	6×5.	11×10.	7×3.	2×3.
5×6.	11×7.	2×11.	2×9.	8×6.

3 × 7.	12 × 9.	9 × 2.	4 × 4.	6 × 7.
4 × 8.	7 × 8.	5 × 9.	6 × 3.	12 × 8.
5 × 12.	9 × 6.	7 × 4.	10 × 11.	10 × 4.
6 × 11.	10 × 10.	9 × 11.	8 × 11.	8 × 10.
7 × 10.	11 × 11.	10 × 7.	7 × 12.	4 × 7.
8 × 9.	12 × 12.	8 × 8.	9 × 10.	10 × 3.
9 × 5.	7 × 7.	4 × 5.	10 × 6.	12 × 2.
5 × 8.	8 × 5.	5 × 10.	11 × 9.	4 × 12.
3 × 10.	2 × 8.	6 × 12.	12 × 11.	3 × 2.
4 × 3.	2 × 12.	7 × 9.	2 × 5.	11 × 3.
3 × 11.	9 × 3.	6 × 10.	3 × 8.	11 × 2.
2 × 10.	3 × 12.	6 × 6.	6 × 2.	11 × 6.
5 × 4.	8 × 3.	12 × 5.	10 × 5.	12 × 10.
10 × 9.	3 × 6.	8 × 2.	11 × 12.	10 × 2.
11 × 8.	6 × 4.	9 × 12.	12 × 4.	4 × 11.

ORAL EXERCISES.

68. 1. At 8 cents each, what will 5 pencils cost?

2. What will 4 pairs of shoes cost at $6 a pair?

3. A boy received $4 per week for his wages. How much did he earn in 8 weeks? 8 times 4 = ?

4. How far can a man walk in 9 hours, if he walks 4 miles per hour? 9 times 4 = ?

5. An orchard contained 8 rows of trees, and there were 7 trees in each row. How many trees were there?

6. A girl attended school every school-day for 9 weeks. How many days was she at school?

7. There are 8 pints in a gallon. How many pints are there in 8 gallons? 8 × 8 = ?

8. A teacher assigned as a lesson 9 written problems each day for 6 days. How many did she assign altogether?

9. How much must I pay for 9 quires of paper at 8 cents per quire? 9 times 8 = ?

10. A contribution for a poor man contained 9 five-cent pieces. How much was that?

11. Most children are in school 6 hours per day. How many hours are they in school per week?

12. Five good long paces are a rod in length. How many paces are there in 7 rods?

13. The railway company offered excursion tickets to Niagara Falls and return at $5 each. How much would they cost for a party of 8 children?

14. Six boys are hoeing corn. If each hoes 4 rows every half-day, how many rows will they all hoe in 5 days?

15. There are 5 roses on a branch. How many roses would there be on 8 such branches? How many are eight 5's?

16. When flour is worth $6 per barrel what will 9 barrels cost?

17. What is the cost of 6 towels at 8 cents apiece?

18. At 9 cents a pound what is the cost of 8 pounds of twine?

19. A set of table knives is 6. How many knives are there in 8 sets?

20. A sheet of note paper has 4 pages. How many pages do 10 sheets have? 8 sheets? 6 sheets?

21. Asa earned $9 per week. How much did he earn in 7 weeks?

22. If 8 times around a certain course is just a mile, how many times around it must I go to walk 8 miles?

23. Seven boys went fishing. James caught 7 fish: if they had each caught as many, how many would all have caught?

24. A window composed of small panes of glass had **10** rows containing **7** in each row. How many panes were there in the window?

25. How many marbles have **8** boys, if each boy has **9** marbles?

26. At the rate of **6** miles an hour, how far will a person travel in **4** hours?

27. If a boy writes **5** words in a minute, how many words can he write in **9** minutes?

28. There are **7** days in a week. How many days are there in **7** weeks?

29. There are **8** quarts in a peck. How many quarts are there in **4** pecks, or a bushel?

30. John is **6** years old, and his father is **5** times as old. How old is his father?

31. Maggie made a quilt with **8** rows of squares in it, and **8** squares in each row. How many squares are there in the quilt?

32. What will 8 quarts of berries cost at 7 cents a quart?

33. If a man can earn $6 in one week, how many dollars can he earn in 6 weeks?

34. I bought 9 sheep for $7 each. How much did I pay for them?

WRITTEN EXERCISES.

69. 1. How many are 5 times 364?

EXPLANATION. — For convenience, the multiplier is written under the multiplicand, and we begin at the right to multiply.

Multiplicand	364
Multiplier	5
Product	1820

5 times 4 units are 20 units, or 2 tens and 0 units. The 0 is written in units' place in the product, and the 2 tens are reserved to add to the tens.

5 times 6 tens are 30 tens, plus 2 tens reserved, are 32 tens, or 3 hundreds and 2 tens. The 2 is written in tens' place in the product, and the 3 hundreds are reserved to add to the hundreds.

5 times 3 hundreds are 15 hundreds, plus 3 hundreds reserved, are 18 hundreds, or 1 thousand and 8 hundreds, which are written in thousands' and hundreds' places in the product.

Hence the product is 1820.

Find the products of the following:

2. 3×342.	16. 6734×4.	30. 4×36895.
3. 4×516.	17. 5921×6.	31. 7×29756.
4. 5×378.	18. 6804×5.	32. 8×38946.
5. 4×427.	19. 5387×7.	33. 9×69138.
6. 3×543.	20. 2956×4.	34. 5×56847.
7. 5×685.	21. 8543×6.	35. 8×38954.
8. 3×379.	22. 7916×8.	36. 9×41689.
9. 6×428.	23. 4438×7.	37. 7×39125.
10. 4×385.	24. 7985×5.	38. 8×86438.
11. 5×619.	25. 9983×6.	39. 9×60854.
12. 11×384.	26. 8974×7.	40. 7×70685.
13. 12×527.	27. 9376×11.	41. 5×71650.
14. 11×627.	28. 8437×12.	42. 9×81459.
15. 12×598.	29. 9546×11.	43. 8×92368.

44. What will 9 pairs of boots cost at $5.25 a pair?

45. A machinist earned $18.75 per week. How much did he earn in 6 weeks?

46. At an auction sale a man bought 7 sewing machines at $13.45 apiece. How much did they all cost him?

47. A builder bought 8 loads of lumber at an average price of $16.35 per load. How much did the lumber cost him?

48. At $19.65 cents each, what would 7 stoves cost?

49. A man bought 5 barrels of flour at $5.75 per barrel. How much did the flour cost him?

50. A drover bought 6 head of cattle at an average cost of $ 37.45 a head. How much did he pay for them?

51. Mr. A bought 8 acres of land at $ 45.75 per acre. How much did the land cost him?

52. If a firkin of butter costs $ 13.85, what must be paid for 5 firkins?

53. There are 5280 feet in a mile. How many feet are there in 6 miles?

54. There are 3600 seconds in 1 hour. How many seconds are there in 8 hours?

55. What will 7 tons of railroad iron cost at $ 64.25 a ton?

56. A merchant sold 9 bales of cotton at $ 37.60 a bale. How much did he receive for it?

57. At a public sale 8 tons of hay were sold for $ 7.85 per ton. How much was paid for the hay?

58. A party of 6 persons hired a schooner, paying $ 3.75 apiece for the use of it. How much did all pay?

59. What will be the cost of 7 organs, if each organ is worth $ 65.75?

60. At $ 75.35 each, what must be paid for 8 wagons?

61. At an average weight of 1267 pounds each, what will 7 oxen weigh?

62. How many bricks can be carried in 6 loads, if 1024 bricks are hauled at a load?

63. A lot cost $ 575. How much will 7 lots cost at the same rate?

64. A family of 3 persons boarded in Albany for 3 weeks at the rate of $ 4.75 a week for each person. What was the cost of their board for the whole time?

70. 1. How many are 10 times 5?   5 times 5?

2. Since 10 times 5 are 50, and 5 times 5 are 25, how many are $(10 + 5)$, or 15 times 5?

3. How many are 10 times 8?   2 times 8?   12 times 8?

4. How many are 10 times 6?   4 times 6?   14 times 6?

5. How many are 10 times 7?   2 times 7?   12 times 7?

6. How many are 12 times 4?   12 times 5?   12 times 3?

7. How may a number be most conveniently multiplied by 15?

8. How many are 10 times 9 plus 2 times 9, or 12 times 9?

9. A foot contains 12 inches. How many inches are there in 12 feet?

10. A pound of sugar weighs 16 ounces. How many ounces do 12 pounds weigh?

11. What will 12 dozen eggs cost at 17 cents per dozen?

12. The fare upon the railroad from a certain city to another is $ 18. How much will 12 tickets cost?

13. What will 18 tons of hay cost at $ 11 per ton?

14. What will 12 pounds of beefsteak cost at 18 cents a pound?

15. How much will 13 brooms cost at 22 cents each?

16. A farmer who owned 15 cows owned 15 times as many sheep. How many sheep did he own?

17. A man earned $ 18 per week for 16 weeks. How much did he earn in all?

18. A lady purchased 15 yards of cloth, paying 18 cents per yard for it. How much did she pay for the whole?

19. How many sheets of paper are there in 15 quires, since each quire contains 24 sheets ?

20. What time will be required to walk 13 miles, if it requires 15 minutes to walk one mile ?

21. A man deposited $15 per month in a savings bank. How much did his deposits amount to in a year ?

22. A circular railroad is 18 miles in length. How far does a train run which makes the circuit 15 times in a day ?

23. A stair has 15 steps. How many steps does a person take who goes up and down it 8 times per day ?

24. How many are 10 times 5 ? 10 times 6 ? 10 times 7 ?

25. What is annexed to a number when it is multiplied by 10 ?

26. How many are 100 times 2 ? 100 times 3 ? 100 times 4 ?

27. What is annexed to a number when it is multiplied by 100 ?

28. How many are 1000 times 2, or 2 times 1000 ? 1000 times 5, or 5 times 1000 ? 1000 times 9, or 9 times 1000 ?

29. How is a number multiplied by 1000 ?

30. How is a number multiplied by 1 with ciphers annexed ?

71. PRINCIPLE. — *A number is multiplied by* 10, 100, 1000, *etc., by annexing to the multiplicand as many ciphers as there are in the multiplier.*

WRITTEN EXERCISES.

72. What are the products of the following ?

1. 274×10	381×100	$9314 \times 1000.$
2. 386×10	610×100	$8167 \times 1000.$

What are the products of the following?

3. 456 × 10   903 × 100   7830 × 10000.

4. 375 × 10   857 × 100   5169 × 10000.

5. 319 × 10   310 × 100   6008 × 100000.

6. 402 × 10   416 × 100   6785 × 100000.

7. What is the product of 3486 × 6000?

3486   EXPLANATION. — Since 6000 is equal to 1000 times 6,
  6000 3486 is first multiplied by 6, giving a product of 20916,
——————— and then that result is multiplied by 1000 by annexing
20916000 three ciphers.

8. 393 × 20   814 × 300   8345 × 2000.

9. 491 × 30   739 × 200   3046 × 8000.

10. 568 × 20   816 × 700   5104 × 4000.

11. 715 × 50   793 × 500   6838 × 3000.

12. 423 × 70   982 × 800   7008 × 8000.

13. 316 × 40   318 × 300   5913 × 9000.

14. 629 × 60   427 × 600   8674 × 7000.

15. 518 × 30   563 × 900   8138 × 6000.

16. Multiply 264 by 142.

EXPLANATION. — For convenience, the multiplier is written under
the multiplicand, units under units, tens under tens,
etc.

  264   Since we cannot multiply by 142 at one operation,
  142   we multiply by the parts, and then add the products.
—————   The parts by which we multiply are 2, 4 tens, and 1
  528   hundred.
10560   2 times 264 equal 528, the *first* partial product;
26400   4 tens, or 40, times 264 equal 10560, the *second*
—————   partial product; 1 hundred, or 100, times 264 equal
37488   26400, the *third* partial product, and the sum of
these, 37488, is the *entire* product.

EXPLANATION. — The ciphers at the right of the partial products may be omitted, the significant figures occupying their proper places without the ciphers.

Thus, in multiplying by 4 *tens*, the lowest order in the product is tens ; hence the first figure of the product is written under tens, and the rest in their proper order.

In multiplying by hundreds, the lowest order of units in the product is hundreds ; hence the first figure of the product is written under hundreds, and the rest in their proper order.

```
 264
 142
 ───
 528
1056
 264
 ───
37488
```

RULE. — *Write the multiplier under the multiplicand, with units under units, tens under tens, etc.*

Multiply each figure of the multiplicand by each significant figure of the multiplier successively, beginning with units. Place the right-hand figure of each product under the figure of the multiplier used to obtain it, and add the partial products.

PROOF. — *Review the work, or multiply the multiplier by the multiplicand. If the results agree, the work is probably correct.*

When there is a cipher in the multiplier, multiply by the significant figures only, taking care to place the first figure in the product under the figure of the multiplier used to obtain it.

17.	18.	19.
3125	4685	3945
403	3007	4800
9375	32795	31560
12500	14055	15780
1259375	14087795	18936000

Multiply :

20. 3842 by 23.

21. 4168 by 32.

22. 3256 by 41.

23. 4187 by 36.

Multiply:

24. 5493 by 27.
25. 8169 by 46.
26. 5768 by 35.
27. 3985 by 71.
28. 4873 by 64.
29. 3567 by 58.
30. 2981 by 49.
31. 6324 by 37.
32. 5237 by 65.
33. 6415 by 79.
34. 7346 by 84.
35. 8125 by 34.
36. 7189 by 67.
37. 3426 by 73.
38. 5763 by 85.
39. 6256 by 99.
40. 7126 by 83.
41. 34567 by 325.
42. 21894 by 216.
43. 46854 by 406.
44. 61854 by 314.
45. 58163 by 248.
46. 48348 by 232.
47. 58194 by 397.
48. 67853 by 206.
49. 38492 by 387.
50. 28637 by 341.
51. 41856 by 416.

52. 32685 by 507.
53. 56736 by 693.
54. 61004 by 372.
55. 52390 by 4225.
56. 43257 by 7056.
57. 654324 by 3097.
58. 683725 by 5618.
59. 398647 by 3009.
60. 318043 by 5960.
61. 346857 by 6807.
62. $468.35 by 3915.
63. $314.27 by 3707.
64. $416.32 by 6850.
65. $527.46 by 4837.
66. $304.25 by 5039.
67. $513.64 by 8106.
68. $425.38 by 9007.
69. $317.24 by 8305.
70. $819.30 by 6804.
71. $364.25 by 5918.
72. $371.58 by 6805.
73. $296.13 by 6432.
74. $324.42 by 3806.
75. $418.56 by 6817.
76. $524.36 by 4026.
77. $327.45 by 3830.
78. $416.32 by 4069.
79. $487.56 by 5830.

80. B sold 17 firkins of butter, each firkin containing 56 pounds, at $.38 a pound. How much did he receive for it?

81. The earth moves in its orbit 19 miles in a second; how far does it move in 60 seconds, or 1 minute? How far in 60 minutes, or 1 hour?

82. Two steamers start from the same place and sail in opposite directions, one at the rate of 18 miles an hour, and the other at the rate of 15 miles an hour. How far will they be apart in 39 hours?

83. Two ships are 7483 miles apart, and are sailing towards each other, one at the rate of 46, the other at the rate of 53 miles a day. How far will they be apart at the end of 73 days?

84. I bought 156 barrels of flour for $1015. Finding 32 barrels of it worthless, I sold the remainder at $9 a barrel. Did I gain or lose, and how much?

85. In an orchard there are 117 rows of trees, and each row contains 69 trees. How many trees are there in the orchard?

86. A freight train consists of 26 cars; each car contains 82 barrels of flour, and each barrel of flour weighs 196 pounds. How many pounds of flour in the entire cargo?

87. Mr. Burns earns $37.60 a week. His expenses are $19.50 a week. How much can he save in 26 weeks?

88. It requires 1972 pickets to fence one side of a square lot. How many pickets will be required to fence 17 lots of the same size and shape?

89. I sold from my farm 270 bushels of wheat at $.98 per bushel, 300 bushels of corn at $.55 per bushel, 175 bushels of oats at $.35 per bushel, and 60 bushels of potatoes at $.45 per bushel. What was the value of the crops sold from the farm?

90. A lady bought at a store 12 yards of silk at 87 cents a yard, 36 yards of ribbon at 15 cents a yard, and 17 yards of muslin at 8 cents a yard. She gave the clerk a 20-dollar bill to pay for it. How much change should she receive?

91. A has $65, B has three times as much as A, and C has as much as both, lacking $25. How much have they all?

92. I bought 80 tons of coal at $3.25 a ton, and paid freight amounting to $13.75. I sold 55 tons for $3.80 a ton, and the balance for $3.95 a ton. How much did I make on the coal?

93. Mr. Hughes sold a farm of 160 acres at $97.50 per acre, and received in payment a note for $3765.27, and the rest in cash. How much cash did he receive?

94. A dealer bought 700 bushels of wheat at $.95 a bushel. He sold 256 bushels at $1.10 a bushel, 44 bushels at $1.15 a bushel, and the remainder for $394. How much did he gain on the entire sale?

95. A speculator bought 640 acres of land at $20 an acre. He sold at one time 350 acres at $25 an acre; at another time 150 acres at $28 an acre. What must he receive for the remainder to gain $4500 on the purchase?

96. A farmer who raised 1160 bushels of oats kept 75 bushels for seed, and enough to winter 12 horses, allowing 45 bushels to each horse, and sold the remainder. How many bushels did he sell?

97. A cloth merchant sold three lots of cassimeres, the first containing 19 pieces of 28 yards each, at $1.75 per yard; the second containing 14 pieces of 27 yards each, at $1.87 per yard; and the third containing 40 pieces averaging 25 yards each, at $1.95 per yard. What was the value of the whole?

DIVISION.

73. 1. How many groups of 2 pencils each can be formed from 6 pencils? How many 2's are there in 6?

2. How many groups containing 3 marbles each can be formed from 9 marbles? How many 3's are there in 9?

3. How many 3's are there in 6? How many 4's in 8? How many times is 3 contained in 6? 2 in 6? 4 in 8?

4. How many cents will each child have when 12 cents are divided equally among 4 children? How many 4's in 12?

5. If 16 cents are divided equally among 8 children, how much will each have?

6. What have you been doing with the above numbers?

7. How many are five 6's? How many 6's in 30?

8. How many are seven 4's? How many 4's in 28?

9. How many are six 3's and 2? How many 3's in 20?

10. How many 5's are there in 22? How many are four 5's and 2?

74. The process of finding how many times one number is contained in another is called **Division**; or,

Division is the process of separating a number into equal parts.

75. The number to be divided is called the **Dividend**.

76. The number by which we divide is called the **Divisor**.

77. The result obtained by division is called the **Quotient.** It shows how many times the divisor is contained in the dividend.

78. The part of the dividend remaining when the division is not exact is called the **Remainder.**

79. The **Sign of Division** is ÷. It is read *divided by.* When it is placed between two numbers, it shows that the one on the left is to be divided by the one on the right.

Thus, 63 ÷ 9 is read 63 divided by 9.

Division is also indicated by writing the dividend above the divisor.

Thus, $\frac{63}{9}$ indicates that 63 is to be divided by 9.

80. PRINCIPLES. — 1. *When the dividend and divisor are like numbers, the quotient must be an abstract number.*

2. *The dividend and remainder are like numbers.*

3. *The product of the divisor and quotient, plus the remainder, is equal to the dividend.*

An example like " How many 6's are there in 30 ? " may be solved by subtraction, but it requires a longer time than by division. Hence, division may be regarded as *a short method of subtracting equal numbers.*

The same example may be solved readily by recalling the products in multiplication. When we wish to know how many *sixes* there are in 30, if we recall the fact that *five* sixes are 30, the answer is found at once. Hence, division is the *converse of multiplication.*

DRILL EXERCISES.

81. Tell the quotients of the following instantly :

40 ÷ 4.	15 ÷ 5.	33 ÷ 3.	36 ÷ 6.	42 ÷ 7.
25 ÷ 5.	30 ÷ 10.	32 ÷ 4.	77 ÷ 7.	60 ÷ 10.
30 ÷ 6.	24 ÷ 2.	40 ÷ 10.	99 ÷ 11.	56 ÷ 8.
18 ÷ 9.	72 ÷ 6.	64 ÷ 8.	28 ÷ 7.	36 ÷ 3.
54 ÷ 6.	36 ÷ 12.	55 ÷ 5.	72 ÷ 9.	14 ÷ 2.

20 ÷ 10.	21 ÷ 7.	48 ÷ 12.	50 ÷ 10.	22 ÷ 2.
8 ÷ 4.	48 ÷ 4.	24 ÷ 4.	27 ÷ 9.	32 ÷ 8.
20 ÷ 2.	42 ÷ 6.	16 ÷ 2.	66 ÷ 6.	60 ÷ 5.
96 ÷ 8.	44 ÷ 11.	24 ÷ 6.	60 ÷ 12.	88 ÷ 11.
6 ÷ 3.	28 ÷ 4.	30 ÷ 5.	63 ÷ 7.	40 ÷ 5.
22 ÷ 11.	36 ÷ 4.	66 ÷ 11.	48 ÷ 8.	44 ÷ 4.
12 ÷ 2.	70 ÷ 10.	8 ÷ 2.	49 ÷ 7.	96 ÷ 12.
20 ÷ 4.	63 ÷ 9.	81 ÷ 9.	35 ÷ 7.	24 ÷ 3.
24 ÷ 12.	88 ÷ 8.	35 ÷ 5.	90 ÷ 10.	45 ÷ 9.
18 ÷ 3.	55 ÷ 11.	80 ÷ 10.	48 ÷ 6.	108 ÷ 9.
60 ÷ 6.	84 ÷ 7.	10 ÷ 2.	110 ÷ 11.	121 ÷ 11.
15 ÷ 3.	16 ÷ 4.	77 ÷ 11.	80 ÷ 8.	108 ÷ 12.
56 ÷ 7.	14 ÷ 7.	6 ÷ 2.	99 ÷ 9.	21 ÷ 3.
90 ÷ 9.	4 ÷ 2.	36 ÷ 9.	40 ÷ 8.	132 ÷ 12.
70 ÷ 7.	16 ÷ 8.	84 ÷ 12.	50 ÷ 5.	120 ÷ 10.
72 ÷ 8.	72 ÷ 12.	18 ÷ 2.	27 ÷ 3.	110 ÷ 10.
20 ÷ 5.	30 ÷ 3.	54 ÷ 9.	100 ÷ 10.	120 ÷ 12.
12 ÷ 6.	18 ÷ 6.	12 ÷ 3.	24 ÷ 8.	132 ÷ 11.
33 ÷ 11.	10 ÷ 5.	12 ÷ 4.	9 ÷ 3.	144 ÷ 12.

ORAL EXERCISES.

82. 1. At 5 cents apiece, how many pencils can be bought for 25 cents? For 35 cents? For 45 cents?

2. How many yards of cloth, at 8 cents per yard, can be bought for 40 cents? How many 8's are there in 40?

3. A field of 70 acres was divided into lots containing 7 acres each. How many lots were there?

4. A dollar was changed into 10-cent pieces. How many were there? How many 7's are there in 56?

5. A girl's entire expenses at boarding school were $6 per week. For how many weeks will $48 pay?

6. How many 5-cent pieces are there in a dime?

7. What is paid per yard for cloth if I get 7 yards for 63 cents ? How many 7's in 63 ? 8's in 72 ?

8. A girl visited at her uncle's for 42 days. How many weeks was that ? How many 7's in 42 ? 6's in 42 ?

9. A freight train averaged 9 miles per hour. In how many hours would it run 72 miles ? How many 8's in 72 ?

10. An orchard contained 54 trees, arranged in 9 rows. How many trees were there in each row ?

11. When oranges sell at 8 cents per dozen, how many dozen can be bought for 80 cents ?

12. A grocer's profit upon a pound of tea was 7 cents. How many pounds must he sell to gain 63 cents ?

13. A stage coach went 8 miles per hour. How long would it require to go 80 miles ? How many 5's in 50 ?

14. A school-room contained 54 seats, arranged in 6 rows. How many seats were there in each row ?

15. When flour sells at $6 per barrel, how many barrels can be purchased for $48 ?

16. How many engravings, worth $7 each, can be bought for $49 ?

17. When coal sells at $5 per ton, how many tons can I buy for $50 ?

18. How many rods of fence, at $8 per rod, can be made for $64 ?

19. A man's wages are $9 per week. In how many weeks can he earn $45 ?

20. If 5 pounds of sugar cost 25 cents, how many pounds can be bought for 40 cents ?

21. My wood cost me $40, at the rate of $5 per cord. How many cords did I purchase ?

22. If writing books sell at 8 cents each, how many can be bought for 72 cents?

23. When 5 yards of cloth cost 35 cents, how many yards can be purchased for 63 cents?

24. If 4 quarts of milk sell for 24 cents, how many quarts can you buy for 42 cents?

25. A boy paid 21 cents for 3 quarts of chestnuts. How many quarts could he have purchased for 35 cents?

26. At the rate of 6 pencils for 48 cents, how many pencils could be bought for 32 cents?

27. A man gave 54 cents to some beggars, giving 9 cents to each. How many beggars were there?

28. If 6 packages of paper cost 42 cents, how many such packages can be obtained for 56 cents?

29. If 8 pounds of lard cost 48 cents, how many pounds can be bought for 42 cents?

30. How many sheep can be bought for $35, if 6 sheep cost $30?

31. If 7 tables can be bought for $56, how many tables, at the same rate, can be purchased for $72?

32. I bought 7 calves for $35. How much was that per head?

33. Mary had 9 packages of paper of the same number of sheets, and in all she had 54 sheets. How many sheets were there in each package?

34. How many sheep, at $4 per head, can be purchased by a man who has $42? *Ans.* 10 sheep, and $2 left.

35. A man who worked for $3 per day earned in a certain time $32. How many days did he work?

Ans. 10⅔ days.

83. From problems 34 and 35 it is apparent that the remainder should sometimes be written *after* the quotient, and sometimes as a *part* of it.

When the *remainder* is written as *part* of the quotient, it is expressed by placing the divisor under it with a line between them, as in the answer to problem 35.

84. When anything is divided into *two* equal parts, *each part* is called *one half;* when into *three* equal parts, *one third;* when into *four* equal parts, *one fourth*, etc.

85. One or more of the equal parts of anything is called a **Fraction.**

Fractions are expressed as follows:

One half by $\frac{1}{2}$. One third by $\frac{1}{3}$. Two thirds by $\frac{2}{3}$.
One fourth by $\frac{1}{4}$. Three fourths by $\frac{3}{4}$. Two fifths by $\frac{2}{5}$.
Five eighths by $\frac{5}{8}$. Seven ninths by $\frac{7}{9}$. Five elevenths by $\frac{5}{11}$.

86. 1. Read the following fractional expressions:

$\frac{3}{10}$	$\frac{8}{11}$	$\frac{12}{23}$	$\frac{15}{19}$	$\frac{14}{27}$	$\frac{18}{35}$	$\frac{15}{24}$	$\frac{12}{27}$
$\frac{13}{24}$	$\frac{11}{29}$	$\frac{10}{47}$	$\frac{12}{36}$	$\frac{15}{30}$	$\frac{37}{44}$	$\frac{31}{80}$	$\frac{35}{39}$
$\frac{25}{30}$	$\frac{18}{64}$	$\frac{19}{27}$	$\frac{31}{49}$	$\frac{29}{35}$	$\frac{16}{83}$	$\frac{29}{98}$	$\frac{67}{145}$

2. What is $\frac{1}{2}$ of 10? 12? 16? 18? 20?

3. What is $\frac{1}{3}$ of 15? 18? 24? 27? 30?

4. What is $\frac{1}{4}$ of 12? 16? 20? 36? 40?

5. What is $\frac{1}{6}$ of 12? 18? 24? 36? 42?

6. What is $\frac{1}{8}$ of 16? 24? 40? 64? 72?

7. What is $\frac{1}{5}$ of 10? 30? 35? 45? 50?

8. What is $\frac{1}{7}$ of 21? 35? 42? 56? 49?

9. A man earned $45 in 9 days. What did he receive per day?

10. In 7 weeks there are 49 days. How many are there in one week?

11. How much does each door cost me, if I pay $56 for 8 of them?

12. If 5 barrels of flour are worth $30, what is the price per barrel?

13. If 6 Christmas cards cost 48 cents, what will be the cost of one at the same rate?

14. A lady paid 64 cents for 8 yards of muslin. How much did she pay per yard?

15. A man's wages for 6 days' work amounted to $24. How much did he receive per day?

16. Mr. B paid $35 for 7 weeks' board. How much did the boarding cost him per week?

17. If a farm hand should earn $20 for laboring 4 weeks, how much would he earn in a week?

18. In 7 weeks a man saved $49. If he saved the same amount each week, what did he save per week?

19. If 8 barrels of sugar are worth $64, what is the price per barrel?

20. If 9 writing desks cost $54, what is the cost of one writing desk?

21. A merchant paid $36 for 9 kegs of nails. How much did he pay per keg?

22. If 9 shawls of a certain quality cost $72, what must you pay for 1 shawl of the same quality?

WRITTEN EXERCISES.

87. 1. Divide 1384 by 4.

EXPLANATION. — For convenience, the divisor is written at the left of the dividend, with a line between them, and the quotient either under the dividend or at the right of it, with a line between them.

Divisor. Dividend.

4)1384

Quotient. 346

4 is not contained in 1 thousand any thousand times, therefore the quotient cannot contain units of any order higher than hundreds. Hence we find how many times 4 is contained in all the hundreds of the dividend. 1 thousand plus 3 hundreds are 13 hundreds. 4 is contained in 13 hundreds 3 hundreds times, with a remainder of 1 hundred. We write the 3 hundreds of the quotient under the hundreds of the dividend.

1 hundred, the remainder, plus 8 tens are 18 tens. 4 is contained in 18 tens 4 tens times, with a remainder of 2 tens. We write the 4 tens of the quotient under the tens of the dividend.

2 tens, the remainder, plus 4 units are 24 units. 4 is contained in 24 units 6 units times, and the 6 is placed under the units of the dividend.

Hence the quotient is 346.

PROOF. — The quotient, 346, multiplied by 4, the divisor, is 1384. Hence the work is correct (Prin. 3).

88. When examples in division are solved without writing the products or remainders, the process is called **Short Division.**

Divide by *short division :*

2.	3.	4.	5.
4)31264	6)216276	5)31250	8)403287
7816	36046	6250	50410⅞

6. 3624 ÷ 4. **10.** 3258 ÷ 6. **14.** 4506 ÷ 3.

7. 2135 ÷ 5. **11.** 4264 ÷ 4. **15.** 4864 ÷ 4.

8. 3852 ÷ 3. **12.** 3042 ÷ 6. **16.** 5274 ÷ 6.

9. 2835 ÷ 5. **13.** 6105 ÷ 5. **17.** 5325 ÷ 5.

Divide by *short division:*

18. $7938 \div 3$.	**37.** $\frac{41\,58}{3}$.	**56.** $619381 \div 9$.
19. $4824 \div 8$.	**38.** $\frac{41\,56}{6}$.	**57.** $492347 \div 7$.
20. $3160 \div 4$.	**39.** $\frac{37\,35}{3}$.	**58.** $583629 \div 6$.
21. $5830 \div 5$.	**40.** $\frac{28\,35}{7}$.	**59.** $510432 \div 8$.
22. $6876 \div 3$.	**41.** $\frac{41\,31}{9}$.	**60.** $617386 \div 9$.
23. $8676 \div 6$.	**42.** $\frac{27\,63}{9}$.	**61.** $\$432.15 \div 5$.
24. $5832 \div 8$.	**43.** $\frac{31\,57}{7}$.	**62.** $\$346.05 \div 9$.
25. $4735 \div 5$.	**44.** $\frac{91\,20}{8}$.	**63.** $\$514.29 \div 7$.
26. $5872 \div 4$.	**45.** $\frac{70\,35}{7}$.	**64.** $\$683.24 \div 8$.
27. $3920 \div 8$.	**46.** $\frac{39\,36}{6}$.	**65.** $\$516.89 \div 6$.
28. $4163 \div 3$.	**47.** $\frac{84\,64}{8}$.	**66.** $\$342.85 \div 4$.
29. $3618 \div 6$.	**48.** $\frac{79\,35}{5}$.	**67.** $\$397.54 \div 9$.
30. $2944 \div 4$.	**49.** $\frac{46\,27}{7}$.	**68.** $\$819.32 \div 7$.
31. $5112 \div 3$.	**50.** $\frac{79\,11}{9}$.	**69.** $\$509.08 \div 6$.
32. $3972 \div 6$.	**51.** $\frac{45\,05}{5}$.	**70.** $\$314.05 \div 9$.
33. $5984 \div 4$.	**52.** $\frac{41\,85}{5}$.	**71.** $\$429.65 \div 8$.
34. $4626 \div 6$.	**53.** $\frac{39\,65}{5}$.	**72.** $\$734.74 \div 6$.
35. $7255 \div 5$.	**54.** $\frac{46\,84}{4}$.	**73.** $\$529.86 \div 7$.
36. $7384 \div 8$.	**55.** $\frac{31\,36}{6}$.	**74.** $\$393.81 \div 9$.

75. A man divided his fortune of $\$7616$ equally among his 6 children. What was the share of each?

76. There are 7 days in a week. How many weeks are there in 1015 days?

77. At $\$6$ a barrel, how many barrels of flour can be purchased with $\$1422$.

78. If 8 horses of equal value are worth $\$2352$, what is each horse worth?

79. A man has 3248 acres of land lying in 7 equal tracts. How many acres are there in each tract?

80. Mr. B bought 6 cows for $182.10. What was the average price of each cow?

81. How many tons of coal, at $5 a ton, can be bought for $3125?

82. I bought 8 yards of broadcloth for $41.60. What was the price per yard?

83. There are 8 quarts in one peck. How many pecks are there in 9136 quarts?

84. If 6 lots are worth $7470, what is the average value of each lot?

85. Divide an estate of $15302 equally among 7 heirs.

86. A lady bought at a store a number of yards of muslin at 8 cents a yard, and paid $3.84 for it. How many yards did she buy?

87. If 7 plows are worth $94.50, what is the average price of a plow?

88. If 6 wagons of the same make, quality, and size, are worth $454.80, what is the value of each?

89. In a nail factory 73,455 nails were made by 5 boys in 2 hours. What was the average number made by each boy?

90. There are 9 square feet in a square yard. How many square yards are there in 36,783 square feet?

ORAL EXERCISES.

89. **1.** At 10 cents each, how many melons can be bought for 90 cents?

2. At $10 each, how many coats can be bought for $60?

3. If a book costs 30 cents, how many can be bought for 60 cents?

4. If a man earns $20 per week, in how many weeks can he earn $60?

5. If there are 80 apple trees arranged in 20 rows, how many trees are there in each row?

6. How many days will I require to travel 150 miles, if I travel 50 miles per day?

7. How many 10's are there in 50? In 60? In 70? In 80? In 130? In 150? In 250? In 350? In 600? In 800?

8. Since 10 is contained 5 times in 50, 6 times in 60, 35 times in 350, 80 times in 800, how may a number be divided by 10?

9. How many 100's are there in 600? In 800? In 3700? In 8500?

10. Since 100 is contained 6 times in 600, 8 times in 800, 37 times in 3700, and 85 times in 8500, how may a number be divided by 100?

90. PRINCIPLE. — *A number may be divided by 10, 100, 1000, etc., by cutting off from the right of the dividend as many figures as there are ciphers upon the right of the divisor.*

WRITTEN EXERCISES.

91. Divide:

1.	2.	3.
1$\vert$00)275$\vert$00	1$\vert$00)394$\vert$63	1$\vert$00)295$\vert$71
275	$394\frac{63}{100}$	$295\frac{71}{100}$

4. $46853 \div 100$.

5. $39278 \div 100$.

6. $38546 \div 100$.

7. $46850 \div 100$.

8. $31700 \div 100$.

9. $68543 \div 1000$.

10. $31927 \div 1000$.

11. $41687 \div 1000$.

12. $38125 \div 1000$.

13. $41736 \div 1000$.

14. $54286 \div 1000$.

15. $31854 \div 10000$.

16. $48653 \div 10000$.

17. $31925 \div 10000$.

18. $46874 \div 10000$.

19. $72840 \div 10000$.

20. $61785 \div 10000$.

21. $42856 \div 10000$.

22. Divide 72595 by 400.

EXPLANATION. — After cutting off the two ciphers from the right of the divisor and two figures from the right of the dividend, the remaining part of the dividend is divided by 4, giving a quotient of 181 and 1 hundred remainder. 1 hundred plus the partial remainder, 95, cut off, gives the entire remainder 195.

$$4|00) 725|95$$
$$181\tfrac{195}{400}$$

Hence the quotient is 181 and 195 remainder or $181\tfrac{195}{400}$.

Divide:

23. 3845 by 30.   **28.** 98357 by 400.   **33.** 316857 by 2000.

24. 4927 by 40.   **29.** 81654 by 700.   **34.** 415684 by 4000.

25. 6839 by 50.   **30.** 32718 by 600.   **35.** 238719 by 6000.

26. 4168 by 70.   **31.** 42513 by 900.   **36.** 418576 by 9000.

27. 6985 by 90.   **32.** 24678 by 800.   **37.** 382456 by 7000.

38. Divide 7975 by 26.

EXPLANATION. — 26 is not contained in 7 thousands any thousands times ; hence the thousands are united with the hundreds, making 79 hundreds. 26 is contained in 79 hundreds, 3 hundreds times with a remainder. The 3 hundreds are written in the quotient, and the divisor is multiplied by them, giving a product of 78 hundreds, or 7 thousands and 8 hundreds, which are written under units of the same order in the dividend. Subtracting, there is a remainder of 1 hundred.

Divisor. Dividend. Quotient.
$$26) \; 7975 \; (306\tfrac{19}{26}$$
$$78$$
$$\overline{175}$$
$$156$$
$$\overline{19}$$

The 1 hundred is united with the 7 tens, making 17 tens. 26 is not contained in 17 tens any tens times ; therefore there are no tens in the quotient, and a cipher is written in tens' place in the quotient.

The 17 tens are united with the 5 units, making 175 units. 26 is contained in 175 units 6 times with a remainder. The 6 is written in units' place in the quotient, and the divisor multiplied by it, giving a product of 156 units, or 1 hundred, 5 tens, and 6 units, which are written under units of the same order in the partial dividend. Subtracting, there is a remainder of 19. The remainder is written over the divisor as part of the quotient.

Hence the quotient is $306\frac{19}{26}$.

PROOF. — $306 \times 26 + 19 = 7975$. Hence the work is correct (Prin. 3).

92. When the steps in the solution of an example in division are written, the process is called *Long Division*.

RULE. — *Write the divisor at the left of the dividend with a curved line between them.*

Find how many times the divisor is contained in the fewest figures on the left hand of the dividend that will contain it, and write the quotient on the right.

Multiply the divisor by this quotient, and place the product under the figures divided. Subtract the result from the partial dividend used, and to the remainder annex the next figure of the dividend.

Divide as before, until all the figures of the dividend have been annexed to the remainder.

If any partial dividend will not contain the divisor, write a cipher in the quotient, then annex the next figure of the dividend, and proceed as before.

If there is a remainder after the last division, write it after the quotient, or with the divisor under it as part of the quotient.

PROOF. — *Multiply the divisor by the quotient, and to the product add the remainder, if any. If the work is correct, the result will equal the dividend.*

1. *To find the quotient figure*, see how many times the first *figure* of the divisor is contained in the *first figures* of the partial dividend that will contain it, making allowance for the addition of the tens from the product of the second figure of the divisor.

2. If the product of the divisor by the quotient figure is greater than the partial dividend from which it is to be subtracted, the quotient figure is *too large*.

3. Each remainder must be less than the divisor ; otherwise the quotient figure is *too small*.

4. When there is no remainder, the divisor is said to be *exact*.

Find the quotients of:

39. $3443 \div 11.$	**53.** $41676 \div 92.$	**67.** $106950 \div 75.$
40. $1728 \div 12.$	**54.** $54250 \div 62.$	**68.** $108320 \div 85.$
41. $4536 \div 21.$	**55.** $52808 \div 82.$	**69.** $126618 \div 94.$
42. $11904 \div 31.$	**56.** $52056 \div 72.$	**70.** $211044 \div 86.$
43. $25133 \div 41.$	**57.** $52542 \div 63.$	**71.** $262656 \div 76.$
44. $12036 \div 51.$	**58.** $46216 \div 53.$	**72.** $507558 \div 87.$
45. $21045 \div 61.$	**59.** $51875 \div 83.$	**73.** $361437 \div 57.$
46. $30885 \div 71.$	**60.** $42628 \div 74.$	**74.** $364450 \div 37.$
47. $26406 \div 81.$	**61.** $50560 \div 64.$	**75.** $429436 \div 49.$
48. $33852 \div 91.$	**62.** $48168 \div 54.$	**76.** $460346 \div 58.$
49. $18832 \div 22.$	**63.** $65940 \div 84.$	**77.** $513282 \div 66.$
50. $24192 \div 32.$	**64.** $63168 \div 94.$	**78.** $522786 \div 89.$
51. $32004 \div 42.$	**65.** $31080 \div 35.$	**79.** $727748 \div 98.$
52. $45292 \div 52.$	**66.** $41220 \div 45.$	**80.** $794061 \div 83.$

81. $11413383 \div 201.$	**93.** $64785278 \div 911.$
82. $21346152 \div 401.$	**94.** $68475384 \div 932.$
83. $23143276 \div 601.$	**95.** $73146254 \div 807.$
84. $30412345 \div 510.$	**96.** $38765893 \div 717.$
85. $34103528 \div 610.$	**97.** $54563524 \div 722.$
86. $51234432 \div 711.$	**98.** $61248638 \div 834.$
87. $45161812 \div 802.$	**99.** $75143920 \div 950.$
88. $36784533 \div 603.$	**100.** $43161726 \div 856.$
89. $25416259 \div 613.$	**101.** $63517429 \div 923.$
90. $31425634 \div 520.$	**102.** $58463471 \div 731.$
91. $48765432 \div 730.$	**103.** $39158167 \div 473.$
92. $45346571 \div 831.$	**104.** $41132516 \div 566.$

Find the quotients of :

105. 31846489 ÷ 1047.   **109.** 241671382 ÷ 8346.

106. 57169438 ÷ 3109.   **110.** 364128796 ÷ 9215.

107. 84365712 ÷ 5186.   **111.** 403214571 ÷ 7843.

108. 136184527 ÷ 7408.   **112.** 754326840 ÷ 9618.

113. If 312 cows are worth $ 11232, what is the value of each cow ?

114. A ship sails 7812 miles in 36 days. How far does it sail in 1 day ?

115. If 49 horses are worth $ 16,758, what is the average value of each ?

116. Into how many farms of 144 acres each can a tract of land containing 10,368 acres be divided ?

117. At $ 82 per acre, how many acres of land can be bought for $ 317,094 ?

118. How many colts, at $ 95 each, can be bought for $ 42,750 ?

119. There are 128 cubic feet in one cord of wood. How many cords of wood are there in 69,248 cubic feet ?

120. The president of the United States receives a yearly salary of $ 50,000. How much is that a day ?

121. A man traveled 83,280 rods. How many miles did he travel, there being 320 rods in a mile ?

122. If a field of 109 acres produces 3379 bushels of wheat, what is the average yield per acre ?

123. A farmer desires to exchange 150 acres of land, at $ 117 an acre, for woodland, at $ 39 per acre. How many acres will he get ?

124. The product of two numbers is 290,625. One of the numbers is 465; what is the other?

125. Mr. King has $8000; he buys a house for $4500, and some land at $140 an acre. How many acres of land can he buy?

126. The circumference of the earth is 25,000 miles; how long would it take to travel round it, going at the rate of 125 miles per day?

127. If the circumference of a wagon wheel is 15 feet, how many turns will the wheel make in going 52800 feet, or ten miles?

128. A man gave $5760 and 128 cows, worth $50 each, for land valued at $64 per acre. How many acres did he receive?

129. A man wills $7000 to his wife, $2000 to a church, $1000 to a school, and the remainder to his 8 children, in equal shares. What does each child receive, the fortune being $42,720?

130. The area of the state of North Carolina is 52,250 square miles, and the population, according to the census of 1890, was 1,617,947. About how many persons, on an average, were there living on a square mile?

131. The state of New York has an area of 49,170 square miles; Rhode Island has an area of 1250 square miles. Into how many states of the size of Rhode Island could New York be divided, and how many square miles would be left over?

132. Texas has an area of 265,780 square miles. Into how many states of the size of New York could Texas be divided, and how many square miles would be left over?

93. When several numbers are to be treated as one number, they are included in parentheses ( ), in braces { }, in brackets [ ], or placed under the vinculum ‾‾‾.

These signs are called **Signs of Aggregation.**

The expressions included by these signs are to be treated as a single number.

Thus, $(5 + 7) \times 5$ or $\overline{5 + 7} \times 5$ means that the sum of 5 and 7 is to be multiplied by 5.

The parts of an expression connected by the signs + or — are the **Terms** of the expression.

Thus, the expression $3+6$ contains two terms. $(3+6)\times 3-(3+2)\times 2$ also contains but two terms, for the numbers in the parentheses are each treated as a single term.

1. $5+10\div 5=5+2$ or 7; but $(5+10)\div 5=15\div 5$ or 3.
2. $2+3\times 10-4=2+30-4$ or 28; but $(2+3)\times 10-4=$ $50-4$ or 46 and $(2+3)\times(10-4)=5\times 6$ or 30.

Hence, to find the value of such expressions:

1st. *Simplify the expressions within the parentheses by performing the operations indicated.* 2d. *Further simplify each term, if necessary, by performing the multiplication or division indicated.* 3d. *Combine the terms.*

When one parenthesis includes another, remove the inner one first.

Find the value of:

3. $(3+4)\times 8.$
4. $(3+4)\times(8-5).$
5. $(5+7)\div(4-2).$
6. $(8+3)-(6-2).$
7. $(9-3)-(7-5).$
8. $(3+4)\times 5-(5+4)\div 3.$
9. $(6+8)\div 2+3\times 5+4.$
10. $7\times 4+3-(12-4)\div 2.$
11. $2+12\div 4-(7+8\div 4)\div 3.$
12. $(3+4)\times 5-(4+10)\div 2-7.$
13. $(325+20)-(415-232)-47.$
14. $(532-40)-(315-116+7)+35.$
15. $(54-16)\times \overline{11+4}-15\times 20.$
16. $\lfloor 84-7\times 6+(3\times 5)-3\rfloor \div 9.$
17. $4+11\times 3-(5+28\div 4+24)\div 6.$

RELATION OF DIVIDEND, DIVISOR, AND QUOTIENT.

94. The value of the quotient depends upon that of the dividend and divisor. If one of these is changed, while the other remains the same, the quotient will be changed. If both are changed, the quotient may or may not be changed.

The changes may be illustrated as follows:

FUNDAMENTAL EQUATION.

$$64 \div 8 = 8.$$

CHANGED EQUATIONS.

1. *Dividend changed.*
- 1. $128 \div 8 = 16$ — 1. Multiplying the dividend by 2 multiplies the quotient by 2.
- 2. $32 \div 8 = 4$ — 2. Dividing the dividend by 2 divides the quotient by 2.

2. *Divisor changed.*
- 1. $64 \div 16 = 4$ — 1. Multiplying the divisor by 2 divides the quotient by 2.
- 2. $64 \div 4 = 16$ — 2. Dividing the divisor by 2 multiplies the quotient by 2.

3. *Both changed.*
- 1. $128 \div 16 = 8$ — Multiplying or dividing both dividend and divisor by 2 does not change the quotient.
- 2. $32 \div 4 = 8$

From these we may deduce the following principles:

95. PRINCIPLES. — 1. *Multiplying the dividend or dividing the divisor by any number, multiplies the quotient by that number.*

2. *Dividing the dividend or multiplying the divisor by any number, divides the quotient by that number.*

3. *Multiplying or dividing both dividend and divisor by the same number, does not change the quotient.*

ANALYSIS AND REVIEW.

96. Analysis is the process of solving problems by tracing the relation of the parts.

In analyzing it is usual to reason from the *given number* to *one*, and then from *one* to the *required number*.

ORAL EXERCISES.

1. If 8 yards of cloth cost $16, what will 12 yards cost?

ANALYSIS. — Since 8 yards cost $16, 1 yard will cost one eighth of $16, or $2; and since 1 yard costs $2, 12 yards will cost 12 times $2, or $24.

2. If 5 coats cost $45, what will 7 coats cost?

3. If 8 oranges cost 32 cents, what will 9 oranges cost?

4. A man bought 6 sheep for $36. What will 7 sheep cost at the same rate?

5. How much will 12 books cost if 8 books cost $16?

6. If 9 tons of coal cost $36, what will be the cost of 7 tons?

7. If 8 barrels of flour are worth $48, what are 12 barrels worth?

8. A man paid $160 for 4 cows. How much would he have paid had he bought 7 cows at the same rate?

9. What must be paid for 14 sheep, if 5 sheep cost $35?

10. In 8 hogsheads there are 504 gallons. How many gallons do 9 hogsheads contain?

11. If 12 men can do a piece of work in 5 days, how long will it take 20 men to do it?

12. If it requires 288 pickets to build a fence 9 rods long, how many pickets will it require to build a fence 15 rods long?

13. If 18 pounds of rice are worth $1.44, how much are 20 pounds worth?

14. In 20 quires of paper there are 480 sheets. How many sheets are there in 8 quires?

15. If a man receives 32 pounds of sugar in exchange for 20 pounds of cheese at 8 cents a pound, what is the price of the sugar per pound?

WRITTEN EXERCISES.

97. 1. A farmer paid $12,880 for a farm of 112 acres. How much did he pay for 8 acres at that rate?

SOLUTION.   112 acres cost $12,880.
                 1 acre costs $115.
                 8 acres cost $920.

2. A man divided $41,185 equally among his children, giving to each $8237. How many children did he have?

3. A merchant bought 175 yards of cloth at $6.50 per yard, and afterwards sold 83 yards at $7 per yard, and the remainder at $7.25 per yard. How much did he gain?

4. I bought at a store 12 pounds of sugar at 5 cents a pound, 3 quarts of syrup at 15 cents a quart, 3 dozen eggs at 24 cents a dozen, 4 pounds of butter at 23 cents a pound, and a sack of flour for 75 cents. I gave the salesman a 5-dollar bill to pay for the groceries. How much change should I have received?

5. A dealer bought 17 harrows at $14 a piece, and gave in exchange 13 cords of wood at $8 per cord, and paid the balance in cash. How much cash did he pay?

6. A farmer bought 7 oxen at $65 each, 9 cows at $42 each, and 120 sheep at $5.50 each. What did he pay for the whole?

7. How many yards of linen, at 28 cents a yard, must be given for 35 bushels of potatoes at 56 cents a bushel?

8. Two men had an equal interest in a herd of cattle; one took 65 at $40 apiece, and the other took the rest at $52 apiece. How many cattle were there in the herd?

9. Mr. A has a sum of money equal to 8214 cents, consisting of an equal number of dollars, dimes, and cents. How many has he of each?

10. What number multiplied by 123, will give a product of 40,221?

11. Mr. Faust has $12,000 to invest in land. How many acres can he buy at $125 an acre?

12. Paid $17,125 for 137 shares of railway stock. How much did each share cost?

13. A drover had 580 sheep; he sold 230 to one man, 213 to another, and then bought enough to make his number 600. How many did he buy?

14. Three men enter into partnership. A puts in $2160; B, $1720; and C twice as much as A and B together. How much did C put in, and how much did all together invest?

15. Rome was founded 753 years before the birth of Christ. How long is it since that time?

16. A dying man willed his estate as follows: To his wife, $4500; to each of his three sons, $2800; to each of his five daughters, $2500; and $3000 to a church. What was the value of the estate?

17. I bought 4 pairs of shoes at $3.75 a pair, 2 pairs of boots at $6.50 a pair, and 3 hats at $2.75 each, and gave the merchant a fifty-dollar bill. How much change did I get?

18. A man earns $60 a week, and spends $28 a week. How much does he save in 12 weeks?

19. Bought 13 cows at $26 each, 9 horses at $125 each, and 100 sheep at $3.75 each, and sold all for $1750. How much did I lose?

20. Two ships, 2500 miles apart, are sailing towards each other, one at the rate of 87 miles a day, and the other at the rate of 85 miles a day. How far apart will they be at the end of 13 days?

21. Two steamships start from New York to Liverpool, one at the rate of 156 miles a day, the other at the rate of 217 miles a day. How far apart will they be at the end of 9 days?

22. Mr. L. had $100. He bought a suit of clothes for $22, a hat for $3, a pair of shoes for $4, and 4 shirts at $1.75 each. How many books at $1.60 apiece can he get for the remainder of his money?

23. How many men, at a salary of $600 a year, will earn $585,000 in a year?

24. It requires 7,020,000 bricks to build a large foundry. How many teams will it require to draw the bricks in 60 days, if each team draws 6 loads per day and 1500 bricks at a load?

25. From a cistern containing 12,572 gallons of water, 9236 gallons were drawn out, and afterwards, during a rainstorm, 7250 gallons ran in. How much water was there then in the cistern?

26. I bought a farm of 163 acres at $ 95 an acre. I paid down $ 2500, and gave bank-stock valued at $ 9000. How much remained unpaid?

27. A certain cistern holds 11,200 gallons of water. When empty, how many barrels of water, each containing 31 gallons, will it take to fill it?

28. A dairy-man has fodder enough to keep 28 cows 4 months. If he sells 12 cows, how many months will the fodder last the rest?

29. If the difference between two numbers is 1320, and the smaller number is 1750, what is the larger number?

30. The sum of two numbers is 3680, and one of the numbers is 1976. What is the other number?

31. The larger of two numbers is 2560, and their difference is 1177. What is the smaller number?

32. What is the product of 14,625 and 12,349?

33. If the product of two numbers is 7,715,962, and one of the numbers is 2566, what is the other number?

34. I paid $ 36 an acre for 50 acres of wood-land. I sold the wood for $ 1576, and the land for $ 17 an acre. Did I gain or lose, and how much?

35. I bought a stock of goods for $ 12,650, paying $ 1650 cash, and the balance in monthly payments of $ 1100 each. How many monthly payments did I make?

36. Twenty-four ladies and 18 gentlemen went on an excursion, and their expenses, which were $ 1.50 each, were paid by the gentlemen. How much did each gentleman pay?

37. A young man worked a year at $ 35 a month. He paid $ 16 a month for his board, and his other expenses amounted to $ 96. How much money did he save?

38. A stationer paid $95 for gold pens, at $1.90 apiece. How many pens did he buy?

39. Find the cost of 118 pounds of ham, at $.11 a pound; and 227 pounds of bacon, at $.09 a pound.

40. A farmer's wheat crop yielded him $565, his corn $362, his oats $175, and his clover seed $57. He paid a farm hand $18 a month for 9 months, $225 for fertilizers, and $195.85 for repairs and other expenses. How much did he gain on his farm?

41. Mr. D. invested $3000 in business. The first year he gained $560, and the second year he lost $475. The next three years his average yearly gain was $843. How much was he worth at the end of the five years?

42. A mechanic receives $1200 a year for his labor, and his expenses are $576. In how many years can he save enough to buy 52 acres of land at $72 an acre?

43. A man paid $450 for a horse and a buggy, the horse being valued at $90 more than the buggy. What did he pay for each?

44. I sold a quantity of wood that cost $920 for $1265, thus gaining $3 a cord. How many cords were there?

45. B bought 30 cows for $1400; but 5 of them died. How much must he receive for each of the rest to incur no loss?

46. A farmer sells 125 acres of land for $85 an acre, and 75 acres of other land at $115 an acre. He invests all the money in another farm that costs him $175 an acre. How many acres are there in the farm?

47. Light travels at the rate of about 186,000 miles a second. How many seconds does it take to reach us from the sun, a distance of about 95,000,000 miles?

FACTORS.

98. 1. What is the product when 7 is multiplied by 5? What are the numbers 7 and 5 of their product?

2. What numbers multiplied one by the other will produce 63? What are the numbers 7 and 9 of 63?

3. What are the factors of a number?

4. Name the factors of the following numbers: 20, 36, 45, 48, 60, 35, 72, 50, 21, 40, 24, 32, 64, 81, 80, 56, 44.

5. What numbers will exactly divide 48? 40? 80? 81?

6. Since 6 exactly divides 48, what part of 48 may it be called?

7. Give the exact divisors of the following numbers: 40, 81, 56, 42, 64, 32, 24, 50, 72, 35, 36, 45, 48, 60.

8. What numbers between 0 and 20 have no exact divisors except themselves and 1? What name is given to such numbers? *Prime Numbers.*

9. What are the prime numbers between 20 and 40?

10. What numbers between 0 and 40 have exact divisors besides themselves and 1? What name is given to such numbers? *Composite Numbers.*

11. Select from the following numbers, *first*, the prime numbers; *secondly*, the composite numbers: 13, 15, 21, 18, 27.

23, 17, 40, 41, 37, 25, 19, 42, 47, 43, 20, 14, 28, 36, 35, 33,
48, 49, 50, 51, 53, 72, 86, 66, 54, 80, 44, 71, 55, 63, 65, 67,
77, 84, 81, 83, 61, 73, 88, 87, 99, 93, 92, 97.

99. A number that expresses whole units is called an **Integer** or **Integral Number.**

Thus, 18, 25, 30, etc., are *integers* or *integral numbers.*

100. The integers which multiplied by one another will produce a number are called the **Factors** of the number.

Thus, 7 and 5 are the factors of 35.

101. An integer that will divide a number without having a remainder is called an **Exact Divisor** of the number.

Thus, 2, 3, 4, and 6 are exact divisors of 12.

The factors of a number are *exact divisors* of it.

102. A number that has no exact divisor except itself and 1 is called a **Prime Number.**

Thus, 1, 3, 5, 7, 11, 13, etc., are prime numbers.

103. A number that has exact divisors besides itself and 1 is called a **Composite Number.** Hence, a composite number is always the product of two or more factors.

Thus, 12, 18, 21, 40, etc., are composite numbers.

104. A number that is exactly divisible by 2 is called an **Even Number.**

Thus, 10, 12, 16, 18, etc., are even numbers.

105. A number that is not exactly divisible by 2 is called an **Odd Number.**

Thus, 3, 5, 9, 11, 13, etc., are odd numbers.

TESTS OF DIVISIBILITY.

106. Illustrate with numbers the truth of each of the following statements:

1. *Two* is an exact divisor of any number whose right-hand digit is 0, 2, 4, 6, or 8.

2. *Three* is an exact divisor of any number, the sum of whose digits is divisible by 3.

3. *Four* is an exact divisor of a number, if the number expressed by its two right-hand digits is divisible by 4.

4. *Five* is an exact divisor of any number whose right-hand digit is 0 or 5.

5. *Six* is an exact divisor of any *even* number, the sum of whose digits is divisible by 3.

6. *Eight* is an exact divisor of a number, if the number expressed by its three right-hand digits is divisible by 8.

7. *Nine* is an exact divisor of any number, the sum of whose digits is divisible by 9.

8. *Twenty-five* is an exact divisor of a number, if the number expressed by its two right-hand digits is divisible by 25.

9. *One hundred twenty-five* is an exact divisor of a number, if the number expressed by its three right-hand digits is divisible by 125.

10. If an *even* number is divisible by an odd number, it is divisible by twice that number.

11. An exact divisor of a number is an exact divisor of any number of times that number.

12. An exact divisor of each of two numbers is an exact divisor of their *sum* and of their *difference*.

EXERCISES.

107. Find by inspection some of the exact divisors of the following numbers :

1. 43844.	9. 72369.	17. 83466.	25. 27324.
2. 39128.	10. 85728.	18. 48324.	26. 34254.
3. 46836.	11. 51650.	19. 51375.	27. 38655.
4. 37125.	12. 43284.	20. 48224.	28. 51750.
5. 48636.	13. 31296.	21. 31959.	29. 62488.
6. 41848.	14. 53712.	22. 40675.	30. 83830.
7. 36444.	15. 48375.	23. 58625.	31. 71127.
8. 52146.	16. 31475.	24. 38169.	32. 92625.

FACTORING.

108. The process of separating a number into its factors is called **Factoring.**

109. Factors that are prime numbers are called **Prime Factors.**

Thus, 5 and 7 are the prime factors of 35.

110. When numbers have no common factor they are said to be **Prime to Each Other.**

Thus, 7 and 16 are prime to each other, though 16 is not a prime number.

111. The number of times a number is used as a factor is indicated by a small figure called an **Exponent.**

It is written above and at the right of the number.

Thus, 5 used as a factor 4 times is indicated by 5^4.

1. What are the prime factors of 1008 ?

2	1008
2	504
2	252
2	126
7	63
3	9
3	3
	1

EXPLANATION. — Since every prime factor of a number is an exact divisor of the number, the prime factors of 1008 may be found by finding all the prime numbers that are exact divisors of 1008. Since the number is *even*, 2 is taken for the first prime divisor. Since the quotient is even, 2 is taken for divisor again, and the division is continued until the last quotient is 1.

Hence the prime factors are 2, 2, 2, 2, 7, 3, 3 or 2^4, 7, 3^2.

RULE. — *Divide the given number by any prime number that will exactly divide it. Divide this quotient by another prime number, and so continue until the quotient is* 1.

The several divisors will be the prime factors.

What are the prime factors of the following :

2.	45.	10.	360.	18.	4862.	26.	21504.
3.	84.	11.	786.	19.	3290.	27.	10010.
4.	125.	12.	1872.	20.	4620.	28.	32320.
5.	210.	13.	2310.	21.	3136.	29.	25600.
6.	315.	14.	3465.	22.	3812.	30.	64384.
7.	432.	15.	2205.	23.	7007.	31.	31570.
8.	330.	16.	6300.	24.	4350.	32.	48500.
9.	484.	17.	7644.	25.	11368.	33.	124416.

CANCELLATION.

112. 1. How many times is 8 times 5 contained in 16 times 5 ? 4 times 12 in 16 times 12 ? 5 times 7 in 15 times 7 ?

2. How many times is 9×8 contained in 27×8 ? 8×6 in 24×6 ? 15×9 in 30×9 ? 4×18 in 12×18 ?

3. In determining the quotient, what numbers may be omitted from both dividend and divisor?

113. The process of shortening computations by rejecting equal factors from both dividend and divisor is called **Cancellation**.

114. PRINCIPLE. — *Rejecting equal factors from both dividend and divisor does not alter the quotient.*

WRITTEN EXERCISES.

115. **1.** Divide $6 \times 12 \times 15 \times 36$ by $3 \times 4 \times 5 \times 48$.

$$\frac{\cancel{6} \times \cancel{12} \times \cancel{15} \times \cancel{36}}{\cancel{3} \times \cancel{4} \times \cancel{5} \times \cancel{48}} = \frac{27}{2} = 13\tfrac{1}{2}.$$

EXPLANATION. — The dividend is written above the divisor with a line between them.

Since 3, 4, and 5 are factors of 6, 12, and 15, respectively, in the dividend, they may be rejected from both dividend and divisor, leaving the factors 2, 3, and 3 in the dividend. Since 12 is a factor of 36 in the dividend and of 48 in the divisor, it may be rejected, leaving 3 in the dividend and 4 in the divisor. Since 2, one of the factors left in the dividend, is a factor of the 4 left in the divisor, it may be rejected, leaving 2 in the divisor.

The product of the factors not canceled in the dividend is 27, and of those in the divisor, 2. Hence, the quotient is $\tfrac{27}{2}$, or $27 \div 2$, or $13\tfrac{1}{2}$.

RULE. — *Reject from the dividend and divisor all factors common to both, and then divide the product of the remaining factors of the dividend by the product of the remaining factors of the divisor.*

When all the factors of both dividend and divisor are canceled, the quotient is 1, for the dividend then contains the divisor exactly *once*.

Divide, using cancellation:

2. $6 \times 9 \times 12 \times 15 \times 20$ by $3 \times 3 \times 4 \times 5 \times 30$.

3. $5 \times 8 \times 24 \times 30$ by $4 \times 3 \times 5 \times 10$.

4. $7 \times 6 \times 5 \times 4 \times 3$ by $8 \times 3 \times 5$.

5. 36×24 by $8 \times 4 \times 6$.

6. $45 \times 30 \times 9$ by $5 \times 9 \times 50$.

7. $12 \times 6 \times 9 \times 20$ by $4 \times 80 \times 3$.

8. $2 \times 3 \times 5 \times 7 \times 9 \times 11$ by $4 \times 6 \times 18 \times 7$.

9. $14 \times 9 \times 7 \times 15 \times 21$ by $42 \times 3 \times 7$.

10. $17 \times 14 \times 13 \times 12$ by $7 \times 3 \times 26 \times 34$.

11. $27 \times 49 \times 38 \times 25$ by $35 \times 18 \times 15$.

12. $28 \times 54 \times 72$ by $14 \times 9 \times 36$.

13. $114 \times 85 \times 75$ by $15 \times 5 \times 57 \times 17$.

14. $140 \times 65 \times 27$ by $13 \times 20 \times 9$.

15. $95 \times 66 \times 81$ by $9 \times 3 \times 11 \times 19$.

16. $78 \times 14 \times 63 \times 5$ by $7 \times 13 \times 7 \times 21$.

17. $69 \times 37 \times 28 \times 45$ by $15 \times 23 \times 7 \times 3$.

18. $144 \times 82 \times 49$ by $7 \times 2 \times 12 \times 41$.

19. $57 \times 148 \times 64$ by $36 \times 19 \times 4$.

20. $84 \times 96 \times 108$ by $27 \times 14 \times 12$.

21. $117 \times 57 \times 49$ by $114 \times 7 \times 13$.

22. $121 \times 8 \times 90$ by $4 \times 10 \times 11 \times 2$.

23. $216 \times 33 \times 72$ by $18 \times 11 \times 36$.

24. $45 \times 56 \times 68 \times 92$ by $7 \times 9 \times 46$.

25. $75 \times 125 \times 33 \times 28$ by $14 \times 16 \times 150$.

26. Divide the product of 47 times 27 times 45, by 9 times 81.

27. Find the quotient of 77 times 360 times 475, divided by 11 times 6 times 35.

28. How many bushels of corn, worth 55 cents a bushel, must be given in exchange for 3 pieces of cloth, each containing 33 yards, at 25 cents a yard ?

29. How many boxes of coffee, each containing 40 pounds, at 28 cents a pound, must be given for 30 firkins of butter, each containing 56 pounds, at 18 cents a pound ?

30. How many barrels of flour, at $6 a barrel, must be given for 3 pieces of linen, each containing 36 yards, at 25 cents a yard?

31. How many bushels of wheat, at 90 cents a bushel, will pay for 3 barrels of sugar, each containing 200 pounds, at 6 cents per pound?

32. A laborer worked 8 days for 24 bushels of potatoes, worth 40 cents a bushel. What were his daily earnings?

33. How many boxes of tea, each containing 24 pounds, worth 45 cents a pound, must be given for 4 loads of wheat, each containing 54 bushels, worth $.95 a bushel?

34. If 34 bushels of wheat make 8 barrels of flour, how many bushels will be necessary to make 72 barrels?

35. A grocer sold 18 boxes of soap, each containing 55 pounds, at 10 cents a pound, and received as pay 66 barrels of apples, each containing 3 bushels. What was the price per bushel of the apples?

36. A farmer exchanged 96 bushels of corn, worth $.55 a bushel, for an equal number of bushels of rye, worth $.75 a bushel, and oats worth $.35 a bushel. How many bushels of each did he receive?

37. If 48 men can dig a trench in 25 days, working 9 hours a day, how many days will be required by 20 men to do the same work if they work 10 hours per day?

38. If 12 barrels of pork, each containing 200 pounds, are worth $192, what will 80 pounds cost at the same rate per pound?

39. How many days' work, at $1.25 a day, will pay for 75 bushels of corn, at $.60 cents a bushel?

FRACTIONS.

116. **1.** When anything is divided into two equal parts, what is each part called? Into three equal parts? Into seven equal parts? Into eight equal parts? Into nine equal parts? Into fifteen equal parts?

2. How many halves are there in anything? How many thirds? How many fifths? How many tenths? How many fifteenths? How many twentieths?

3. What part of an apple will each boy receive when it is divided equally among 7 boys? Among 8 boys?

4. How much is one fifth of 10 cents? Of 15 cents? Of 30 cents?

5. How much is one sixth of 12 cents? Of 18 cents? Of 24 cents?

6. How much is one seventh of 14 oranges? Of 21 oranges? Of 28 oranges?

7. In 6 hours James earned 36 cents. How much did he earn per hour?

8. A school has 4 classes of the same size, and the whole number of pupils in the classes is 40. How many are there in each class?

117. One or more of the equal parts of anything is called a **Fraction**.

Two numbers, written one above the other with a line between them, are used to *express* a fraction.

118. The number which shows into how many parts **a** thing has been divided is called the **Denominator**.

It is written below the line.

Thus, in the fraction $\frac{7}{9}$, 9 is the denominator. It shows that something has been divided into 9 equal parts.

119. The number which shows how many parts form the fraction is called the **Numerator**.

It is written above the line.

Thus, in the fraction $\frac{7}{9}$, 7 is the numerator. It shows that the fraction contains 7 of the 9 equal parts.

120. The numerator and denominator together are called the **Terms of the Fraction**.

121. A fraction whose numerator is less than its denominator is called a **Proper Fraction**.

Thus, $\frac{3}{4}$, $\frac{5}{9}$, and $\frac{15}{27}$ are proper fractions.
The value of a proper fraction is, therefore, *less than* 1.

122. A fraction whose numerator equals or exceeds its denominator is called an **Improper Fraction**.

Thus, $\frac{7}{7}$, $\frac{15}{8}$, and $\frac{41}{23}$ are improper fractions.
The value of an improper fraction is, therefore, 1 *or more than* 1.

123. A number expressed by an integer and a fraction is called a **Mixed Number**.

Thus, $3\frac{5}{7}$, $8\frac{7}{9}$, and $14\frac{12}{23}$ are mixed numbers.

124. The unit which is divided into equal parts is called the **Unit of the Fraction**.

A fraction whose unit has been divided into *any number* of equal parts is called a *Common Fraction*.

A fraction whose unit has been divided into tenths, hundredths, thousandths, etc., is called a *Decimal Fraction*.

125. One of the equal parts into which a unit has been divided is called a **Fractional Unit.**

126. A fraction also expresses *unexecuted division.*

Thus, $\frac{10}{5}$ is equal to $10 \div 5$; $\frac{19}{4}$ is equal to $19 \div 4$.

127. Fractions are read by naming first the number of fractional units, and then the kind of them.

Thus, $\frac{3}{8}$ is read three eighths; $\frac{9}{31}$ nine thirty-firsts.

128. Read the following:

$\frac{5}{7}$	$\frac{6}{8}$	$\frac{3}{24}$	$\frac{18}{27}$	$\frac{15}{33}$	$\frac{24}{81}$	$\frac{53}{67}$	$\frac{68}{80}$	$\frac{58}{83}$	$\frac{71}{90}$
$\frac{2}{13}$	$\frac{5}{18}$	$\frac{7}{21}$	$\frac{8}{27}$	$\frac{16}{43}$	$\frac{35}{37}$	$\frac{52}{61}$	$\frac{39}{42}$	$\frac{17}{29}$	$\frac{31}{44}$
$\frac{26}{305}$	$\frac{31}{419}$	$\frac{46}{527}$	$\frac{43}{816}$	$\frac{112}{719}$	$\frac{224}{439}$	$\frac{512}{639}$	$\frac{783}{518}$	$\frac{314}{463}$	$\frac{520}{649}$

Express in figures:

1. Seven ninths. Eight elevenths. Four fifteenths.

2. Six nineteenths. Nine fourteenths. Five seventeenths.

3. Three twentieths. Six forty-fifths. Nine eighteenths.

4. Seventeen twentieths. Thirteen forty-sevenths.

5. Twelve thirtieths. Fifty-five eighty-fifths.

6. Seventeen fifty-fifths. Thirty-four ninety-eighths.

129. 1. Interpret the expression $\frac{7}{9}$.

EXPLANATION. — $\frac{7}{9}$ represents 7 of 9 equal parts of a thing. It also represents one ninth of 7, and 7 divided by 9. It is read seven ninths.

In like manner interpret the following:

2.	$\frac{3}{8}$	$\frac{5}{12}$	$\frac{16}{23}$	$\frac{18}{45}$	$\frac{47}{38}$	$\frac{53}{33}$	$\frac{81}{90}$	$\frac{85}{76}$
3.	$\frac{5}{11}$	$\frac{8}{15}$	$\frac{21}{42}$	$\frac{33}{84}$	$\frac{39}{40}$	$\frac{85}{40}$	$\frac{83}{00}$	$\frac{85}{02}$
4.	$\frac{13}{24}$	$\frac{17}{35}$	$\frac{45}{86}$	$\frac{41}{73}$	$\frac{47}{65}$	$\frac{81}{72}$	$\frac{76}{45}$	$\frac{86}{73}$

REDUCTION.

130. **To reduce fractions to higher terms.**

1. In $\frac{1}{2}$ yard, how many fourths are there? How many eighths?

2. In $\frac{1}{3}$ of a foot, how many sixths are there? How many ninths?

3. Since $\frac{1}{2}$ is equal to $\frac{2}{4}$, how may the terms of the fraction $\frac{2}{4}$ be obtained from $\frac{1}{2}$? $\frac{4}{8}$ from $\frac{1}{2}$? $\frac{2}{6}$ from $\frac{1}{3}$? $\frac{3}{9}$ from $\frac{1}{3}$?

4. Since the terms of the fraction $\frac{4}{8}$ may be obtained from $\frac{1}{2}$ by multiplying them by 4, how may the terms of the fraction $\frac{1}{2}$ be obtained from $\frac{4}{8}$?

5. What changes, then, may be made in the terms of a fraction without changing its value?

Change the following:

6. $\frac{3}{4}$ to 12ths.	13. $\frac{4}{9}$ to 18ths.	20. $\frac{5}{9}$ to 18ths.
7. $\frac{4}{5}$ to 20ths.	14. $\frac{5}{8}$ to 24ths.	21. $\frac{3}{5}$ to 25ths.
8. $\frac{5}{7}$ to 14ths.	15. $\frac{4}{9}$ to 27ths.	22. $\frac{4}{8}$ to 16ths.
9. $\frac{3}{8}$ to 16ths.	16. $\frac{2}{3}$ to 24ths.	23. $\frac{3}{7}$ to 14ths.
10. $\frac{4}{7}$ to 21sts.	17. $\frac{5}{6}$ to 18ths.	24. $\frac{4}{5}$ to 25ths.
11. $\frac{2}{5}$ to 15ths.	18. $\frac{3}{4}$ to 20ths.	25. $\frac{7}{9}$ to 18ths.
12. $\frac{2}{3}$ to 18ths.	19. $\frac{2}{3}$ to 21sts.	26. $\frac{3}{5}$ to 30ths.

131. The process of changing the forms of fractions without changing their values is called **Reduction of Fractions.**

132. A fraction is expressed in *higher* terms, when its numerator and denominator are expressed by larger numbers.

133. PRINCIPLE. — *Multiplying or dividing both terms of a fraction by the same number does not change the value of the fraction.*

WRITTEN EXERCISES.

134. 1. Change $\frac{7}{16}$ to 48ths.

$48 \div 16 = 3$

$\dfrac{7 \times 3 = 21}{16 \times 3 = 48}$

EXPLANATION. — Since there are 48 forty-eighths in 1, in $\frac{1}{16}$ there are $\frac{1}{16}$ of $\frac{48}{48}$, or $\frac{3}{48}$; and in $\frac{7}{16}$ there are 7 times $\frac{3}{48}$, or $\frac{21}{48}$. Or,

Since the denominator of the fraction is to be 48, both terms of the fraction must be multiplied by 3.

RULE. — *Multiply the terms of the fraction by such a number as will change the given denominator to the required denominator.*

Change the following:

2. $\frac{13}{35}$ to 70ths.   9. $\frac{22}{36}$ to 108ths.   16. $\frac{33}{53}$ to 212ths.

3. $\frac{14}{27}$ to 54ths.   10. $\frac{31}{45}$ to 135ths.   17. $\frac{21}{45}$ to 180ths.

4. $\frac{12}{32}$ to 64ths.   11. $\frac{18}{72}$ to 216ths.   18. $\frac{36}{73}$ to 219ths.

5. $\frac{18}{29}$ to 58ths.   12. $\frac{42}{55}$ to 165ths.   19. $\frac{25}{59}$ to 236ths.

6. $\frac{19}{26}$ to 78ths.   13. $\frac{51}{37}$ to 111ths.   20. $\frac{27}{38}$ to 152nds.

7. $\frac{15}{31}$ to 93ds.   14. $\frac{63}{72}$ to 144ths.   21. $\frac{25}{49}$ to 196ths.

8. $\frac{18}{42}$ to 84ths.   15. $\frac{55}{84}$ to 168ths.   22. $\frac{43}{71}$ to 355ths.

135. To reduce fractions to lower terms.

1. How many *halves* are there in $\frac{4}{8}$? $\frac{3}{6}$? $\frac{5}{10}$? $\frac{6}{12}$?

2. How many *thirds* are there in $\frac{2}{6}$? $\frac{3}{9}$? $\frac{4}{12}$? $\frac{5}{15}$?

Reduce the following to lower terms:

?. $\frac{5}{15}$ $\frac{6}{18}$ $\frac{9}{18}$ $\frac{8}{24}$ $\frac{10}{30}$ $\frac{9}{27}$ $\frac{12}{24}$ $\frac{8}{32}$.

4. $\frac{7}{14}$ $\frac{5}{20}$ $\frac{6}{24}$ $\frac{4}{16}$ $\frac{3}{15}$ $\frac{2}{16}$ $\frac{3}{21}$ $\frac{7}{28}$.

5. $\frac{5}{30}$ $\frac{6}{36}$ $\frac{8}{56}$ $\frac{5}{45}$ $\frac{6}{42}$ $\frac{4}{40}$ $\frac{9}{30}$ $\frac{7}{49}$.

6. $\frac{7}{56}$ $\frac{5}{40}$ $\frac{8}{40}$ $\frac{9}{63}$ $\frac{6}{48}$ $\frac{4}{36}$ $\frac{9}{72}$ $\frac{8}{64}$.

136. A **common divisor** of two or more numbers is a number that will exactly divide each of them.

137. A fraction is expressed in *lower* terms when its numerator and denominator are expressed in smaller numbers.

A fraction is expressed in its *lowest* terms when its numerator and denominator have no common divisor.

WRITTEN EXERCISES.

138. 1. Reduce $\frac{45}{60}$ to its lowest terms.

$$5)\overline{45} \atop 5)\overline{60} = \frac{9}{12}$$

$$3)\overline{9} \atop 3)\overline{12} = \frac{3}{4}$$

EXPLANATION. — Since the fraction is to be reduced to its lowest terms, the terms are first divided by 5 (Prin., Art. 133), and the terms of the resulting fraction by 3. Inasmuch as no number will exactly divide the terms of the fraction $\frac{3}{4}$, the fraction is reduced to its lowest terms.

RULE. — *Divide the terms of the fraction by any common divisor, and continue thus to divide until the terms have no common divisor.* See also Art. 511.

Reduce to their lowest terms:

2. $\frac{18}{54}, \frac{54}{81}$.

3. $\frac{36}{72}, \frac{63}{84}$.

4. $\frac{48}{72}, \frac{29}{87}$.

5. $\frac{20}{45}, \frac{48}{96}$.

6. $\frac{36}{96}, \frac{45}{60}$.

7. $\frac{32}{64}, \frac{55}{66}$.

8. $\frac{40}{75}, \frac{80}{95}$.

9. $\frac{44}{76}, \frac{77}{99}$.

10. $\frac{55}{80}, \frac{75}{125}$.

11. $\frac{56}{84}, \frac{75}{100}$.

12. $\frac{240}{480}, \frac{120}{168}$.

13. $\frac{115}{253}, \frac{105}{225}$.

14. $\frac{121}{396}, \frac{245}{364}$.

15. $\frac{155}{217}, \frac{96}{144}$.

16. $\frac{192}{216}, \frac{72}{248}$.

17. $\frac{168}{192}, \frac{120}{210}$.

18. $\frac{175}{210}, \frac{176}{220}$.

19. $\frac{288}{480}, \frac{126}{162}$.

20. $\frac{121}{132}, \frac{195}{210}$.

21. $\frac{240}{312}, \frac{126}{198}$.

22. $\frac{125}{375}, \frac{300}{480}$.

23. $\frac{272}{425}, \frac{195}{585}$.

24. $\frac{216}{414}, \frac{182}{196}$.

25. $\frac{192}{224}, \frac{252}{396}$.

26. $\frac{144}{192}, \frac{210}{840}$.

27. $\frac{108}{144}, \frac{176}{192}$.

28. $\frac{182}{196}, \frac{210}{300}$.

29. $\frac{315}{378}, \frac{450}{675}$.

30. $\frac{420}{660}, \frac{360}{576}$.

31. $\frac{264}{480}, \frac{567}{783}$.

32. $\frac{132}{144}, \frac{125}{625}$.

33. $\frac{363}{605}, \frac{504}{616}$.

34. $\frac{400}{450}, \frac{648}{720}$.

35. $\frac{378}{594}, \frac{726}{792}$.

36. $\frac{480}{560}, \frac{391}{667}$.

37. $\frac{288}{864}, \frac{253}{782}$.

38. $\frac{693}{792}, \frac{435}{957}$.

39. $\frac{704}{792}, \frac{750}{900}$.

40. $\frac{528}{984}, \frac{856}{936}$.

41. $\frac{728}{784}, \frac{615}{915}$.

139. To reduce integers and mixed numbers to improper fractions.

1. How many fourths are there in an orange? In 2 oranges?

2. How many sixths are there in a cake? In 3 cakes?

3. How many fifths are there in 1? In 2? In 3? In 4?

4. How many eighths are there in 1? In 2? In 5? In 8? In 9? In 10?

5. How many sevenths are there in 1? In $1\frac{4}{7}$? In 2? In $2\frac{5}{7}$? In 6?

Reduce the following to improper fractions.

6. $2\frac{1}{2}$ $3\frac{2}{7}$ $4\frac{2}{5}$ $5\frac{3}{8}$ $6\frac{2}{5}$ $7\frac{1}{6}$.

7. $3\frac{1}{4}$ $5\frac{3}{4}$ $3\frac{5}{7}$ $4\frac{3}{5}$ $7\frac{3}{4}$ $5\frac{2}{5}$.

8. $4\frac{1}{2}$ $4\frac{2}{7}$ $2\frac{5}{9}$ $3\frac{2}{7}$ $8\frac{2}{3}$ $8\frac{3}{4}$.

9. $5\frac{1}{3}$ $3\frac{6}{9}$ $4\frac{3}{6}$ $2\frac{7}{9}$ $9\frac{1}{4}$ $3\frac{7}{8}$.

10. $2\frac{2}{3}$ $6\frac{1}{4}$ $6\frac{2}{7}$ $5\frac{2}{3}$ $4\frac{3}{8}$ $7\frac{3}{6}$.

11. $3\frac{3}{4}$ $5\frac{2}{5}$ $5\frac{1}{4}$ $2\frac{6}{7}$ $2\frac{5}{9}$ $6\frac{5}{6}$.

WRITTEN EXERCISES.

140. 1. Reduce $18\frac{3}{5}$ to an improper fraction.

$18 = \frac{90}{5}$ EXPLANATION. — Since in 1 there are 5 fifths, in 18
$\frac{90}{5} + \frac{3}{5} = \frac{93}{5}$ there are 18 times 5 fifths, or $\frac{90}{5}$; and in $18 + \frac{3}{5}$ there
     are $\frac{90}{5} + \frac{3}{5}$, or $\frac{93}{5}$. Hence, $18\frac{3}{5}$ is equal to $\frac{93}{5}$.

RULE. — *Multiply the integer by the given denominator, to this product add the numerator, and write the result over the given denominator.*

Reduce the following to improper fractions:

2. $18\frac{7}{9}$.	8. $36\frac{15}{18}$.	14. $421\frac{13}{24}$.	20. $526\frac{18}{47}$.
3. $24\frac{5}{8}$.	9. $48\frac{17}{19}$.	15. $347\frac{17}{28}$.	21. $635\frac{23}{25}$.
4. $36\frac{9}{10}$.	10. $51\frac{19}{20}$.	16. $423\frac{37}{42}$.	22. $717\frac{35}{48}$.
5. $47\frac{10}{11}$.	11. $68\frac{21}{25}$.	17. $450\frac{45}{49}$.	23. $694\frac{54}{77}$.
6. $53\frac{12}{13}$.	12. $72\frac{27}{37}$.	18. $479\frac{55}{81}$.	24. $800\frac{67}{81}$.
7. $60\frac{14}{17}$.	13. $89\frac{65}{99}$.	19. $399\frac{87}{90}$.	25. $815\frac{41}{100}$.

26. Change 24 to 5ths; 13 to 8ths; 45 to 7ths; 37 to 12ths; 37 to 15ths; 24 to 17ths; 36 to 25ths; 41 to 40ths.

141. To reduce improper fractions to integers or mixed numbers.

1. To how many dollars are 8 quarter-dollars equal? 16? 20? 25? 30?

2. To how many bushels are 12 fourths of a bushel equal? 20? 25? 50?

3. How many units are there in 5 fifths? In 10 fifths? In 15 fifths?

Reduce to integers or mixed numbers:

4. $\frac{15}{3}$	$\frac{21}{4}$	$\frac{31}{5}$	$\frac{45}{7}$	$\frac{39}{6}$	$\frac{54}{6}$	$\frac{50}{8}$.
5. $\frac{18}{6}$	$\frac{32}{5}$	$\frac{43}{6}$	$\frac{47}{5}$	$\frac{41}{8}$	$\frac{53}{7}$	$\frac{49}{7}$.
6. $\frac{16}{4}$	$\frac{41}{8}$	$\frac{71}{8}$	$\frac{35}{4}$	$\frac{32}{4}$	$\frac{57}{6}$	$\frac{55}{6}$.
7. $\frac{20}{5}$	$\frac{33}{6}$	$\frac{35}{6}$	$\frac{37}{6}$	$\frac{46}{5}$	$\frac{61}{7}$	$\frac{67}{8}$.
8. $\frac{30}{6}$	$\frac{50}{7}$	$\frac{46}{6}$	$\frac{63}{7}$	$\frac{53}{6}$	$\frac{80}{9}$	$\frac{71}{9}$.

WRITTEN EXERCISES.

142. 1. Reduce $\frac{356}{9}$ to a mixed number.

$$\frac{356}{9} = 356 \div 9 = 39\frac{5}{9}$$

EXPLANATION. — Since 9 ninths are equal to 1 unit, 356 ninths are equal to as many units as 9 ninths are contained times in 356 ninths, or $39\frac{5}{9}$. Therefore, $\frac{356}{9} = 39\frac{5}{9}$.

Rule. — *Divide the numerator by the denominator.*

Reduce to integers or mixed numbers :

2. $\frac{98}{15}$, $\frac{52}{23}$. 9. $\frac{224}{24}$, $\frac{148}{27}$. 16. $\frac{3475}{36}$. 23. $\frac{34256}{116}$.

3. $\frac{87}{12}$, $\frac{68}{21}$. 10. $\frac{179}{31}$, $\frac{235}{39}$. 17. $\frac{3885}{43}$. 24. $\frac{41216}{120}$.

4. $\frac{91}{13}$, $\frac{72}{25}$. 11. $\frac{251}{41}$, $\frac{265}{47}$. 18. $\frac{5261}{56}$. 25. $\frac{48314}{123}$.

5. $\frac{86}{17}$, $\frac{78}{26}$. 12. $\frac{341}{52}$, $\frac{436}{67}$. 19. $\frac{4877}{63}$. 26. $\frac{51417}{215}$.

6. $\frac{93}{11}$, $\frac{93}{43}$. 13. $\frac{514}{25}$, $\frac{600}{40}$. 20. $\frac{7108}{84}$. 27. $\frac{53418}{314}$.

7. $\frac{88}{19}$, $\frac{87}{61}$. 14. $\frac{735}{57}$, $\frac{751}{60}$. 21. $\frac{7952}{72}$. 28. $\frac{64721}{375}$.

8. $\frac{99}{18}$, $\frac{98}{27}$. 15. $\frac{828}{79}$, $\frac{864}{98}$. 22. $\frac{9680}{80}$, 29. $\frac{75682}{400}$.

143. To reduce dissimilar fractions to similar fractions.

1. How many eighths are there in $\frac{1}{2}$? In $\frac{1}{4}$?

2. How many sixths are there in $\frac{1}{2}$? In $\frac{1}{3}$? In $\frac{2}{3}$?

3. How many twelfths are there in $\frac{1}{2}$? In $\frac{1}{3}$? In $\frac{1}{4}$? In $\frac{1}{6}$?

4. Into what parts, then, of the same size, may $\frac{1}{2}$, $\frac{1}{3}$, $\frac{1}{4}$, and $\frac{1}{6}$ be divided?

5. Into what parts of the same size may $\frac{1}{2}$ and $\frac{1}{4}$ be divided? $\frac{1}{4}$ and $\frac{1}{8}$? $\frac{1}{8}$ and $\frac{1}{16}$? $\frac{1}{2}$ and $\frac{1}{8}$? $\frac{1}{4}$ and $\frac{1}{16}$? $\frac{1}{2}$, $\frac{1}{4}$, and $\frac{1}{8}$? $\frac{1}{2}$, $\frac{1}{4}$, $\frac{1}{8}$, and $\frac{1}{16}$?

Reduce the following to fractions having the same denominators :

6. $\frac{1}{2}$ and $\frac{1}{3}$. 11. $\frac{2}{3}$ and $\frac{3}{8}$. 16. $\frac{1}{2}$, $\frac{3}{5}$, and $\frac{4}{10}$.

7. $\frac{1}{4}$ and $\frac{1}{8}$. 12. $\frac{3}{4}$ and $\frac{5}{6}$. 17. $\frac{1}{2}$, $\frac{3}{8}$, and $\frac{5}{12}$.

8. $\frac{1}{4}$ and $\frac{1}{6}$. 13. $\frac{3}{8}$ and $\frac{1}{6}$. 18. $\frac{1}{4}$, $\frac{3}{8}$, and $\frac{5}{6}$.

9. $\frac{1}{2}$ and $\frac{3}{8}$. 14. $\frac{2}{5}$ and $\frac{3}{6}$. 19. $\frac{1}{3}$, $\frac{1}{4}$, and $\frac{3}{8}$.

10. $\frac{1}{3}$ and $\frac{2}{9}$. 15. $\frac{3}{4}$ and $\frac{3}{5}$. 20. $\frac{1}{4}$, $\frac{1}{5}$, and $\frac{3}{10}$.

144. Fractions that have the same denominators are called **Similar Fractions**.

145. Fractions that have not the same denominators are called **Dissimilar Fractions**.

146. The denominator of similar fractions is called a **Common Denominator**.

147. When similar fractions are expressed in their lowest terms, they have their **Least Common Denominator**.

WRITTEN EXERCISES.

148. 1. Reduce $\frac{3}{4}$, $\frac{5}{8}$, and $\frac{11}{12}$, to similar fractions.

$$\frac{3}{4} = \frac{3 \times 6}{4 \times 6} = \frac{18}{24}$$

$$\frac{5}{8} = \frac{5 \times 3}{8 \times 3} = \frac{15}{24}$$

$$\frac{11}{12} = \frac{11 \times 2}{12 \times 2} = \frac{22}{24}$$

EXPLANATION. — Since the fractions are to be changed to other fractions having a common denominator, the terms of each fraction must be multiplied by some number which will cause them to have the same denominator. (Prin., Art. 133.)

By examining the denominators 4, 8, and 12, it is evident that the denominators of all the fractions can be made 24, and the fractions will then be similar. To make the denominators 24, the terms of the first fraction must be multiplied by 6; the terms of the second, by 3; the terms of the third, by 2. And thus, the fractions are changed to the similar fractions $\frac{18}{24}$, $\frac{15}{24}$, $\frac{22}{24}$.

Reduce to similar fractions :

2. $\frac{2}{3}$, $\frac{5}{6}$, $\frac{5}{12}$.

3. $\frac{3}{4}$, $\frac{1}{2}$, $\frac{5}{8}$.

4. $\frac{1}{2}$, $\frac{2}{3}$, $\frac{3}{4}$.

5. $\frac{3}{4}$, $\frac{5}{8}$, $\frac{7}{16}$.

6. $\frac{5}{10}$, $\frac{7}{15}$, $\frac{8}{30}$.

7. $\frac{5}{8}$, $\frac{5}{12}$, $\frac{5}{24}$.

8. $\frac{5}{6}$, $\frac{5}{8}$, $\frac{5}{12}$.

9. $\frac{7}{12}$, $\frac{5}{24}$, $\frac{5}{6}$.

10. $\frac{3}{4}$, $\frac{2}{5}$, $\frac{3}{10}$.

11. $\frac{3}{5}$, $\frac{5}{6}$, $\frac{1}{15}$.

12. $\frac{3}{10}$, $\frac{3}{20}$, $\frac{3}{30}$.

13. $\frac{4}{5}$, $\frac{5}{12}$, $\frac{7}{20}$.

14. $\frac{5}{9}$, $\frac{5}{15}$, $\frac{3}{5}$.

15. $\frac{4}{9}$, $\frac{7}{36}$, $\frac{7}{18}$.

16. $\frac{5}{24}$, $\frac{3}{8}$, $\frac{7}{12}$.

17. $\frac{7}{16}$, $\frac{5}{8}$, $\frac{11}{32}$.

18. $\frac{1}{4}$, $\frac{1}{3}$, $\frac{1}{8}$, $\frac{1}{12}$.

19. $\frac{1}{5}$, $\frac{3}{4}$, $\frac{3}{10}$, $\frac{7}{20}$.

20. $\frac{3}{7}$, $\frac{5}{14}$, $\frac{9}{28}$, $\frac{1}{2}$.

21. $\frac{3}{10}$, $\frac{4}{5}$, $\frac{7}{20}$, $\frac{9}{30}$.

22. $\frac{3}{4}$, $\frac{4}{11}$, $\frac{5}{22}$, $\frac{3}{8}$.

23. $\frac{3}{7}$, $\frac{4}{21}$, $\frac{6}{7}$, $\frac{5}{14}$.

24. $\frac{4}{9}$, $\frac{7}{36}$, $\frac{8}{18}$, $\frac{3}{4}$.

25. $\frac{4}{5}$, $\frac{7}{15}$, $\frac{9}{30}$, $\frac{11}{20}$.

26. Reduce $\frac{2}{3}$, $\frac{3}{4}$, $\frac{7}{12}$, and $\frac{9}{16}$ to similar fractions having their least common denominator.

$$
\begin{array}{c|cccc}
3 & 3 & 4 & 12 & 16 \\
\hline
2 & 1 & 4 & 4 & 16 \\
\hline
2 & 1 & 2 & 2 & 8 \\
\hline
& 1 & 1 & 1 & 4
\end{array}
$$

$3 \times 2 \times 2 \times 4 = 48$

EXPLANATION. — The least common denominator cannot always be easily found by inspection. It may then be found as in the margin.

Since the least common denominator must be the smallest number that will contain each of the denominators, it must contain each of the prime factors of the denominators and *no other factors*. The prime factors are found as in the margin. 3 is a prime factor of 3 and 12, and consequently a factor of the least common denominator. Dividing by 3, and writing below the quotients and numbers of which 3 is not a factor, we have, 1, 4, 4, 16. Dividing by 2, and again by 2, the factors of the denominator are found to be the divisors 3, 2, 2, and the factor 4 in the last row. Their product is 48, the least common denominator. The fractions thus become $\frac{32}{48}$, $\frac{36}{48}$, $\frac{28}{48}$, $\frac{27}{48}$.

NOTE. — Fractions should first be reduced to their lowest terms. In finding the factors of the least common denominator a number that is a factor of another number may be disregarded. Thus, since 3 and 4 are factors of 12, they might have been disregarded, and the factors of 12 and 16 only found. See also pages 389–391.

Change to similar fractions having their least common denominator:

27. $\frac{3}{4}$, $\frac{5}{6}$, $\frac{7}{8}$, $\frac{7}{12}$.

28. $\frac{1}{4}$, $\frac{3}{8}$, $\frac{5}{6}$, $\frac{7}{9}$.

29. $\frac{1}{2}$, $\frac{3}{4}$, $\frac{5}{8}$, $\frac{7}{16}$.

30. $\frac{2}{5}$, $\frac{5}{6}$, $\frac{7}{15}$, $\frac{11}{30}$.

31. $\frac{3}{5}$, $\frac{7}{10}$, $\frac{11}{20}$, $\frac{13}{40}$.

32. $\frac{1}{3}$, $\frac{4}{7}$, $\frac{5}{6}$, $\frac{8}{21}$.

33. $\frac{4}{9}$, $\frac{7}{12}$, $\frac{11}{36}$, $\frac{19}{24}$.

34. $\frac{2}{3}$, $\frac{1}{5}$, $\frac{7}{8}$, $\frac{5}{6}$.

35. $\frac{3}{10}$, $\frac{7}{15}$, $\frac{9}{20}$, $\frac{13}{30}$.

36. $\frac{5}{12}$, $\frac{8}{21}$, $\frac{11}{28}$, $\frac{13}{42}$.

37. $\frac{3}{5}$, $\frac{11}{12}$, $\frac{9}{20}$, $\frac{29}{60}$.

38. $\frac{4}{9}$, $\frac{13}{35}$, $\frac{23}{45}$, $\frac{17}{63}$.

39. $\frac{7}{9}$, $\frac{5}{11}$, $\frac{16}{18}$, $\frac{6}{22}$.

40. $\frac{3}{11}$, $\frac{6}{13}$, $\frac{15}{33}$, $\frac{3}{39}$.

41. $\frac{3}{5}$, $\frac{15}{30}$, $\frac{28}{36}$, $\frac{4}{15}$.

42. $\frac{16}{21}$, $\frac{12}{16}$, $\frac{11}{14}$, $\frac{6}{7}$.

43. $\frac{3}{11}$, $\frac{2}{14}$, $\frac{15}{18}$, $\frac{9}{36}$.

44. $\frac{11}{30}$, $\frac{8}{15}$, $\frac{10}{60}$, $\frac{7}{120}$.

45. $4\frac{3}{5}$, $6\frac{4}{7}$, $\frac{11}{14}$, $\frac{9}{10}$.

46. $7\frac{5}{9}$, $9\frac{3}{7}$, $8\frac{2}{3}$, $4\frac{1}{21}$.

ADDITION.

149. **1.** James spent $\frac{2}{5}$ of a dollar for an arithmetic, $\frac{1}{5}$ for a slate, and $\frac{4}{5}$ for a geography. How much did he spend for all ?

2. I bought $\frac{1}{2}$ of a yard of silk, but afterward I was compelled to buy $\frac{3}{4}$ of a yard more. How much did I buy ?

3. A boy caught a fish that weighed $\frac{2}{3}$ of a pound, and his sister caught one weighing $\frac{3}{4}$ of a pound. How much did both weigh ?

4. What is the sum of $\$\frac{3}{4}$, $\$\frac{1}{2}$, and $\$\frac{1}{4}$?

5. A boy worked $\frac{2}{3}$ of a day for A, and $\frac{3}{4}$ of a day for B. How long did he work for both ?

6. A man planted $\frac{2}{3}$ of an acre with potatoes, and $\frac{5}{6}$ of an acre with corn. How much land was planted with both ?

7. A grocer sold $1\frac{1}{2}$ dozen eggs to one person, $\frac{3}{4}$ dozen to another, and $1\frac{1}{3}$ dozen to another. How many did he sell to all ?

8. A man sold three lots, the first containing $\frac{3}{5}$ of an acre, the second $\frac{7}{10}$ of an acre, and the third 1 acre. How much land did he sell ?

9. A girl paid $\$1\frac{3}{4}$ for a sled, $\$\frac{1}{2}$ for a book, and $\$1\frac{1}{4}$ for a doll. How much did her purchases cost ?

10. James had $\$3\frac{1}{2}$, Henry had $\$4\frac{3}{4}$, and Samuel had $\$3\frac{3}{4}$. How much had they all ?

11. A dressmaker deposited in a savings-bank $\$3\frac{2}{5}$ at one time, $\$4\frac{3}{4}$ at another, and $\$3\frac{1}{2}$ at another. What was the sum of the deposits ?

12. A fruiterer sold Mr. A $3\frac{3}{4}$ dozen bananas, Mr. B $2\frac{5}{6}$ dozen, Mr. C $4\frac{5}{12}$ dozen. How many dozen did he sell them all?

13. A carpenter worked $4\frac{5}{9}$ days one week, $3\frac{2}{3}$ days the next, and $5\frac{1}{3}$ days the next. How many days did he work in the three weeks?

14. The expenses of a party were $\$3\frac{4}{5}$ for railroad tickets, $\$2\frac{3}{4}$ for carriages, $\$5\frac{7}{10}$ for provisions. How much were the expenses?

15. What must be done to dissimilar fractions before they can be added?

What is the sum of the following:

16. $\frac{3}{4}$, $\frac{1}{2}$, and $\frac{5}{8}$.

17. $\frac{7}{8}$, $\frac{1}{3}$, and $\frac{0}{4}$.

18. $\frac{1}{3}$, $\frac{1}{6}$, and $\frac{4}{9}$.

19. $\frac{1}{5}$, $\frac{3}{10}$, and $\frac{4}{5}$.

20. $\frac{5}{6}$, $\frac{2}{3}$, and $\frac{1}{6}$.

21. $\frac{1}{3}$, $\frac{5}{12}$, and $\frac{3}{4}$.

22. $\frac{1}{4}$, $\frac{7}{8}$, and $\frac{1}{2}$.

23. $\frac{1}{2}$, $\frac{7}{10}$, and $\frac{2}{5}$.

24. $\frac{1}{3}$, $\frac{3}{4}$, and $\frac{1}{6}$.

25. $\frac{1}{5}$, $\frac{3}{10}$ and $\frac{1}{2}$.

26. $1\frac{1}{2}$, $2\frac{1}{4}$, and $2\frac{1}{8}$.

27. $1\frac{1}{3}$, $2\frac{3}{4}$, and $3\frac{1}{2}$.

28. $2\frac{1}{4}$, $3\frac{1}{0}$, and $4\frac{5}{12}$.

29. $3\frac{1}{3}$, $4\frac{2}{9}$, and $5\frac{2}{3}$.

30. $3\frac{1}{5}$, $2\frac{3}{10}$, and $3\frac{4}{5}$.

150. PRINCIPLE. — *Only similar fractions can be added.*

WRITTEN EXERCISES.

151. **1.** What is the sum of $\frac{5}{8}$, $\frac{3}{5}$, and $\frac{7}{10}$?

$\frac{5}{8} + \frac{3}{5} + \frac{7}{10} = \frac{25}{40} + \frac{24}{40} + \frac{28}{40} = \frac{77}{40}$
$\frac{77}{40} = 1\frac{37}{40}.$

EXPLANATION. — Since the fractions are dissimilar, they must be changed to similar fractions before adding.

The least common denominator of the given fractions is 40, and $\frac{5}{8} = \frac{25}{40}$; $\frac{3}{5} = \frac{24}{40}$; and $\frac{7}{10} = \frac{28}{40}$. Hence the sum is $\frac{77}{40}$, or $1\frac{37}{40}$.

2. What is the sum of $3\frac{1}{4}$, $5\frac{7}{8}$, and $4\frac{1}{6}$.

$3\frac{1}{4} = 3\frac{6}{24}$
$5\frac{7}{8} = 5\frac{21}{24}$
$4\frac{1}{6} = 4\frac{4}{24}$
$\overline{13\frac{7}{24}}$

EXPLANATION.— Since the numbers are composed of both integers and fractions, they may be added separately and their sums united. Thus, the sum of the fractions is $\frac{31}{24}$, or $1\frac{7}{24}$; the sum of the integers 12; and the sum of both $13\frac{7}{24}$.

RULE. — *Reduce the given fractions to similar fractions, add their numerators, and write the sum over the common denominator.*

When there are mixed numbers, or integers, add the fractions and integers separately, and then add the results.

If the sum is an improper fraction, reduce it to an integral or mixed number.

Find the sum of the following:

3. $\frac{2}{3}$, $\frac{5}{6}$, $\frac{7}{9}$, $\frac{5}{12}$.

4. $\frac{3}{4}$, $\frac{5}{8}$, $\frac{2}{3}$, $\frac{5}{24}$.

5. $\frac{5}{7}$, $\frac{3}{14}$, $\frac{4}{21}$, $\frac{5}{14}$.

6. $\frac{3}{8}$, $\frac{5}{9}$, $\frac{7}{18}$, $\frac{3}{4}$.

7. $\frac{5}{4}$, $\frac{6}{7}$, $\frac{3}{14}$, $\frac{1}{2}$.

8. $\frac{5}{8}$, $\frac{5}{7}$, $\frac{5}{4}$, $\frac{5}{14}$.

9. $\frac{2}{3}$, $\frac{5}{9}$, $\frac{7}{18}$, $\frac{3}{4}$.

10. $\frac{7}{8}$, $\frac{5}{12}$, $\frac{7}{24}$, $\frac{2}{3}$.

11. $\frac{6}{7}$, $\frac{5}{28}$, $\frac{3}{14}$, $\frac{3}{4}$.

12. $\frac{2}{5}$, $\frac{7}{10}$, $\frac{5}{30}$, $\frac{2}{3}$.

13. $\frac{5}{8}$, $\frac{5}{6}$, $\frac{3}{9}$, $\frac{5}{24}$.

14. $\frac{4}{7}$, $\frac{4}{8}$, $\frac{4}{14}$, $\frac{4}{28}$.

15. $\frac{3}{10}$, $\frac{7}{15}$, $\frac{7}{30}$, $\frac{7}{20}$.

16. $\frac{7}{12}$, $\frac{9}{16}$, $\frac{13}{24}$, $\frac{11}{18}$.

17. $\frac{5}{9}$, $\frac{7}{18}$, $\frac{7}{36}$, $\frac{7}{12}$.

18. $\frac{5}{8}$, $\frac{4}{9}$, $\frac{3}{4}$, $\frac{5}{6}$.

19. $\frac{7}{12}$, $\frac{8}{15}$, $\frac{15}{36}$, $\frac{8}{24}$.

20. $\frac{8}{9}$, $\frac{7}{18}$, $\frac{7}{16}$, $\frac{5}{24}$.

21. $\frac{3}{10}$, $\frac{8}{9}$, $\frac{3}{8}$, $\frac{13}{15}$.

22. $\frac{2}{3}$, $\frac{5}{12}$, $\frac{17}{24}$, $\frac{11}{14}$.

23. $\frac{14}{15}$, $\frac{17}{30}$, $\frac{23}{28}$, $\frac{19}{20}$.

24. $\frac{7}{12}$, $\frac{19}{24}$, $\frac{31}{36}$, $\frac{9}{10}$.

25. $\frac{9}{16}$, $\frac{11}{12}$, $\frac{13}{20}$, $\frac{11}{18}$.

26. $\frac{3}{8}$, $\frac{5}{6}$, $\frac{13}{24}$, $\frac{23}{36}$.

27. $\frac{8}{9}$, $\frac{5}{36}$, $\frac{13}{24}$, $\frac{7}{48}$.

28. $\frac{14}{15}$, $\frac{13}{18}$, $\frac{9}{10}$, $\frac{7}{30}$.

29. $6\frac{5}{8}$, $7\frac{3}{5}$, $8\frac{6}{10}$.

30. $5\frac{3}{4}$, $8\frac{5}{8}$, $7\frac{2}{3}$.

31. $7\frac{5}{7}$, $6\frac{3}{14}$, $5\frac{3}{10}$.

32. $8\frac{3}{4}$, $9\frac{3}{10}$, $4\frac{13}{15}$.

33. $7\frac{8}{9}$, $3\frac{5}{36}$, $6\frac{7}{8}$.

34. $8\frac{5}{7}$, $5\frac{12}{21}$, $2\frac{5}{14}$.

35. $9\frac{3}{5}$, $8\frac{8}{15}$, $6\frac{38}{45}$.

36. $15\frac{1}{4}$, $16\frac{3}{15}$, $18\frac{5}{12}$.

37. $22\frac{7}{12}$, $18\frac{47}{60}$, $19\frac{13}{15}$.

38. $35\frac{17}{18}$, $26\frac{11}{12}$, $84\frac{15}{18}$.

39. $41\frac{10}{21}$, $23\frac{17}{42}$, $36\frac{13}{15}$.

40. $32\frac{14}{23}$, $18\frac{11}{46}$, $45\frac{3}{5}$.

41. $43\frac{18}{85}$, $19\frac{3}{10}$, $21\frac{11}{15}$.

42. What is the sum of $126\frac{3}{8}$ pounds, $92\frac{3}{4}$ pounds, and $206\frac{5}{12}$ pounds?

43. What is the sum of 1250 bushels, $720\frac{4}{15}$ bushels, and $640\frac{7}{12}$ bushels?

44. I bought four pieces of cloth containing $32\frac{5}{6}$, $38\frac{1}{2}$, $40\frac{7}{8}$, and $45\frac{3}{4}$ yards, respectively. How many yards did I buy in all?

45. Five men weigh, respectively, $156\frac{1}{4}$, $160\frac{7}{8}$, $165\frac{1}{2}$, $162\frac{5}{16}$, and $168\frac{5}{8}$ pounds. What is their entire weight?

46. John has $\$1\frac{1}{10}$; James, $\$5\frac{2}{5}$; Charles, $\$17\frac{17}{20}$; and Edward, $\$12\frac{6}{40}$. How much have they together?

47. A farmer received $\$17\frac{3}{4}$ for oats, $\$28\frac{1}{2}$ for corn, $\$76\frac{3}{5}$ for wheat, and $\$150\frac{7}{10}$ for a horse. How much did he receive for all?

48. Sarah is $11\frac{1}{3}$ years old; Mary is $3\frac{1}{2}$ years older than Sarah; and Henry is $5\frac{7}{12}$ years older than Mary. How old is Henry?

49. From A to B is $18\frac{2}{7}$ miles, from B to C 20 miles, from C to D $81\frac{5}{8}$ miles, from D to E $37\frac{19}{112}$ miles. What is the distance from A to E?

50. A merchant sold $3\frac{2}{5}$ yards of cloth for $\$16\frac{1}{5}$, $5\frac{1}{4}$ yards for $\$24\frac{1}{4}$, and $8\frac{3}{8}$ yards for $\$28\frac{1}{5}$. How many yards did he sell, and how much money did he receive?

51. A has $13\frac{1}{2}$ acres of land, B has $17\frac{3}{4}$ acres more than A, C has as much as both A and B. How many acres has B, how many has C, and how many have they all together?

52. A man has three fields containing, respectively, $16\frac{4}{5}$ acres, $18\frac{19}{80}$ acres, and $15\frac{17}{36}$ acres. How many acres are there in the three fields?

53. Mr. B walked $23\frac{2}{3}$ miles on Monday, $25\frac{3}{20}$ miles on Tuesday, $27\frac{14}{64}$ miles on Wednesday, and $29\frac{47}{100}$ miles on Thursday. How far did he walk in all?

SUBTRACTION.

152. **1.** Mary had \$$\frac{9}{10}$ and spent \$$\frac{3}{10}$. How much had she left?

2. From a lot containing $\frac{7}{8}$ of an acre $\frac{1}{4}$ of an acre was sold. How large a lot was left? $\frac{7}{8} - \frac{1}{4} = ?$ $\frac{7}{8} - \frac{2}{4} = ?$

3. A boy paid \$$\frac{7}{8}$ for his skates, but sold them for \$$\frac{1}{4}$ less than he paid for them. What did he get for them?

4. If I have \$$\frac{9}{10}$ and spend \$$\frac{1}{20}$ how much will I have left?

5. A girl paid \$$\frac{2}{5}$ for a grammar and \$$\frac{3}{4}$ for a geography. How much more did she pay for the geography than for the grammar?

6. A lad hoed $\frac{7}{8}$ of a field of corn. If he hoed $\frac{3}{4}$ of the field in the forenoon, how much did he do in the afternoon?

7. What must be done to dissimilar fractions before they can be subtracted?

Find the value of:

8. $\frac{3}{4} - \frac{3}{8}$.	**15.** $\frac{3}{8} - \frac{1}{4}$.	**22.** $2 - \frac{3}{4}$.
9. $\frac{5}{10} - \frac{1}{4}$.	**16.** $\frac{9}{10} - \frac{1}{4}$.	**23.** $3 - 1\frac{3}{4}$.
10. $\frac{5}{8} - \frac{1}{2}$.	**17.** $\frac{9}{16} - \frac{3}{8}$.	**24.** $2\frac{3}{4} - 1\frac{1}{2}$.
11. $\frac{7}{10} - \frac{2}{5}$.	**18.** $\frac{7}{15} - \frac{1}{3}$.	**25.** $2\frac{1}{2} - 1\frac{3}{4}$.
12. $\frac{8}{9} - \frac{2}{3}$.	**19.** $\frac{17}{20} - \frac{4}{5}$.	**26.** $3\frac{1}{4} - 1\frac{1}{2}$.
13. $\frac{7}{12} - \frac{1}{3}$.	**20.** $\frac{13}{16} - \frac{3}{4}$.	**27.** $2\frac{3}{4} - 1\frac{3}{8}$.
14. $\frac{8}{15} - \frac{1}{3}$.	**21.** $\frac{19}{30} - \frac{1}{30}$.	**28.** $2\frac{3}{8} - 1\frac{3}{4}$.

153. PRINCIPLE. — *Only similar fractions can be subtracted.*

WRITTEN EXERCISES.

154. 1. From $\frac{9}{11}$ subtract $\frac{3}{4}$.

$\frac{9}{11} - \frac{3}{4} = \frac{36}{44} - \frac{33}{44} = \frac{3}{44}$ EXPLANATION. — Since the fractions are not similar they must be made similar before subtracting. The least common denominator of the given fractions is 44. $\frac{9}{11} = \frac{36}{44}$ and $\frac{3}{4} = \frac{33}{44}$. $\frac{36}{44} - \frac{33}{44} = \frac{3}{44}$.

2. From $4\frac{1}{3}$ subtract $2\frac{5}{8}$.

$4\frac{1}{3} = 4\frac{8}{24}$
$2\frac{5}{8} = 2\frac{15}{24}$

$1\frac{17}{24}$

EXPLANATION. — Since the numbers are composed of integers and fractions, the integers and the fractions may be subtracted separately.

The fractions must be first reduced to similar fractions. It is evident that $\frac{15}{24}$ cannot be subtracted from $\frac{8}{24}$, hence 1 or $\frac{24}{24}$ is taken from **4** and united with the $\frac{8}{24}$, making $\frac{32}{24}$. $\frac{15}{24}$ from $\frac{32}{24}$ leaves $\frac{17}{24}$, and 2 from 3 (the number left after 1 has been united with the fraction $\frac{8}{24}$) leaves 1. Hence the remainder is $1\frac{17}{24}$.

RULE. — *Reduce the fractions to similar fractions. Find the difference between the numerators and write it over the common denominator.*

When there are mixed numbers or integers, subtract the fractions and the integers separately.

Mixed numbers may be reduced to improper fractions and subtracted according to the first part of the rule.

Find the value of :

3. $\frac{7}{8} - \frac{3}{5}$.	11. $\frac{11}{30} - \frac{5}{19}$.	19. $\frac{25}{31} - \frac{3}{8}$.
4. $\frac{2}{3} - \frac{3}{11}$.	12. $\frac{8}{21} - \frac{6}{25}$.	20. $\frac{19}{20} - \frac{5}{16}$.
5. $\frac{6}{13} - \frac{7}{26}$.	13. $\frac{17}{30} - \frac{7}{24}$.	21. $\frac{27}{40} - \frac{4}{15}$.
6. $\frac{7}{10} - \frac{4}{15}$.	14. $\frac{18}{35} - \frac{8}{25}$.	22. $\frac{33}{34} - \frac{6}{51}$.
7. $\frac{9}{15} - \frac{4}{45}$.	15. $\frac{16}{45} - \frac{12}{39}$.	23. $\frac{27}{35} - \frac{8}{30}$.
8. $\frac{7}{24} - \frac{5}{48}$.	16. $\frac{22}{34} - \frac{8}{17}$.	24. $\frac{30}{36} - \frac{18}{25}$.
9. $\frac{13}{15} - \frac{18}{75}$.	17. $\frac{16}{33} - \frac{7}{30}$.	25. $\frac{31}{40} - \frac{9}{40}$.
10. $\frac{28}{36} - \frac{14}{26}$.	18. $\frac{19}{39} - \frac{5}{13}$.	26. $\frac{42}{49} - \frac{21}{98}$.

27. $\frac{65}{77} - \frac{45}{88}$.   32. $\frac{75}{99} - \frac{54}{88}$.   37. $7\frac{5}{8} - 2\frac{13}{15}$.

28. $\frac{70}{72} - \frac{19}{60}$.   33. $5\frac{1}{4} - 3\frac{1}{3}$.   38. $8\frac{3}{10} - 5\frac{10}{21}$.

29. $\frac{63}{75} - \frac{36}{50}$.   34. $6\frac{7}{8} - 4\frac{5}{12}$.   39. $9 \quad - 4\frac{3}{4}$.

30. $\frac{71}{85} - \frac{45}{70}$.   35. $9 \quad - 3\frac{7}{15}$.   40. $8\frac{1}{9} - 5\frac{7}{12}$.

31. $\frac{83}{92} - \frac{30}{46}$.   36. $8\frac{1}{3} - 4\frac{3}{7}$.   41. $9\frac{3}{15} - 3\frac{13}{50}$.

Find the value of :

42. $\frac{1}{4} + \frac{2}{3} - \frac{1}{5} + \frac{3}{10}$.   50. $3\frac{1}{4} + 2\frac{1}{3} + 3\frac{4}{7} + 3\frac{5}{12} + 6\frac{1}{8}$.

43. $\frac{2}{7} - \frac{3}{12} + \frac{5}{6} - \frac{1}{5}$.   51. $5\frac{3}{5} + 6\frac{4}{7} - 3\frac{2}{15} - \frac{23}{30} + 7\frac{7}{10}$.

44. $\frac{8}{9} + \frac{4}{5} - \frac{7}{15} + \frac{2}{30}$.   52. $8\frac{1}{8} - 3\frac{3}{4} + 2\frac{4}{5} - 2\frac{1}{6} + 5$.

45. $\frac{5}{8} + \frac{7}{9} - \frac{1}{36} - \frac{7}{18}$.   53. $9\frac{1}{10} + 3\frac{4}{15} - 3\frac{7}{12} - 1\frac{5}{6} - 2\frac{3}{4}$.

46. $\frac{3}{10} + \frac{9}{15} - \frac{1}{40} - \frac{4}{15}$.   54. $7\frac{3}{8} + 2\frac{5}{6} - 3\frac{5}{24} - 4\frac{2}{3} + 3\frac{3}{4}$.

47. $\frac{8}{11} + \frac{3}{4} - \frac{3}{8} - \frac{5}{44}$.   55. $5 \quad + 6\frac{5}{9} - 3\frac{3}{4} - 2\frac{1}{8} + 1\frac{11}{36}$.

48. $\frac{7}{10} - \frac{1}{3} + \frac{3}{4} - \frac{4}{5}$.   56. $7\frac{4}{10} - 3\frac{5}{7} + 8\frac{12}{35} - 5\frac{3}{5} + 9$.

49. $\frac{3}{7} + \frac{5}{9} - \frac{5}{21} + \frac{2}{3}$.   57. $6\frac{2}{7} + 4\frac{5}{9} + 8\frac{2}{3} - 4\frac{5}{21} - 4\frac{5}{7}$.

58. A piece of flannel containing $25\frac{7}{8}$ yards shrank $1\frac{5}{6}$ yards in dyeing. How much did the cloth then measure ?

59. From a lot containing $\frac{19}{20}$ of an acre of land, I sold $\frac{3}{25}$ of an acre to one man, and $\frac{3}{8}$ of an acre to another. How much land had I left ?

60. If $19\frac{3}{16}$ yards are cut from a piece of cloth containing $42\frac{17}{20}$ yards, how many yards will be left ?

61. A boy gave $18\frac{3}{4}$ cents for a slate, $62\frac{1}{2}$ cents for a book, and $37\frac{1}{2}$ cents for some paper. How much change should he receive if he gave in payment a two-dollar bill ?

62. If 6 is added to each term of $\frac{2}{3}$, is the value of the fraction increased or diminished, and how much ?

MULTIPLICATION.

155. 1. How much is $\frac{1}{2}$ of $\frac{1}{2}$ of a yard? $\frac{1}{2}$ of $\frac{1}{4}$ of a yard?

2. How much is $\frac{1}{4}$ of $\frac{1}{2}$ of a yard? $\frac{3}{4}$ of $\frac{1}{2}$ of a yard?

3. How much is $\frac{1}{2}$ of $\frac{1}{3}$ of an orange? $\frac{1}{3}$ of $\frac{1}{2}$ of an orange?

4. How much is $\frac{1}{2}$ of $\frac{1}{5}$ of an acre? $\frac{1}{5}$ of $\frac{1}{2}$ of an acre?

5. Since $\frac{1}{5}$ of $\frac{1}{2}$ of an acre is $\frac{1}{10}$ of an acre, what part of an acre is $\frac{2}{5}$ of $\frac{1}{2}$ of an acre? $\frac{3}{5}$ of $\frac{1}{2}$ of an acre? $\frac{4}{5}$ of $\frac{1}{2}$ of an acre?

6. How much is $\frac{1}{2}$ of $\frac{1}{6}$ of a foot? $\frac{1}{6}$ of $\frac{1}{2}$ of a foot?

7. Since $\frac{1}{6}$ of $\frac{1}{2}$ of a foot is $\frac{1}{12}$ of a foot, what part of a foot is $\frac{2}{6}$ of $\frac{1}{2}$ of a foot? $\frac{3}{6}$ of $\frac{1}{2}$ of a foot? $\frac{4}{6}$ of $\frac{1}{2}$ of a foot? $\frac{5}{6}$ of $\frac{1}{2}$ of a foot?

8. How much is $\frac{3}{5}$ of $\frac{1}{2}$? $\frac{1}{2}$ of $\frac{3}{5}$? $\frac{4}{5}$ of $\frac{1}{2}$? $\frac{1}{2}$ of $\frac{4}{5}$?

9. How much is $\frac{1}{2}$ of $\frac{1}{7}$? $\frac{1}{4}$ of $\frac{1}{7}$? $\frac{1}{5}$ of $\frac{1}{7}$? $\frac{1}{6}$ of $\frac{1}{7}$?

10. How much is $\frac{1}{2}$ of $\frac{3}{7}$? $\frac{1}{4}$ of $\frac{3}{7}$? $\frac{1}{5}$ of $\frac{3}{7}$? $\frac{1}{6}$ of $\frac{3}{7}$?

11. How much is $\frac{3}{4}$ of $\frac{3}{7}$? $\frac{3}{5}$ of $\frac{3}{7}$? $\frac{3}{7}$ of $\frac{3}{7}$? $\frac{3}{10}$ of $\frac{3}{7}$?

12. A cistern was $\frac{3}{4}$ full, but $\frac{2}{5}$ of the water was drawn out. What part of the amount the cistern would hold was drawn out?

13. Mr. Ames, who owned a lot containing $\frac{3}{7}$ of an acre, sold $\frac{1}{10}$ of it. What part of an acre did he sell?

14. If he had sold $\frac{3}{10}$ of it, what part of an acre would he have sold? $\frac{3}{10}$ of $\frac{3}{7} = $?

15. A man's farm was such that $\frac{3}{4}$ of it only was tilled. He sold $\frac{4}{5}$ of that part. What part of the farm did he sell?

16. A girl who had $$\frac{4}{5}$ spent $\frac{3}{8}$ of it for candy. What part of a dollar did she spend? $\frac{4}{5} \times \frac{3}{8} = ?$ $\frac{4}{5} \times \frac{5}{8} = ?$

17. A yard of crape costs $$\frac{2}{5}$. What will $\frac{3}{4}$ of a yard cost? $\frac{3}{4}$ of $\frac{2}{5} = ?$ $\frac{3}{4}$ of $\frac{4}{5} = ?$ $\frac{3}{5}$ of $\frac{3}{4} = ?$

18. A man who owned $\frac{3}{7}$ of a mill sold $\frac{3}{4}$ of his share. What part of the mill did he sell? $\frac{3}{7}$ of $\frac{3}{4} = ?$

19. A fruit seller had $\frac{3}{4}$ of a dozen cocoanuts and sold $\frac{2}{3}$ of them? What part of a dozen did he sell?

20. A train ran $\frac{3}{4}$ of the distance between two places in an hour. What part of the distance did it run in $\frac{3}{4}$ of an hour?

21. Two boys counting their money found that one had $$\frac{3}{4}$ and the other had $\frac{3}{4}$ as much. What part of a dollar had each?

WRITTEN EXERCISES.

156. **1.** Find $\frac{3}{8}$ of $\frac{4}{5}$, or multiply $\frac{4}{5}$ by $\frac{3}{8}$.

$$\frac{3}{8} \text{ of } \frac{4}{5} = \frac{\overset{}{4}}{5} \times \frac{3}{\underset{2}{8}} = \frac{3}{10}$$

EXPLANATION. — To multiply $\frac{4}{5}$ by $\frac{3}{8}$ is to find $\frac{3}{8}$ of $\frac{4}{5}$, or 3 times $\frac{1}{8}$ of $\frac{4}{5}$. $\frac{1}{8}$ of $\frac{4}{5} = \frac{4}{40}$, and $\frac{3}{8}$ of $\frac{4}{5} = \frac{12}{40}$, or $\frac{3}{10}$.

RULE. — *Reduce all integers and mixed numbers to improper fractions.*

Find the product of the numerators for the numerator of the product, and of the denominators, for its denominator.

1. When possible use cancellation.
2. The word *of*, between fractions, is equivalent to the *sign of multiplication*. Such expressions are sometimes called *compound fractions.* Thus, $\frac{3}{4}$ of $\frac{7}{5}$ is equal to $\frac{3}{4} \times \frac{7}{5}$.
3. Integers may be expressed, in the form of fractions, by writing 1 as a denominator. Thus, 4 may be written as $\frac{4}{1}$.

Find the product of:

2. $\frac{3}{5} \times \frac{8}{9}$.

3. $\frac{5}{18} \times \frac{6}{5}$.

4. $\frac{12}{27} \times \frac{9}{4}$.

5. $\frac{12}{25} \times \frac{5}{6}$.

6. $\frac{30}{49} \times \frac{7}{10}$.

7. $\frac{25}{48} \times \frac{8}{10}$.

8. $\frac{42}{50} \times \frac{10}{14}$.   15. $\frac{18}{25} \times \frac{10}{7} \times \frac{3}{9}$.   22. $2\frac{1}{2} \times 4\frac{1}{2} \times \frac{4}{5}$.

9. $\frac{20}{33} \times \frac{10}{30}$.   16. $\frac{18}{44} \times \frac{11}{10} \times \frac{3}{9}$.   23. $\frac{15}{24} \times \frac{3}{5} \times 6\frac{3}{4}$.

10. $\frac{21}{16} \times \frac{12}{14}$.   17. $\frac{56}{72} \times \frac{18}{8} \times \frac{4}{7}$.   24. $\frac{16}{10} \times \frac{4}{8} \times 25\frac{1}{2}$.

11. $\frac{15}{27} \times \frac{9}{20} \times \frac{4}{15}$.   18. $\frac{27}{40} \times \frac{10}{36} \times \frac{3}{8}$.   25. $\frac{35}{36} \times \frac{12}{20} \times 8$.

12. $\frac{36}{49} \times \frac{7}{12} \times \frac{5}{3}$.   19. $\frac{42}{48} \times \frac{6}{9} \times \frac{8}{9}$.   26. $\frac{30}{49} \times 3\frac{1}{4} \times \frac{7}{10}$.

13. $\frac{33}{40} \times \frac{8}{11} \times \frac{3}{10}$.   20. $\frac{3}{4} \times \frac{4}{7} \times 2\frac{1}{2}$.   27. $\frac{48}{81} \times \frac{9}{24} \times 4\frac{1}{2}$.

14. $\frac{25}{32} \times \frac{12}{20} \times \frac{3}{8}$.   21. $\frac{3}{5} \times 7\frac{1}{2} \times \frac{2}{3}$.   28. $\frac{27}{40} \times \frac{8}{9} \times 9$.

29. Multiply $2\frac{3}{8}$ by 10.

$2\frac{3}{8}$
10
——
20

$3\frac{3}{4}$
——
$23\frac{3}{4}$

EXPLANATION. — In examples like this, it is best to multiply the fraction and integer separately and to add the results. Thus, 10 times 2 are 20. 10 times $\frac{3}{8}$ are $\frac{30}{8}$, or $3\frac{6}{8}$, or $3\frac{3}{4}$. This added to 20, gives the entire product, $23\frac{3}{4}$. Or their product may be found by the general rule. Thus,

$$2\frac{3}{8} = \frac{19}{8}, \text{ and } \frac{19}{8} \times \frac{10}{1} = \frac{190}{8} = 23\frac{3}{4}.$$

Multiply the following:

30. $12\frac{3}{5}$ by 15.   35. $29\frac{8}{13}$ by 26.   40. $24\frac{15}{32}$ by 48.

31. $15\frac{5}{8}$ by 24.   36. $41\frac{3}{10}$ by 41.   41. $25\frac{12}{25}$ by 35.

32. $24\frac{3}{7}$ by 20.   37. $32\frac{5}{13}$ by 39.   42. $31\frac{15}{22}$ by 33.

33. $36\frac{4}{5}$ by 18.   38. $24\frac{5}{18}$ by 32.   43. $18\frac{24}{56}$ by 25.

34. $42\frac{8}{9}$ by 36.   39. $29\frac{6}{17}$ by 34.   44. $39\frac{20}{81}$ by 27.

45. Multiply 10 by $2\frac{3}{8}$.

10
$2\frac{3}{8}$
——
20

$3\frac{3}{4}$
——
$23\frac{3}{4}$

EXPLANATION. — Multiply by the integer and the fraction separately, and add the results.

Thus, 2 times $10 = 20$. $\frac{1}{8}$ of $10 = \frac{10}{8}$, and $\frac{3}{8}$ of $10 = \frac{30}{8}$ or, $3\frac{6}{8}$. This added to 20 gives the entire product, $23\frac{3}{4}$. Or, the product may be found by the general rule. Thus,

$$\frac{10}{1} \times \frac{19}{8} = \frac{190}{8}, \text{ or } 23\frac{3}{4}.$$

Multiply:

46. 25 by $3\frac{4}{5}$.   **54.** 52 by $4\frac{3}{5}$.   **62.** $8\frac{3}{4}$ by 20.

47. 30 by $4\frac{3}{10}$.   **55.** 61 by $8\frac{3}{8}$.   **63.** $9\frac{8}{15}$ by 25.

48. 56 by $7\frac{3}{8}$.   **56.** 59 by $7\frac{2}{8}$.   **64.** $8\frac{5}{27}$ by 21.

49. 63 by $8\frac{5}{9}$.   **57.** 43 by $4\frac{5}{7}$.   **65.** $9\frac{10}{21}$ by 18.

50. 64 by $7\frac{5}{8}$.   **58.** 63 by $6\frac{7}{8}$.   **66.** $9\frac{5}{13}$ by 26.

51. 60 by $8\frac{7}{12}$.   **59.** 71 by $8\frac{5}{9}$.   **67.** $7\frac{5}{17}$ by 34.

52. 72 by $9\frac{3}{8}$.   **60.** $3\frac{5}{8}$ by 24.   **68.** $6\frac{8}{21}$ by 27.

53. 42 by $8\frac{5}{7}$.   **61.** $5\frac{7}{10}$ by 35.   **69.** $8\frac{11}{12}$ by 28.

70. $9\frac{13}{24}$ by 26.   **79.** $36 \times 5\frac{3}{7} \times 4\frac{2}{3}$.

71. $7\frac{6}{29}$ by 38.   **80.** $38 \times 6\frac{5}{9} \times 5\frac{3}{4}$.

72. $9\frac{17}{42}$ by 84.   **81.** $42 \times 7\frac{7}{10} \times 4\frac{3}{8}$.

73. $9\frac{23}{30}$ by 52.   **82.** $45 \times 8\frac{4}{5} \times 7\frac{5}{12}$.

74. $25 \times 3\frac{5}{8} \times 4\frac{1}{2}$.   **83.** $47 \times 6\frac{5}{13} \times 5\frac{4}{9}$.

75. $15 \times 4\frac{2}{7} \times 5\frac{1}{4}$.   **84.** $49 \times 2\frac{5}{6} \times 4\frac{4}{7}$.

76. $24 \times 6\frac{5}{12} \times 6\frac{2}{3}$.   **85.** $50 \times 3\frac{7}{10} \times 7\frac{3}{5}$.

77. $25 \times 3\frac{4}{5} \times 6\frac{2}{15}$.   **86.** $52 \times 7\frac{3}{13} \times 4\frac{5}{9}$.

78. $40 \times 4\frac{5}{8} \times 3\frac{2}{5}$.   **87.** $55 \times 6\frac{3}{20} \times 6\frac{7}{11}$.

88. A coat cost $\$12\frac{7}{10}$, and a hat $\frac{2}{5}$ as much. What was the cost of the hat?

89. How much will $12\frac{1}{2}$ yards of cloth cost, at $\$3\frac{3}{5}$ a yard?

90. I bought $66\frac{2}{3}$ yards of flannel, at $\$.37\frac{1}{2}$ per yard. How much did I pay for it?

91. What will $43\frac{3}{4}$ bushels of potatoes cost, at $\$.62\frac{1}{2}$ per bushel?

92. A man sold $7\frac{2}{5}$ tons of hay, at $\$15\frac{7}{20}$ per ton. How much did he receive for it?

93. If a man earns $1\frac{3}{4}$ per day, how much can he earn in 35 days?

94. James has $4\frac{3}{4}$, and Mary has $\frac{3}{5}$ as much. How much money has Mary?

95. At $1\frac{5}{8}$ each, what will 65 Latin grammars cost?

96. What are $18\frac{1}{2}$ bushels of apples worth, at $\frac{7}{8}$ per bushel?

97. If one load of hay is worth $6\frac{3}{4}$, how much are 18 loads worth?

98. A has $\frac{3}{4}$ of $125, and B has $\frac{2}{3}$ as much as A. How much money has B?

99. Mr. B owns $\frac{5}{8}$ of a farm valued at $16728. What is the value of his portion of the farm?

100. A hotel in one month used 31 pounds of coffee, and $7\frac{3}{5}$ times as much sugar. How much sugar was used?

101. A merchant bought a piece of cloth for $57\frac{3}{4}$, but was obliged to sell it for $\frac{4}{5}$ of what it cost him. How much did he lose?

102. John can walk $21\frac{3}{16}$ miles in a day. How far can he walk in 24 days?

103. What must be paid for 17 tables, at $7\frac{3}{5}$ apiece?

104. A and B bought a mowing machine for $75. A paid $\frac{4}{9}$ of the cost, and B $\frac{5}{9}$. How much did each pay?

105. A wheel in making one revolution travels $15\frac{3}{10}$ feet. How far will it travel in making 25 revolutions?

106. What will be the cost of $\frac{3}{7}$ of a piece of cloth containing $23\frac{1}{2}$ yards, at $3\frac{1}{2}$ per yard?

107. If a ship sails $18\frac{5}{9}$ miles an hour, how far will she sail in 15 hours?

DIVISION.

157. **1.** How many times is $\frac{1}{3}$ contained in 1?

2. Since $\frac{1}{3}$ is contained in 1 three times, what part of three times is $\frac{2}{3}$ contained in 1?

3. How many times is $\frac{1}{5}$ contained in 1? Since $\frac{1}{5}$ is contained in 1 five times, what part of 5 times is $\frac{2}{5}$ contained in 1? $\frac{3}{5}$? $\frac{4}{5}$?

4. Since $\frac{2}{5}$ is contained in 1 $\frac{5}{2}$ times, how many times will it be contained in $\frac{1}{2}$? In $\frac{1}{3}$? In $\frac{1}{4}$? In $\frac{2}{3}$?

5. How many times is $\frac{1}{7}$ contained in 1? $\frac{2}{7}$? $\frac{3}{7}$? $\frac{5}{7}$?

6. Since $\frac{5}{7}$ is contained in 1 $\frac{7}{5}$ times, how many times will it be contained in $\frac{1}{2}$? In $\frac{1}{3}$? In $\frac{2}{3}$? In $\frac{3}{4}$?

7. How many quires of paper, at $\$\frac{1}{5}$ per quire, can be purchased for $\$\frac{3}{10}$? For $\$\frac{7}{10}$? For $\$\frac{9}{10}$?

8. At $\$\frac{2}{3}$ per yard, how much cloth can be bought for $\$\frac{5}{6}$? For $\$\frac{7}{6}$? For $\$\frac{3}{4}$?

9. At $\$\frac{3}{5}$ per pound, how many pounds of raisins can be bought for $\$1$? For $\$\frac{1}{2}$? For $\$\frac{3}{4}$?

10. When rye is worth $\$\frac{4}{5}$ per bushel, how much can be purchased for $\$1$? For $\$\frac{1}{2}$? For $\$1\frac{1}{2}$?

11. At $\$\frac{2}{5}$ per pound, how much honey can be bought for $\$1$? For $\$2$? For $\$\frac{1}{2}$? For $\$3$?

12. How many pictures, worth $\$\frac{3}{4}$ each, can be purchased for $\$3$? For $\$6$? For $\$9$?

13. How long will it take a boy to earn $\$1\frac{1}{4}$, if he earns $\$\frac{3}{4}$ per day? How long to earn $\$2\frac{1}{4}$?

14. If a man pays $\$\frac{4}{5}$ per day for his board, for how many days' board will $\$4$ pay? $\$8$? $\$12$?

15. The cost of coal is $\$\frac{2}{7}$ per hundred-weight. How many hundred-weight can be bought for $\$1$? How many for $\$2$?

16. Some diaries are sold for $\$\frac{3}{5}$ each. How many can be bought for $\$3$? How many for $\$6$?

WRITTEN EXERCISES.

158. 1. Divide $\frac{4}{5}$ by $\frac{3}{7}$, or find how many times $\frac{3}{7}$ is contained in $\frac{4}{5}$.

$\frac{4}{5} \div \frac{3}{7} = \frac{4}{5} \times \frac{7}{3} = \frac{28}{15}$, or $1\frac{13}{15}$.   EXPLANATION. — $\frac{1}{7}$ is contained in 1 seven times, and $\frac{3}{7}$ is contained in 1, one third of 7 times, or $\frac{7}{3}$ times.

Since $\frac{3}{7}$ is contained in 1 $\frac{7}{3}$ times, in $\frac{4}{5}$ it will be contained $\frac{4}{5}$ of $\frac{7}{3}$ times, or $\frac{28}{15}$ times, or $1\frac{13}{15}$ times.

RULE. — *Multiply the dividend by the divisor inverted.*

1. When possible, use cancellation.
2. Integers and mixed numbers must be reduced to improper fractions.

Find the quotients of:

2. $\frac{3}{7} \div \frac{3}{5}$.	**13.** $\frac{32}{46} \div \frac{4}{5}$.	**24.** $2\frac{1}{4} \div \frac{3}{7}$.	**35.** $17 \div 3\frac{1}{8}$.
3. $\frac{4}{15} \div \frac{2}{5}$.	**14.** $\frac{33}{56} \div \frac{11}{16}$.	**25.** $3\frac{1}{5} \div \frac{8}{9}$.	**36.** $18 \div 4\frac{1}{5}$.
4. $\frac{5}{18} \div \frac{3}{4}$.	**15.** $\frac{19}{52} \div \frac{13}{14}$.	**26.** $5\frac{2}{3} \div \frac{17}{5}$.	**37.** $17 \div 3\frac{1}{4}$.
5. $\frac{15}{28} \div \frac{3}{7}$.	**16.** $\frac{45}{99} \div \frac{25}{27}$.	**27.** $8\frac{4}{9} \div \frac{4}{3}$.	**38.** $20 \div 3\frac{3}{4}$.
6. $\frac{20}{49} \div \frac{4}{7}$.	**17.** $\frac{4}{4} \div \frac{3}{8}$.	**28.** $9\frac{2}{4} \div \frac{19}{20}$.	**39.** $\frac{5}{7} \div 10$.
7. $\frac{12}{25} \div \frac{6}{7}$.	**18.** $5 \div \frac{2}{7}$.	**29.** $7\frac{2}{6} \div \frac{11}{12}$.	**40.** $\frac{3}{5} \div 8$.
8. $\frac{17}{33} \div \frac{5}{6}$.	**19.** $6 \div \frac{5}{12}$.	**30.** $8\frac{3}{4} \div 2\frac{1}{2}$.	**41.** $\frac{4}{7} \div 19$.
9. $\frac{18}{41} \div \frac{3}{5}$.	**20.** $8 \div \frac{3}{4}$.	**31.** $8\frac{4}{5} \div 3\frac{1}{10}$.	**42.** $\frac{6}{13} \div 12$.
10. $\frac{20}{27} \div \frac{5}{7}$.	**21.** $9 \div \frac{5}{7}$.	**32.** $5\frac{3}{7} \div 3\frac{1}{6}$.	**43.** $\frac{7}{15} \div 18$.
11. $\frac{24}{29} \div \frac{3}{8}$.	**22.** $8 \div \frac{7}{9}$.	**33.** $4\frac{2}{3} \div 2\frac{1}{6}$.	**44.** $\frac{8}{23} \div 16$.
12. $\frac{25}{36} \div \frac{5}{6}$.	**23.** $7 \div \frac{8}{13}$.	**34.** $15 \div 3\frac{3}{4}$.	**45.** $\frac{20}{33} \div 30$.

Divide:

46. $\frac{3}{7} \times \frac{5}{8}$ by $16 \div \frac{6}{7}$.

47. $\frac{15}{28} \div \frac{5}{7}$ by $\frac{3}{4}$ of 9.

48. $\frac{25}{36} \times \frac{9}{10}$ by $\frac{3}{7}$ of $2\frac{1}{3}$.

49. $\frac{20}{21} \times \frac{3}{7}$ by $\frac{4}{5}$ of $2\frac{1}{2}$.

50. $\frac{16}{35} \times \frac{15}{42}$ by $\frac{4}{7}$ of 3.

51. $\frac{19}{22} \times \frac{5}{8}$ by $\frac{17}{21} \times \frac{3}{4}$.

52. $\frac{31}{42} \times \frac{21}{62} \times \frac{9}{16}$ by $2\frac{7}{8}$.

53. $\frac{18}{45} \times \frac{9}{27} \times \frac{7}{11}$ by $8\frac{2}{5}$.

54. $\frac{57}{64}$ by $\frac{4}{5} \times \frac{8}{3} \times \frac{5}{16}$.

55. $6\frac{5}{12}$ by $\frac{7}{15} \times \frac{25}{76} \times 19$.

56. $14\frac{2}{3} \times \frac{4}{9}$ by $\frac{19}{21} \times \frac{9}{14}$.

57. $16\frac{3}{7} \times 7$ by $\frac{81}{91}$.

58. $9\frac{1}{2} \times 4\frac{2}{3}$ by $6 \times \frac{5}{8}$.

59. $12\frac{5}{9} \times \frac{6}{5}$ by $18\frac{3}{4}$.

60. $\frac{7}{8} \times 4\frac{5}{9}$ by $\frac{3}{4} \times 3\frac{3}{5}$.

61. $\frac{28}{55} \times \frac{20}{48}$ by $\frac{16}{41} \times \frac{11}{18}$.

62. $\frac{39}{65} \times \frac{4}{13} \times \frac{13}{16}$ by $14\frac{3}{8}$.

63. $\frac{48}{77} \times \frac{55}{91} \times 8$ by $17\frac{2}{3}$.

64. $\frac{65}{81} \times 7\frac{4}{13}$ by $\frac{3}{7} \times 5\frac{5}{7}$.

65. $\frac{68}{95} \times \frac{19}{27} \times 5\frac{1}{6}$ by $18\frac{3}{4}$.

66. $\frac{44}{87} \times 14\frac{5}{8}$ by $20\frac{4}{7}$.

67. $\frac{85}{99} \times \frac{11}{17} \times 3\frac{1}{6}$ by $27 \times \frac{4}{19}$.

68. Divide $\frac{3}{5}$ of $\frac{5}{7}$ of $\frac{4}{9}$ of $3\frac{1}{4}$ by $\frac{5}{8}$ of $\frac{12}{25}$ of $\frac{4}{9}$ of $\frac{2}{3}$ of 6.

SUGGESTION. — Change the integers and mixed numbers to improper fractions, and invert *all factors* of the divisor. Use cancellation.

$\frac{3}{5}$ of $\frac{5}{7}$ of $\frac{4}{9}$ of $3\frac{1}{4}$ divided by $\frac{5}{8}$ of $\frac{12}{25}$ of $\frac{4}{9}$ of $\frac{2}{3}$ of 6

$= \frac{3}{5} \times \frac{5}{7} \times \frac{4}{9} \times \frac{13}{4} \times \frac{8}{5} \times \frac{25}{12} \times \frac{9}{4} \times \frac{3}{2} \times \frac{1}{6} = \frac{65}{56} = 1\frac{9}{56}$.

69. Divide $\frac{2}{3}$ of $\frac{4}{5}$ of $\frac{7}{8}$ of $\frac{5}{9}$ by $\frac{5}{6}$ of $\frac{8}{9}$ of $\frac{3}{10}$ of 4.

70. Divide $\frac{5}{12}$ of $\frac{18}{23}$ of $\frac{17}{25}$ of $4\frac{1}{6}$ by $\frac{4}{7}$ of $\frac{12}{14}$ of $\frac{16}{35}$.

71. Divide $\frac{7}{8}$ of $\frac{13}{56}$ of $\frac{16}{27}$ of $7\frac{2}{3}$ by $\frac{15}{19}$ of $\frac{14}{29}$ of $14\frac{1}{2}$.

72. Divide $\frac{4}{13}$ of $\frac{39}{64}$ of $\frac{14}{27}$ of $\frac{18}{42}$ by $\frac{16}{35}$ of $\frac{85}{91}$ of $2\frac{1}{5}$.

73. Divide $\frac{9}{16}$ of $\frac{14}{6}$ of $\frac{21}{47}$ of $7\frac{5}{6}$ by $\frac{14}{9}$ of $\frac{13}{27}$ of $\frac{16}{45}$.

74. Divide $\frac{17}{65}$ of $\frac{14}{29}$ of $\frac{17}{50}$ of $\frac{21}{68}$ by $\frac{13}{15}$ of $\frac{34}{35}$ of $\frac{5}{9}$ of $8\frac{1}{6}$.

75. Divide $\frac{8}{9}$ of $\frac{74}{85}$ of $\frac{5}{7}$ of $5\frac{3}{7}$ by $\frac{8}{19}$ of $\frac{12}{27}$ of $\frac{6}{11}$ of $4\frac{4}{5}$.

76. Divide $\frac{19}{42}$ of $\frac{28}{33}$ of $\frac{11}{14}$ of $7\frac{1}{9}$ by $\frac{23}{35}$ of $\frac{5}{8}$ of $\frac{16}{23}$ of $\frac{8}{35}$ of $24\frac{5}{12}$.

77. Divide $16\frac{3}{4}$ by 5.

$5)16\frac{3}{4}$

$3\frac{7}{20}$

EXPLANATION. — The division may be performed in the ordinary way, but it is often more convenient to divide as follows:

5 is contained in $16\frac{3}{4}$, 3 times with a remainder of $1\frac{3}{4}$ or $\frac{7}{4}$; and $\frac{7}{4}$ divided by 5 equals $\frac{7}{20}$. Therefore the quotient is $3\frac{7}{20}$.

Divide:

78. $28\frac{3}{5}$ by 6.	**83.** $42\frac{5}{8}$ by 8.	**88.** $24\frac{5}{8}$ by 7.
79. $35\frac{2}{9}$ by 8.	**84.** $33\frac{3}{5}$ by 6.	**89.** $32\frac{3}{5}$ by 5.
80. $61\frac{5}{7}$ by 7.	**85.** $36\frac{2}{3}$ by 9.	**90.** $40\frac{4}{7}$ by 6.
81. $52\frac{7}{8}$ by 5.	**86.** $28\frac{3}{5}$ by 6.	**91.** $26\frac{1}{8}$ by 5.
82. $41\frac{1}{4}$ by 8.	**87.** $30\frac{4}{7}$ by 7.	**92.** $33\frac{5}{9}$ by 4.

93. Divide 27 by $3\frac{1}{4}$.

$\begin{array}{c|c} 3\frac{1}{4} & 27 \\ 4 & 4 \\ \hline 13 & 108 \\ & 8\frac{4}{13} \end{array}$

EXPLANATION. — It is frequently convenient to reduce the numbers to equivalent fractions having the same denominator, and then to divide the numerator of the dividend by the numerator of the divisor.

Thus, $3\frac{1}{4} = 13$ fourths, and $27 = 108$ fourths.

Then $108 \div 13 = 8\frac{4}{13}$, the quotient.

94. 35 by $4\frac{2}{3}$.	**98.** 54 by $5\frac{1}{8}$.	**102.** 61 by $10\frac{1}{6}$.
95. 42 by $3\frac{2}{5}$.	**99.** 36 by $4\frac{2}{5}$.	**103.** $24\frac{3}{4}$ by $8\frac{1}{2}$.
96. 37 by $6\frac{1}{2}$.	**100.** 48 by $7\frac{5}{8}$.	**104.** $18\frac{2}{5}$ by $2\frac{1}{10}$.
97. 29 by $4\frac{2}{3}$.	**101.** 35 by $6\frac{1}{5}$.	**105.** $13\frac{1}{3}$ by $4\frac{1}{3}$.

106. If a yard of silk costs $\$2\frac{1}{5}$, how many yards can be bought for $\$15\frac{1}{2}$?

107. At $\$6\frac{3}{4}$ per barrel, how many barrels of flour can be bought for $\$74\frac{1}{4}$?

108. If a man can walk $3\frac{2}{5}$ miles an hour, in how many hours can he walk $30\frac{2}{3}$ miles?

109. Mr. Hill can cut $3\frac{3}{4}$ cords of wood in one day. How many days will he require to cut $38\frac{3}{10}$ cords?

110. I bought 18 turkeys for $\$32\frac{2}{5}$. What was the average price of each?

111. A man divided $\$16$ among some poor children, giving to each $\$1\frac{3}{5}$. How many children received a share?

112. A shoe dealer paid $\$60$ for a case of overshoes, at $\$\frac{3}{4}$ a pair. How many pairs of shoes were there in the case?

113. Mr. Long earns $\$26\frac{2}{5}$ in a week, or six working days. How much does he earn per day?

114. How many yards of cloth can be bought for $\$65$, at $\$\frac{7}{8}$ a yard?

115. What is the average weight of 12 men whose united weight is $1768\frac{5}{8}$ pounds?

116. A farmer raised $536\frac{3}{4}$ bushels of wheat from a field containing 21 acres. What was the average yield per acre?

117. How many steps will it take to walk a mile, or 5280 feet, each step being $2\frac{1}{2}$ feet in length?

118. At $\$33\frac{1}{3}$ per acre, how many acres of land can be purchased for $\$6750\frac{2}{3}$?

119. I paid $\$15\frac{3}{4}$ for 25 bushels of potatoes. What did I pay per bushel?

120. In a field containing $3\frac{3}{4}$ acres there were raised 87 bushels of grain. What was the yield per acre?

121. Four men in partnership gain $\$4327\frac{1}{4}$. If they share equally, what will be each one's share of the gain?

122. What is the price of hay, when $5\frac{4}{7}$ tons are worth $\$65$?

123. I paid $\$36\frac{1}{2}$ for $6\frac{7}{8}$ cords of wood. What was the price per cord?

FRACTIONAL FORMS.

159. Expressions of *unexecuted division* of fractions are often written in *the form of a fraction.* Such expressions are usually termed *Complex Fractions.*

Thus, $\frac{3}{4} \div 5$, written $\frac{\frac{3}{4}}{5}$, and $6\frac{1}{4} \div \frac{3}{5}$, written $\frac{6\frac{1}{4}}{\frac{3}{5}}$, are complex fractions.

1. Find the value of $\dfrac{3\frac{2}{3}}{\frac{3}{5}}$.

EXPLANATION. — The expression means $3\frac{2}{3} \div \frac{3}{5}$, and is solved like other examples in division of fractions.

Reduce to simple fractions :

2. $\dfrac{\frac{12}{15}}{\frac{7}{5}}$.

3. $\dfrac{\frac{18}{27}}{\frac{9}{5}}$.

4. $\dfrac{\frac{21}{25}}{\frac{7}{15}}$.

5. $\dfrac{\frac{27}{42}}{\frac{6}{14}}$.

6. $\dfrac{\frac{23}{26}}{1\frac{3}{8}}$.

7. $\dfrac{6}{\frac{3}{5}}$.

8. $\dfrac{21}{\frac{7}{9}}$.

9. $\dfrac{\frac{35}{5}}{12}$.

10. $\dfrac{48}{\frac{9}{15}}$.

11. $\dfrac{55}{2\frac{2}{27}}$.

12. $\dfrac{5\frac{3}{4}}{6\frac{1}{2}}$.

13. $\dfrac{5\frac{1}{5}}{\dfrac{2}{6\frac{1}{4}}}$.

14. $\dfrac{3\frac{2}{3}}{\dfrac{2\frac{1}{4}}{2}}$.

15. $\dfrac{5\frac{1}{6}}{\dfrac{3}{2\frac{1}{8}}}$.

16. $\dfrac{15\frac{1}{8}}{\dfrac{2\frac{1}{5}}{10}}$.

17. $\dfrac{\frac{3}{4}1 \text{ of } \frac{2}{3}}{\frac{2}{7} \text{ of } 2\frac{1}{2}}$.

18. $\dfrac{\frac{5}{8} \text{ of } 2\frac{1}{4}}{\frac{4}{5} \text{ of } \frac{5}{8}}$.

19. $\dfrac{\frac{7}{8} \text{ of } 3\frac{2}{3}}{\frac{5}{6} \text{ of } 2\frac{4}{7}}$.

20. $\dfrac{\frac{15}{4} \text{ of } 5\frac{3}{8}}{\frac{41}{5} \text{ of } 5\frac{5}{6}}$.

21. $\dfrac{\frac{8}{17} \text{ of } 11\frac{5}{12}}{\frac{16}{34} \text{ of } 9\frac{3}{16}}$.

FRACTIONAL RELATION OF NUMBERS.

160. To find what part one number is of another.

1. What part of 8 is $2\frac{1}{2}$?

SOLUTION. —1 is $\frac{1}{8}$ of 8 ; hence, $2\frac{1}{2}$ is $2\frac{1}{2}$ times $\frac{1}{8}$ of 8, or $\dfrac{2\frac{1}{2}}{8}$ of 8, or $\frac{5}{16}$ of 8.

What part of

2. 8 is 7 ?	**6.** 13 is 11 ?	**10.** 10 is $3\frac{1}{5}$?	**14.** 18 is $\frac{3}{4}$?
3. 9 is 3 ?	**7.** 15 is 8 ?	**11.** 12 is $3\frac{1}{4}$?	**15.** 15 is $\frac{4}{5}$?
4. 18 is 5 ?	**8.** 14 is 7 ?	**12.** 15 is $4\frac{1}{2}$?	**16.** 21 is $\frac{3}{7}$?
5. 21 is 6 ?	**9.** 24 is 13 ?	**13.** 13 is $2\frac{3}{4}$?	**17.** 35 is $\frac{3}{5}$?

18. What part of $4\frac{1}{2}$ is 2 ?

SOLUTION. —$4\frac{1}{2} = \frac{9}{2}$, and $2 = \frac{4}{2}$. $\frac{4}{2}$ is $\frac{4}{9}$ of $\frac{9}{2}$. Therefore 2 is $\frac{4}{9}$ of $4\frac{1}{2}$.

What part of

19. $5\frac{1}{4}$ is 3 ?	**23.** $4\frac{2}{3}$ is 2 ?	**27.** $8\frac{3}{5}$ is 6 ?	**31.** $\frac{3}{5}$ is 12 ?
20. $5\frac{2}{5}$ is 5 ?	**24.** $5\frac{1}{3}$ is 3 ?	**28.** $7\frac{4}{9}$ is 5 ?	**32.** $\frac{4}{5}$ is 8 ?
21. $7\frac{1}{8}$ is 2 ?	**25.** $3\frac{2}{7}$ is 2 ?	**29.** $8\frac{3}{7}$ is 6 ?	**33.** $\frac{6}{7}$ is 10 ?
22. $6\frac{1}{5}$ is 4 ?	**26.** $6\frac{2}{3}$ is 5 ?	**30.** $9\frac{1}{8}$ is 8 ?	**34.** $\frac{7}{8}$ is 9 ?

35. What part of $4\frac{1}{2}$ is $2\frac{1}{3}$?

SOLUTION. —$4\frac{1}{2} = \frac{27}{6}$ and $2\frac{1}{3} = \frac{14}{6}$. $\frac{14}{6}$ is $\frac{14}{27}$ of $\frac{27}{6}$. Therefore $2\frac{1}{3}$ is $\frac{14}{27}$ of $4\frac{1}{2}$.

What part of

36. $2\frac{1}{2}$ is $3\frac{1}{3}$?	**40.** $3\frac{1}{4}$ is $2\frac{3}{5}$?	**44.** $6\frac{1}{5}$ is $3\frac{1}{4}$?	**48.** $\frac{3}{4}$ is $\frac{2}{3}$?
37. $3\frac{1}{5}$ is $4\frac{1}{2}$?	**41.** $3\frac{5}{8}$ is $1\frac{1}{2}$?	**45.** $5\frac{2}{5}$ is $4\frac{1}{10}$?	**49.** $\frac{5}{7}$ is $\frac{3}{4}$?
38. $4\frac{2}{3}$ is $3\frac{1}{9}$?	**42.** $5\frac{2}{7}$ is $2\frac{3}{7}$?	**46.** $3\frac{6}{7}$ is $2\frac{3}{4}$?	**50.** $\frac{6}{11}$ is $\frac{5}{8}$?
39. $6\frac{1}{5}$ is $3\frac{1}{4}$?	**43.** $8\frac{4}{9}$ is $3\frac{2}{3}$?	**47.** $4\frac{8}{9}$ is $3\frac{1}{4}$?	**51.** $\frac{4}{9}$ is $\frac{3}{5}$?

161. A number and its relation to another number given, to find the other number.

1. 120 is $\frac{4}{5}$ of what number?

SOLUTION.—Since 120 is $\frac{4}{5}$ of a number, $\frac{1}{5}$ of the number is $\frac{1}{4}$ of 120, or 30; and since 30 is $\frac{1}{5}$ of the number, the number must be 5 times 30, or 150.   Hence, 120 is $\frac{4}{5}$ of 150.

Find the number of which

2. 160 is $\frac{2}{3}$.	7. 240 is $\frac{6}{7}$.	12. 380 is $\frac{5}{8}$.	17. 510 is $\frac{17}{20}$.
3. 180 is $\frac{3}{4}$.	8. 252 is $\frac{7}{8}$.	13. 392 is $\frac{4}{9}$.	18. 756 is $\frac{18}{25}$.
4. 176 is $\frac{4}{5}$.	9. 275 is $\frac{5}{9}$.	14. 415 is $\frac{5}{11}$.	19. 589 is $\frac{19}{30}$.
5. 180 is $\frac{5}{6}$.	10. 320 is $\frac{8}{9}$.	15. 474 is $\frac{6}{13}$.	20. 609 is $\frac{21}{36}$.
6. 192 is $\frac{3}{5}$.	11. 364 is $\frac{7}{6}$.	16. 497 is $\frac{7}{15}$.	21. 625 is $\frac{25}{32}$.

22. A man spent $450, which was $\frac{5}{9}$ of his money.   How much money had he?

23. Mr. B bought a house for $1260.   The house cost him $\frac{3}{8}$ as much as his store.   What did he pay for the store?

24. A drover paid $2914 for a lot of sheep, which is $\frac{9}{10}$ of what he sold them for.   How much did he receive for them?

25. C bought a cow for $31.50, which was $\frac{5}{21}$ of what he paid for a horse.   What was the cost of the horse?

26. A lady bought a dress for $21.65 and found that she had spent $\frac{5}{8}$ of her money.   How much money had she?

27. D has a library which contains 1264 books.   His library contains $\frac{4}{7}$ as many books as E's.   How many books are there in E's library?

28. A farmer raised 672 bushels of wheat, which was $\frac{3}{11}$ of the number of bushels of corn he raised. How much corn did he raise?

29. Mr. H built a barn which cost him $2513. The barn cost him $\frac{7}{12}$ as much as his house. What was the cost of the house?

30. A man burned 1560 bushels of lime in September, which was $\frac{6}{7}$ of the number of bushels burned in October. How much lime did he burn in October?

31. A merchant sold on Monday goods amounting to $376.70, which was $\frac{5}{6}$ of the amount received for goods on Tuesday. What was the amount received for Tuesday's sale?

32. Mr. K deposited in one bank $1936, which was $\frac{11}{13}$ of the money which he deposited in another bank. How much did he deposit in the latter bank?

33. A man left his son $19,000, which was $\frac{2}{5}$ the value of his estate. What was the value of his estate?

34. 3300 feet are $\frac{5}{8}$ of a mile? How many feet are there in a mile?

35. A man sold his house for $36,000, which was $\frac{6}{7}$ of its cost. How much did the house cost?

36. Mr. Black spends $48 a week, which is $\frac{3}{8}$ of his weekly income. Mr. Cutler spends $60 a week, which is $\frac{5}{6}$ of his weekly income. Which of them has the greater income, and how much greater?

37. A man has debts amounting to $2193. This amount is equal to $\frac{17}{35}$ of his resources. How much money is he worth?

38. A man expended $\frac{19}{20}$ of his fortune in buying a farm for $4826. What was his fortune?

REVIEW EXERCISES.

ORAL EXERCISES.

162. **1.** A boy having $\frac{1}{4}$ earned $\frac{2}{5}$. What part of a dollar had he then?

2. Mr. A, having $3\frac{3}{4}$ acres of land, bought $6\frac{3}{5}$ acres. How much land did he then have? He then sold $\frac{7}{20}$ of an acre. How much had he left?

3. A man owning $\frac{5}{8}$ of a ship sold $\frac{2}{3}$ of his share. What part of the ship does he still own?

4. Mr. A buying a farm paid $\frac{1}{3}$ cash, $\frac{1}{4}$ the second year, and $\frac{2}{5}$ the next year. How much more must he pay to own the farm?

5. A boy bought a watch for $27, which was $4\frac{1}{2}$ times the cost of the chain. What did the chain cost?

6. Mr. K is 45 years old and his wife is $\frac{4}{5}$ of his age. How old is his wife?

7. A horse costs $160, and $\frac{3}{4}$ of its cost is 3 times the cost of a cow. What is the cost of the cow?

8. If to the height of a certain tree in California you add $\frac{9}{4}$ of its height, the sum will equal 266 feet. How high is the tree?

9. How many pounds of coffee, at $\frac{3}{10}$ of a dollar a pound, can be bought for $6?

10. A man bought turkeys at $1\frac{3}{4}$ dollars apiece. How many did he get for $21? How many for $28? For $35? For $56?

11. If a man can plow $\frac{1}{3}$ of a field containing 5 acres in a day, how much can he plow in $\frac{2}{3}$ of a day?

12. How much will 5 carpenters earn in 4 days if they each receive $$ 2\frac{4}{10} per day ?

13. If there are $2\frac{3}{4}$ bushels of apples in a barrel, how many barrels will contain 22 bushels ?

14. A can do a certain piece of work in 3 days, and B can do it in 4 days. How long will it take them to do it working together ?

SOLUTION. — Since A can do the work in 3 days, he can do $\frac{1}{3}$ of it in 1 day ; and since B can do the work in 4 days, he can do $\frac{1}{4}$ of it in 1 day. Both together can therefore do the sum of $\frac{1}{3}$ and $\frac{1}{4}$ or $\frac{7}{12}$ of it in 1 day. If both did $\frac{1}{12}$ of the work in a day, they could do the whole in 12 days, but inasmuch as they do $\frac{7}{12}$ of the work in 1 day, they can do the whole in $\frac{1}{7}$ of 12 days, or $1\frac{5}{7}$ days.

15. A can do a certain piece of work in 2 days, B in 3 days, and C in 4 days. How long will it take them to do it working together ?

16. Charles lost $\frac{4}{7}$ of his marbles, and then had 21 left. How many marbles had he at first ? How many marbles did he lose ?

17. A grocer sold $10\frac{1}{2}$ pounds of butter for $$ 4.20. What was the price per pound ?

18. After selling $4\frac{1}{2}$ acres to A, and $5\frac{3}{5}$ acres to B, I find that I have $\frac{3}{4}$ of my land left. How much had I at first ?

19. If 8 men eat 4 loaves of bread in one day, how many loaves will 5 men eat in 3 days ?

20. A man is 42 years of age, and $\frac{2}{7}$ of his age is $\frac{1}{3}$ of his wife's age. How old is his wife ?

21. Mr. H bought a cow for $$ 35 and sold it for $\frac{6}{7}$ of what it cost. How much did he lose ?

22. A farmer sold 60 sheep, which were $\frac{2}{5}$ of what remained. How many had he at first ?

23. A man sold $\frac{2}{5}$ of his farm for $1500. At this rate what was the value of the farm?

24. A man sold $\frac{2}{5}$ of his farm and had 30 acres left. How many acres had he at first?

25. Edward gave $.60 for a book and a slate, and the slate cost $\frac{3}{7}$ as much as the book. What did each cost?

SOLUTION. — The book cost a certain sum and the slate cost $\frac{3}{7}$ as much; hence both must have cost $1\frac{3}{7}$ or $\frac{10}{7}$ times the cost of the book. Then, since $\frac{10}{7}$ of the cost of the book was 60 cents, $\frac{1}{7}$ of the cost was $\frac{1}{10}$ of 60 cents, or 6 cents. Since $\frac{1}{7}$ of the cost of the book was 6 cents, the entire cost of the book was 7 times 6 cents, or 42 cents. Hence the book cost 42 cents and the slate 60 cents — 42 cents, or 18 cents.

26. A horse cost $125, and $\frac{4}{5}$ of the cost of the horse is 4 times the cost of the harness. What did the harness cost?

27. If a rod 4 feet long casts a shadow $6\frac{2}{3}$ feet long, what is the length of the shadow that a rod 12 feet long will cast at the same time of day?

28. A can do a piece of work in 6 days, and B can do it in 10 days. In what time can both do it?

29. If $\frac{3}{4}$ of a yard of cloth costs $3\frac{3}{4}$, what will 5 yards cost?

30. A market woman bought eggs at the rate of 4 for 5 cents, and sold them at the rate of 5 for 9 cents. How much did she gain on each egg?

31. How many oranges, at $7\frac{1}{2}$ cents apiece, can be exchanged for 60 pears, at $2\frac{1}{2}$ cents apiece?

32. A fruit grower sold 28 bushels of peaches, and had $\frac{1}{5}$ of his peaches left. How many peaches did he have?

33. If the yearly rent of a house is $600, what will be the rent for $7\frac{1}{2}$ months at the same rate?

34. If 3 boxes of oranges cost $\$5\frac{2}{3}$, how many boxes can be bought for $17.

35. Henry hoed $3\frac{3}{4}$ acres of corn, hoeing $\frac{3}{5}$ of an acre each day. How many days did it take him?

36. Mary is $\frac{3}{8}$ as old as her mother, who is 40 years of age. Her mother is $\frac{4}{7}$ of the age of her grandmother. How old is Mary, and how old is her grandmother?

37. $\frac{3}{4}$ of a cord of wood, at $6 per cord, will pay ror what part of a ton of coal, at $8 per ton?

38. A sold B $\frac{2}{3}$ of his land, and then bought back $\frac{1}{3}$ of what he had sold. What part of the land did each then have?

39. I raised from my orchard 75 bushels of apples. I kept 25 bushels for my own use, gave $10\frac{3}{4}$ bushels to a friend, and $4\frac{1}{2}$ bushels decayed. The rest I sold. How many bushels did I sell?

40. Jacob and Rebecca have each $\$3\frac{1}{2}$. They agree to buy a book costing $\$3\frac{1}{4}$ as a Christmas present for their mother. How much has each left if they share the expense equally?

41. Charles lives $1\frac{1}{2}$ miles from the schoolhouse. If it takes him $6\frac{2}{3}$ minutes to go $\frac{1}{3}$ of a mile, how long will it take him to go to school?

42. How many bushels of potatoes, at $\$\frac{3}{4}$ a bushel, will pay for a barrel of sugar, at $\$7\frac{1}{2}$?

43. A pole is $\frac{1}{5}$ in the mud, $\frac{1}{4}$ in the water, and 44 feet in the air. How long is the pole?

44. A fox is 60 rods in advance of a hound. The fox runs 62 rods a minute, the hound 66. How many minutes will it take the hound to catch the fox?

45. What is the value of 20 bushels of grain, at the rate of $3\frac{1}{3}$ bushels for $\$2$?

46. What is the value of $\frac{8}{9}$ of an acre of land, if $\frac{7}{8}$ of an acre is worth $\$84$?

47. How much will $6\frac{1}{2}$ barrels of flour cost, if $\frac{5}{8}$ of a barrel costs $\$2\frac{1}{2}$?

48. If $3\frac{1}{2}$ yards of cloth are worth $\$9\frac{4}{5}$, what is a yard worth?

49. A man worked $11\frac{2}{3}$ days, and after paying his board and other expenses with $\frac{4}{7}$ of his earnings, had $\$15$ left. How much did he receive a day?

50. A and B do a piece of work in 7 days, and B can do $\frac{1}{4}$ of the same in $3\frac{1}{2}$ days. How long will it take each to do it alone?

SOLUTION. — Since B can do $\frac{1}{4}$ of the work in $3\frac{1}{2}$ days, he can do the whole work in 4 times $3\frac{1}{2}$ days, or 14 days, and $\frac{1}{14}$ of it in 1 day. Since A and B can do $\frac{1}{7}$ of it in 1 day, and B can do $\frac{1}{14}$ of it in 1 day, $\frac{1}{7} - \frac{1}{14}$, or $\frac{1}{14}$, is the part that A can do in 1 day. Since A can do $\frac{1}{14}$ of the work in 1 day, he can do the whole work in 14 days. Hence each can do the work in 14 days.

WRITTEN EXERCISES.

163. **1.** A farm is divided into five fields containing respectively $19\frac{3}{4}$, $28\frac{2}{3}$, $30\frac{2}{5}$, $36\frac{5}{8}$, and $39\frac{1}{2}$ acres. How many acres are there in the farm?

2. I bought a barrel of flour for $\$6\frac{3}{8}$, 3 bushels of potatoes at $\$\frac{3}{8}$ per bushel, and a ham for $\$3\frac{5}{8}$, and gave the clerk a twenty-dollar bill. How much change did I get?

3. If a man working $8\frac{1}{2}$ hours a day can finish a piece of work in 12 days, how many hours per day must he work to complete it in $8\frac{3}{4}$ days?

4. What is the value of 700 eggs, at 25 cents per dozen?

5. The quotient is 347 and the divisor $26\frac{1}{8}$. What is the dividend?

6. A sold $\frac{2}{5}$ of his land, and then had $115\frac{3}{4}$ acres. How much land had he before the sale?

7. There are $30\frac{1}{4}$ square yards in a square rod. How many square rods are there in 1000 square yards?

8. A man bequeathed to his wife $ 5604, which was $\frac{12}{19}$ of his estate. What was the value of his estate?

9. If 6 is added to both terms of the fraction $\frac{7}{9}$, will the value of the fraction be increased or diminished, and how much?

10. If 6 is subtracted from both terms of the fraction $\frac{7}{8}$, will its value be increased or diminished, and how much?

11. A merchant bought 450 pounds of sugar at $4\frac{1}{2}$ cents a pound, 50 pounds of tea at $37\frac{1}{2}$ cents a pound, and 80 pounds of rice at $8\frac{3}{4}$ cents a pound. What was the entire cost?

12. A grocer, after selling $\frac{1}{8}$, $\frac{1}{10}$, $\frac{1}{5}$, and $\frac{1}{4}$ of a quantity of sugar, had 260 pounds left. How many pounds had he at first?

13. A owns $\frac{5}{7}$ of a section of land, B $\frac{3}{4}$ of a section, and C $\frac{3}{10}$ as much as A and B together. What part of a section does C own?

14. Divide $\frac{2}{5}$ of $\frac{4}{8}$ of $\frac{5}{7}$ of $3\frac{3}{4}$ by $6 \times \frac{3}{4}$ of $\frac{4}{9}$ of 5.

15. If $12\frac{3}{4}$ bushels of potatoes, at 40 cents a bushel, are given for a quantity of molasses, at $18\frac{3}{4}$ cents a gallon, how many gallons of molasses are obtained?

16. From a barrel of vinegar containing $41\frac{1}{2}$ gallons, $\frac{1}{10}$ leaked out. If I paid $ 6.75 for it, at what price per gallon must I sell the remainder to still gain $ 1 on the vinegar?

17. A saleswoman earns $ $\frac{9}{10}$ a day, and her expenses are $ $3\frac{19}{20}$ a week. How much money can she save in a year, or 52 weeks?

18. A stock of goods was owned by three partners. A owned $\frac{2}{5}$ of it, B $\frac{3}{8}$ of it, and C the remainder. The goods were sold at a profit of $ 4260. What was each one's share of the gain?

19. A man worked $24\frac{3}{4}$ days, and after paying for his board and other expenses with $\frac{3}{7}$ of his earnings, he had $ 24 remaining. What were his daily wages?

20. If a miller takes $\frac{1}{8}$ of the quantity of grain for grinding it, how many bushels must a farmer carry to the mill that he may take away 21 bushels of ground grain?

21. I paid 9 cents a pound for a live turkey that weighed $16\frac{3}{4}$ pounds, and the waste in dressing was $\frac{2}{7}$ of its weight. How much a pound did the dressed turkey cost me?

22. Divide $\frac{5}{6}$ of $\frac{8}{9}$ of $1\frac{2}{15}$ of $1\frac{8}{24}$ of $6\frac{1}{4}$ by $\frac{4}{7}$ of $\frac{9}{16}$ of $\frac{21}{36}$ of $7\frac{1}{2}$.

23. Divide $\frac{7}{8}$ of $1\frac{4}{17}$ of $\frac{34}{37}$ of $\frac{5}{12}$ of $8\frac{1}{2}$ by $\frac{2}{3}$ of $\frac{41}{56}$ of $1\frac{4}{25}$ of $1\frac{8}{19}$.

24. A merchant tailor has $45\frac{3}{4}$ yards of cloth, from which he wishes to cut an equal number of coats, trousers, and vests. How many of each can be cut from it if the garments contain $4\frac{1}{4}$ yards, $2\frac{3}{4}$ yards, and $\frac{5}{8}$ of a yard, respectively?

25. A farmer sold at market 20 sheep at $ $2\frac{7}{8}$ each, and bought 8 yards of cloth at $1\frac{3}{5}$ per yard. How much money had he left?

26. A man having 100 fowls, sold $\frac{1}{4}$ of them to E, and $\frac{2}{3}$ of the remainder to F. What was the value of what remained, if they were worth 25 cents apiece?

27. How many tons of hay will be required to keep 2 horses for 6 months, if 8 horses eat 15 tons in that time?

28. A walked at the rate of $3\frac{1}{4}$ miles an hour for $5\frac{7}{12}$ hours, and B at the rate of $4\frac{1}{2}$ miles an hour for $4\frac{3}{15}$ hours. Which walked the greater distance, and how much?

29. A young man received \$1000 from his father. He spent $\frac{1}{20}$ of it for clothes, $\frac{1}{8}$ of it in traveling, and invested the rest in land. How much did he pay for the land?

30. Two thirds of a stock of goods was destroyed by fire, $\frac{2}{5}$ of the remainder was destroyed by water, and the rest was sold at cost for \$2575. What was the cost of the entire stock?

31. Five eighths of A's money increased by the difference between $\frac{2}{3}$ and $\frac{3}{4}$ of his money equals \$1020. How much money has A?

32. A pole 63 feet long was broken into two unequal pieces, and $\frac{3}{5}$ of the longer piece equaled $\frac{3}{4}$ of the shorter. What was the length of each piece?

SOLUTION. — Since $\frac{3}{5}$ of the longer piece $=\frac{3}{4}$ of the shorter piece, $\frac{1}{5}$ of the longer piece $=\frac{1}{3}$ of $\frac{3}{4}$, or $\frac{1}{4}$ of the shorter piece.

Since $\frac{1}{5}$ of the longer piece $=\frac{1}{4}$ of the shorter, the longer piece $=\frac{5}{4}$ of the shorter piece.

Since the longer piece was $\frac{5}{4}$ of the shorter, both pieces must have been $1\frac{5}{4}$ or $\frac{9}{4}$ times the shorter piece, which is 63 feet.

Since $\frac{9}{4}$ of the shorter piece $=63$ feet, $\frac{1}{4}$ of the shorter piece was $\frac{1}{9}$ of 63 feet, or 7 feet, and the entire length of the shorter piece was 28 feet.

63 feet -28 feet $=35$ feet, the length of the longer piece.

33. Divide $\frac{13}{20}$ of $\frac{16}{21}$ of $\frac{7}{12}$ of $\dfrac{3\frac{1}{2}}{4}$ by $\frac{2}{5}$ of $\frac{8}{9}$ of 15.

34. I have a farm of 80 acres. On $\frac{2}{5}$ of the farm corn is planted, on $\frac{2}{3}$ of the remainder wheat, and on the rest, oats. How many acres are there of each kind of grain?

35. The length of a room is $15\frac{2}{3}$ feet, and the width is $12\frac{3}{4}$ feet. What will be the cost of a moulding extending entirely around it at $4\frac{1}{2}$ cents a foot?

36. A owned $\frac{5}{7}$ of a ship and sold $\frac{3}{4}$ of his share to B; B sold $\frac{5}{8}$ of what he bought to C for $2500. At that rate what was the whole ship worth?

37. From $4\frac{3}{4}$ acres I sell to E $\frac{7}{8}$ of an acre, to F $\frac{5}{8}$ of an acre, to G $\frac{6}{7}$ of an acre, and to H $\frac{7}{16}$ of an acre. How much is the remainder worth at $850 per acre?

38. A gentleman paid $60 for keeping 2 horses 12 weeks. What would it cost, at the same rate, to keep one horse $3\frac{1}{2}$ weeks?

39. Two brothers together own $\frac{1}{3}$ of a flouring mill valued at $12520. One owns $\frac{3}{7}$ as much as the other. What is the value of each one's share?

40. A lady has $55\frac{3}{4}$ in her purse. She spends $13\frac{1}{2}$ for a shawl, $4\frac{3}{5}$ for cloth, $3\frac{1}{4}$ for a hat, and $2\frac{7}{10}$ for lace. How much has she left?

41. A stove manufacturer purchases old iron at $\frac{83}{100}$ per hundred pounds, and makes out of it stoves weighing 125 pounds each, which he sells at $15\frac{1}{2}$ apiece. How much does he gain on each 100 pounds of old iron?

42. A carpenter alone can build a shop in 18 days, and with the help of his son he can build it in 12 days. In how many days can the son alone build the shop?

43. A man who had spent $\frac{2}{3}$ of his money and $\frac{1}{3}$ more, found he had $21 left. How much money had he at first?

44. Simplify $\dfrac{\frac{2}{9}}{\frac{1}{2} \text{ of } \frac{1}{3}} \div \dfrac{\frac{3}{4} \text{ of } \frac{6}{10}}{4\frac{1}{5}}$.

45. I bought 26 yards of carpet at $1\frac{9}{10}$ a yard, 3 curtains at $5\frac{2}{3}$ each, and 6 chairs at $1\frac{3}{4}$ each. What was my bill?

46. A huckster bought 75 bushels of apples at $\frac{3}{4}$ per bushel, 65 bushels at $\frac{5}{8}$ per bushel, and 20 bushels at $\frac{13}{20}$ per bushel. At what average price per bushel must he sell them to gain $25?

47. A and B hire a pasture for $15.50. A puts in 8 cows, and B puts in 12 cows. What must each pay?

48. Two men hire a pasture for $20. The one puts in 9 horses, and the other puts in 48 sheep. If 18 sheep eat as much as 3 horses, what must each man pay?

49. A can walk a mile in $\frac{1}{3}$ of an hour, and B in $\frac{3}{11}$ of an hour. In a race of 15 miles, which will win, and by how much?

50. James, William, and Joseph can remove a pile of wood in 12 hours. James and William together can remove it in 18 hours. In how many hours can Joseph alone remove it?

51. A flour dealer bought 130 barrels of flour at $6\frac{2}{3}$ per barrel. He sold 85 barrels at $6\frac{9}{10}$ per barrel, and the remainder at $7. What did he gain?

52. A and B together have $9500. Two thirds of A's money equals $\frac{2}{5}$ of B's. How much money has each?

53. A lady divided $7\frac{1}{5}$ among some children, giving them $\frac{9}{10}$ each. What was the number of children?

54. R, O, and W bought a drove of cattle. R paid for $\frac{3}{8}$ of the drove, O for $\frac{4}{15}$ of it, and W for the remainder. It was found that R paid $56 more than W. What did each pay, and what was the cost of the drove?

55. Simplify $\dfrac{2\frac{2}{3} \text{ of } 5\frac{1}{6}}{7\frac{1}{12}} + \dfrac{3\frac{1}{2}}{4} \div \dfrac{1}{2}$.

56. A farmer brought to market 3 jars of butter, weighing 27, 29, and 40 pounds, respectively. The empty jars weighed $4\frac{1}{3}$, $4\frac{8}{9}$, and $7\frac{1}{4}$ pounds. The butter was sold for $28. What was the price per pound?

57. A man bequeathed to his son $7500, which was $3\frac{3}{4}$ times what he gave his daughter. What did the daughter receive?

58. A owns $\frac{2}{7}$ of a mill, and B the remainder; $\frac{5}{8}$ of the difference between their shares is valued at $8500. What is the value of the mill?

59. What is the value of $17\frac{1}{2}$ bales of cotton, each weighing $4\frac{3}{4}$ hundred-weight, at $18\frac{3}{4}$ per hundred-weight?

60. A spends $\frac{4}{5}$ of his income, and B, having the same income, spends $1\frac{1}{3}$ times as much as A, and finds himself $75 in debt at the end of the year. What is the income of each?

61. I bought 75 acres of land at $63 an acre. I sold $\frac{3}{16}$ of it at $71 an acre, $\frac{7}{20}$ at $65 an acre, and the remainder for 3\frac{1}{2}$ more per acre than I paid for it. What did I gain on the whole?

62. A farmer sold $320\frac{2}{5}$ pounds of maple sugar at $15\frac{3}{4}$ cents a pound, and took his pay in cloth at $67\frac{1}{2}$ cents a yard. How many yards did he receive?

63. A ship is worth $85000. A man owns $\frac{7}{16}$ of it. If he sells $\frac{3}{5}$ of his share, what is the value of the part of his share which is left?

64. The water flows from one spring at the rate of $71\frac{1}{2}$ gallons in 11 minutes; from another spring at the rate of 113 gallons in 19 minutes. Which spring flows the faster, and what is the difference in the flow per minute?

65. A merchant sold a quantity of sugar for $1180, and thereby gained $\frac{1}{4}$ of the cost. If he had sold it for $1000, would he have gained or lost, and how much?

66. What is the exact value of $\left(3 + 2\frac{1}{2} - \frac{3}{4} \text{ of } \frac{6}{2} + \dfrac{4}{\frac{2}{3}}\right) \div 4\frac{1}{5}$?

67. A owes $1140. By saving $\frac{6}{19}$ of his income annually for 5 years, he can pay his debt and have $1200 left. What is his yearly income?

68. A man has three creditors. To the first he owes $1360½, to the second $1087¼, and to the third $876¾. The man fails, and the creditors seize all his property, which amounts to only $2350. How much should each creditor receive?

69. Two men cleared a piece of woodland for $69. The one worked 19½ days and cut 71¾ cords; the other worked twice as many days as the first cut cords per day. How much did each receive, if they shared in proportion to the time they worked?

70. A stock-broker bought 7 shares of Northern Pacific Railroad stock at $97½ per share, and 15 shares of Union Pacific Railroad stock at $101¾ per share. He sold them all at $105¼ a share. How much did he gain?

71. If a miller takes ⅛ for toll, and a bushel of wheat produces 40 pounds of flour, how many bushels must be carried to the mill to obtain 196 pounds of flour, or 1 barrel?

72. A merchant bought three pieces of cloth for $365¾. The first contained 31½ yards, the second 42¼ yards, and the third 47⅝ yards. He wishes to sell the cloth so as to gain ¼ of the cost. At what price must he sell it per yard?

73. An estate was divided between two brothers and a sister. The elder brother received $\frac{5}{13}$ of the estate, the younger $\frac{3}{10}$, and the sister the remainder, which was $1623 more than the younger brother received. What was the value of the estate, and what did each receive?

74. Divide 9 times the product of $\dfrac{2\frac{2}{3}}{2\frac{2}{9}}$ and $\dfrac{\frac{1}{4} \text{ of } \frac{1}{5}}{20}$ by $\dfrac{4\frac{3}{7}}{5\frac{1}{6}}$.

75. A and B can perform a piece of work in $23\frac{10}{19}$ days. A alone can perform it in 37¾ days. In how many days can B do the work alone?

76. A boat whose rate of sailing in still water is 14 miles an hour, was accelerated $3\frac{1}{2}$ miles per hour in going downstream, and retarded the same distance per hour in coming up. How long would it take the boat to come up the same distance that it could go down in 10 hours?

77. Eight men cut $97\frac{1}{2}$ cords of wood in $4\frac{7}{8}$ days, for which they received $\$48\frac{1}{2}$. What was the average daily pay of each man?

78. Two men dug a ditch for $\$75$; one man worked $3\frac{1}{2}$ days and dug 14 rods; the other worked as many days as the first dug rods per day. How much did each receive, if they shared in proportion to the time they worked?

79. A man has $\frac{1}{8}$ of his property invested in real estate, $\frac{3}{7}$ of the remainder in bonds, $\frac{4}{5}$ of what still remains in bank stock, and the rest, which is $\$3500$, he has invested in business. What is the value of his entire property?

80. The sum of two numbers equals $5\dfrac{3\frac{1}{2}}{7\frac{1}{3}}$, and one of them is the difference between $\dfrac{49\frac{3}{10}}{11}$ and $\dfrac{22\frac{1}{5}}{9}$. What is the other number?

81. A and B together can do a piece of work in 12 days. If A can do only $\frac{3}{4}$ as much as B, how long will it take each of them to do the work?

82. A man bought a house and paid $\frac{1}{3}$ of the price in cash at the time of the purchase. A year afterward he paid $\frac{1}{3}$ of what then remained unpaid, and the two payments amounted to $\$5260$. How much did he pay for the house?

83. A cistern which holds 280 gallons is empty. It has a supply pipe which will fill it in 10 hours, and a discharge pipe which will empty it in 7 hours. If the supply pipe has been running into it for 4 hours, and then both pipes are opened, in what time will it be emptied?

DECIMAL FRACTIONS.

164. **1.** What is 1 of the ten equal parts of anything?

2. What is 1 of the ten equal parts of $\frac{1}{10}$? 3 parts?

3. What is 1 of the ten equal parts of $\frac{1}{100}$? 35 parts?

4. What is 1 of the ten equal parts of $\frac{1}{1000}$? 43 parts?

5. What part of $\frac{1}{10}$ is $\frac{1}{100}$? Of $\frac{1}{100}$ is $\frac{1}{1000}$? Of $\frac{1}{1000}$ is $\frac{1}{10000}$?

6. What part of $\frac{7}{10}$ is $\frac{7}{100}$? Of $\frac{5}{100}$ is $\frac{5}{1000}$? Of $\frac{9}{1000}$ is $\frac{9}{10000}$?

165. The divisions of anything into *tenths, hundredths, thousandths,* etc., are called *Decimal Divisions.*

166. One or more of the decimal divisions of a unit are called a **Decimal Fraction.**

The word *decimal* is derived from the Latin word *decem, ten.*

Decimal fractions are commonly called *decimals.*

167. Since tenths are equal to ten times as many hundredths, hundredths equal to ten times as many thousandths, etc., decimals have the same law of increase and decrease as integers, and the *denominator* may be indicated by the *position of the figures.*

In the decimal system of notation, the representative value of a figure is decreased tenfold by each removal one place to the right; hence:

The figure at the *right of units* expresses *tenths.*

The figure at the *right of tenths* expresses *hundredths*.

The figure at the *right of hundredths* expresses *thousandths*.

The figure at the *right of thousandths* expresses *ten-thousandths*.

The figure at the *right of ten-thousandths* expresses *hundred-thousandths*, etc.

168. A period, called the **Decimal Point,** is placed before the decimal.

Thus, .5 represents $\frac{5}{10}$; .58 represents $\frac{58}{100}$.

$.6 = \frac{6}{10}$ $.08 = \frac{8}{100}$ $.008 = \frac{8}{1000}$ $.0007 = \frac{7}{10000}$

$.9 = \frac{9}{10}$ $.09 = \frac{9}{100}$ $.003 = \frac{3}{1000}$ $.0235 = \frac{235}{10000}$

$.7 = \frac{7}{10}$ $.05 = \frac{5}{100}$ $.004 = \frac{4}{1000}$ $.1461 = \frac{1461}{10000}$

NUMERATION TABLE.

MILLIONS.	HUNDRED-THOUSANDS.	TEN-THOUSANDS.	THOUSANDS.	HUNDREDS	TENS.	UNITS.		TENTHS.	HUNDREDTHS.	THOUSANDTHS.	TEN-THOUSANDTHS	HUNDRED-THOUSANDTHS.	MILLIONTHS.
3	4	1	5	6	7	3	.	4	1	3	2	0	7

The number is read, 3 million, 415 thousand, 673 *and* 413 thousand 207 millionths.

The orders of decimals below millionths are ten-millionths, hundred-millionths, billionths, ten-billionths, hundred-billionths, trillionths, etc.

EXERCISES IN NUMERATION.

169. **1**. Read the expression 5.239.

The whole expression is read, 5 and 239 thousandths.

RULE. — *Read the decimal as an integral number, and give it the denomination of the right-hand figure.*

Read the following:

2. .324.	**9.** 323.56.	**16.** 385.043685.
3. .457.	**10.** 4.5283.	**17.** 42.0004367.
4. .3856.	**11.** 46738.4.	**18.** 916.380043.
5. .2834.	**12.** 50.0037.	**19.** 74348.0435.
6. .5169.	**13.** 310.009.	**20.** 8.04045006.
7. .0045.	**14.** 346.009.	**21.** 91873.0009.
8. .0008.	**15.** 92080.9.	**22.** 90.90900009.

EXERCISES IN NOTATION.

170. **1.** Express decimally seventy-nine thousandths.

EXPLANATION. — Since thousandths occupy the third place, three figures are required to express the decimal. Hence, the number seventy-nine is written, and a cipher prefixed to cause the figures to occupy their proper position. Hence, the decimal is written .079.

RULE. — *Write the numerator of the decimal, prefix ciphers if necessary to indicate the denominator, and place the decimal point before tenths.*

Express decimally:

2. Eight tenths. Three tenths. Five tenths. Four hundredths. Eight hundredths. Six hundredths.

3. Five thousandths. Three hundred four thousandths. Seven ten-thousandths. Eight hundred sixty-five ten-thousandths. Sixty-eight thousandths.

4. Fifteen hundredths. Twelve hundred-thousandths. Forty-eight thousandths. Four hundred-millionths.

5. Ninety-five ten-thousandths. Ninety billionths. Sixty-two hundred-thousandths. Fifty-five thousandths.

6. 210 millionths. 403 thousandths. 15 hundredths. 4256 hundred-thousandths. 1268 hundred-millionths.

7. 56345 millionths. 389 ten-thousandths. 3854 hundred-thousandths. 518 ten-millionths.

8. Sixty-seven, and three hundred forty-nine ten-thousandths. Fifty, and fifty-five millionths.

9. Eighty-eight, and five thousand five hundred-thousandths. Nine, and nine ten-thousandths.

10. $\frac{4}{10}$. **13.** $\frac{1585}{10000}$. **16.** $\frac{5}{10}$. **19.** $\frac{5}{10}$.

11. $\frac{14}{100}$. **14.** $\frac{15}{100000}$. **17.** $\frac{50}{100}$. **20.** $\frac{5}{100}$.

12. $\frac{125}{1000}$. **15.** $5\frac{4}{10}$ **18.** $\frac{500}{1000}$. **21.** $\frac{5}{1000}$.

22. How do the fractions in 16, 17, and 18 compare in value? How do the decimals compare? What is the effect of *annexing* ciphers to decimals?

23. How do the fractions in 19, 20, and 21 compare in value? How do the decimals compare? What is the effect of *prefixing* decimal ciphers to a decimal?

24. How does the number of places in a decimal compare with the number of ciphers in the denominator.

171. PRINCIPLES. — 1. *Annexing ciphers to a decimal does not alter its value.*

2. *Each decimal cipher, prefixed to a decimal, diminishes the value of the decimal tenfold.*

3. *The denominator of a decimal, when expressed, is 1 with as many ciphers annexed as there are figures in the decimal.*

172. In expressions of the currency of the United States, the cents, mills, etc., may be read as decimals of a dollar:

Thus, $5.375 may be read 5 dollars and 375 thousandths, or 5 dollars $37\frac{5}{10}$ cents.

Read the following as dollars and decimals of a dollar:

1. $6.495. **3.** $7.394 **5.** $4.004.

2. $5.083. **4.** $5.865. **6.** $8.056.

REDUCTION.

173. To reduce dissimilar to similar decimals.

1. Reduce .5, .25, .046, and 2.0506 to similar decimals.

$$.5 \quad = .5000$$
$$.25 \quad = .2500$$
$$.046 = .0460$$
$$2.0506 = 2.0506$$

EXPLANATION. — Since the lowest order of decimals in the given numbers is ten-thousandths, all the decimals must be changed to ten-thousandths. This may be done by annexing ciphers (Prin. 1, Art. 171).

RULE. — *Give all the decimals the same number of places by annexing ciphers.*

Reduce to similar decimals:

2. .4, .65, .175.

3. .05, .015, .75, .0104.

4. .045, .476, .00055.

5. .0043, .1, .140, .07865.

6. 1.2, .43, .105, .10017.

7. 3.27, .0005, .584.

8. .3460, .17, .4, 17.6.

9. 4.08, .7, .0004.

10. 9, .9, .009, 90.

11. 6.1, 1.054, 12.36876.

12. 75, 4.1, .268, .0057.

13. 100, .001, 1000, .000001.

174. To reduce decimals to common fractions.

1. Reduce .75 to a common fraction.

$$.75 = \tfrac{75}{100} = \tfrac{3}{4}$$

EXPLANATION. — .75 expressed as a common fraction is $\tfrac{75}{100}$, or $\tfrac{3}{4}$, when it is reduced to its lowest terms.

RULE. — *Omit the decimal point, supply the proper denominator, and reduce the fraction to its lowest terms.*

2. .25.	4. .65.	6. .38.	8. .375.
3. .75.	5. .52.	7. .54.	9. .875.

10. .435.	14. .0375.	18. .7024.	22. .05165.
11. .568.	15. .0215.	19. .0475.	23. .01235.
12. .405.	16. .1135.	20. .05625.	24. .41275.
13. .635.	17. .0025.	21. .03435.	25. .00015.

26. Reduce $.87\frac{1}{2}$ to a common fraction.

$$.87\frac{1}{2} = \frac{87\frac{1}{2}}{100} = \frac{\frac{175}{2}}{100} = \frac{175}{200} = \frac{7}{8}.$$

EXPLANATION. — The expression written as a common fraction becomes $\frac{\frac{175}{2}}{100}$. Performing the division indicated, or reducing the denominator also to halves, it becomes $\frac{175}{200}$, or $\frac{7}{8}$.

Reduce to common fractions :

27. $.12\frac{1}{2}$.	31. $.62\frac{1}{2}$.	35. $.416\frac{2}{3}$.	39. $.0014\frac{1}{6}$.
28. $.18\frac{3}{4}$.	32. $.41\frac{1}{3}$.	36. $.003\frac{3}{4}$.	40. $12.095\frac{5}{8}$.
29. $.37\frac{1}{2}$.	33. $.24\frac{3}{5}$.	37. $.075\frac{3}{10}$.	41. $22.71\frac{2}{3}$.
30. $.49\frac{1}{8}$.	34. $.56\frac{5}{6}$.	38. $.643\frac{4}{5}$.	42. $43.87\frac{2}{5}$.

175. To reduce a common fraction to a decimal.

1. How many tenths are there in 1 ? In $\frac{1}{5}$? In $\frac{2}{5}$? In $\frac{3}{5}$? In $\frac{4}{5}$?

2. How many hundredths are there in 1 ? In $\frac{1}{4}$? In $\frac{3}{4}$? In $\frac{1}{5}$? In $\frac{2}{5}$?

3. How many hundredths are there in 3 ? In $\frac{1}{4}$ of 3, or $\frac{3}{4}$?

4. How many hundredths are there in 4 ? In $\frac{1}{5}$ of 4, or $\frac{4}{5}$?

5. How many thousandths are there in 1 ? In $\frac{1}{5}$?

6. How many thousandths are there in 2 ? In $\frac{2}{5}$?

7. Reduce $\frac{7}{8}$ to an equivalent decimal.

$8\overline{)7.000}$
$\quad.875$

EXPLANATION. — $\frac{7}{8}$ is $\frac{1}{8}$ of 7. In 7 there are 70 tenths, and $\frac{1}{8}$ of 70 tenths is 8 tenths and 6 tenths remainder. 6 tenths are equal to 60 hundredths, and $\frac{1}{8}$ of 60 hundredths is 7 hundredths and 4 hundredths remainder. 4 hundredths are equal to 40 thousandths, and $\frac{1}{8}$ of 40 thousandths is 5 thousandths. Hence $\frac{7}{8}$ is equal to 8 tenths + 7 hundredths + 5 thousandths, or .875.

RULE. — *Annex ciphers to the numerator and divide by the denominator. Point off as many decimal places in the quotient as there are ciphers annexed.*

1. In many cases the division is not exact. In such instances the remainder may be expressed as a common fraction, or the sign + may be employed after the decimal to show that the result is not complete; thus $\frac{1}{6} = .166\frac{2}{3}$, or .166 +.

2. Common fractions in their *lowest terms* cannot be reduced to exact decimal values or pure decimals when their denominators contain any prime factors besides 2 or 5. This truth is evident, from the fact that when ciphers are annexed to the numerator, that is, when it is multiplied by 10, only the factors 2 and 5 are introduced into the numerator; consequently if any other prime factor is found in the denominator, the division cannot be exact.

3. It is evident also that fractions whose denominators are composed of the factors 2 or 5 have exact decimal values.

Change the following to decimals:

8. $\frac{3}{5}$.	17. $\frac{5}{9}$.	26. $\frac{3}{16}$.	35. $\frac{27}{63}$.	44. $37\frac{1}{2}$.
9. $\frac{1}{4}$.	18. $\frac{6}{25}$.	27. $\frac{50}{68}$.	36. $\frac{58}{71}$.	45. $.45\frac{1}{4}$.
10. $\frac{3}{8}$.	19. $\frac{4}{7}$.	28. $\frac{6}{11}$.	37. $\frac{74}{75}$.	46. $16.4\frac{4}{9}$.
11. $\frac{4}{5}$.	20. $\frac{12}{13}$.	29. $\frac{9}{44}$.	38. $\frac{80}{55}$.	47. $48.5\frac{3}{10}$.
12. $\frac{3}{4}$.	21. $\frac{8}{15}$.	30. $\frac{7}{125}$.	39. $12\frac{1}{2}$.	48. $.23\frac{5}{8}$.
13. $\frac{3}{20}$.	22. $\frac{7}{24}$.	31. $\frac{14}{40}$.	40. $18\frac{3}{4}$.	49. $60.0\frac{4}{5}$.
14. $\frac{14}{25}$.	23. $\frac{72}{48}$.	32. $\frac{27}{60}$.	41. $24\frac{3}{5}$.	50. $.000\frac{13}{75}$.
15. $\frac{2}{5}$.	24. $\frac{1}{18}$.	33. $\frac{5}{30}$.	42. $\frac{13}{52}$.	51. $513.00\frac{2}{3}$.
16. $\frac{1}{3}$.	25. $\frac{3}{25}$.	34. $\frac{6}{24}$.	43. $\frac{7}{147}$.	52. $75.000\frac{1}{2}$.

ADDITION.

176. 1. What is the sum of .29, 3.314, 41.2356?

.29
3.314
41.2356
—————
44.8396

EXPLANATION. — The numbers are written so that units of the same order stand in the same column, and they are added precisely as in integers. The decimal part of the sum is separated from the integral part by the decimal point.

The decimals may be made similar by annexing ciphers until all the decimals have the same number of places, and then added; but this is not commonly done.

Find the sum of the following:

2. 3.25, 1.6, 32.043, .341, 15.   5. .004, 5.75, .026, 4.1.

3. 1.14, 70, .014, .6413, 24.   6. 6.845, .137, 2.5, .1004.

4. .45, .076, 41.7, .0457.   7. .964, .0034, 46, 7.37, .08.

8. .125, 1.25, 12.5, 125, .0125.

9. 37, 5.4, 62.5, .44, 3.845.

10. 4.2, .034, 78.9, 62.5, 148.9.

11. 12.34, 1.2, 16.5, 27.4, 15.35, 174.8.

12. 4.1, 67.5, 42.001, 13.18, .0004.

13. 146.9, .00412, 31.416, 125.001, 231.8.

14. 47.25, 5.00695, 193.5, 5.875, 9.0000105.

15. $7.28, $213.09, $.21, $13.42, $.15.

16. $10.25, $8.95, $3.02, $135.24, $185.64.

17. $200, $.20, $2.05, $.12$\frac{1}{2}$, 3.18\frac{3}{4}$.

18. $1.35, $16.50, 2.37\frac{1}{2}$, $.56$\frac{1}{4}$, $2000.

19. A family used .85 of a ton of coal in January, .75 of a ton in February, .675 of a ton in March, and .5 of a ton in April. How many tons of coal did they use?

20. A man earned $ 6.75 in one week, $ 7.25 in another, $ 7.37½ in another, $ 8.12½ in another, and $ 9 in another. How much did he earn in the five weeks ?

21. In four piles of wood there are respectively 5.316 cords, 8¼ cords, 12.25 cords, and 13.569 cords. How many cords are there in all the piles ?

22. Find the sum of three hundred and five hundredths, two thousand one hundred eight and four thousandths, three millionths, one hundred seventeen thousand seven hundred seven and forty-five millionths.

23. A bookseller bought 5 complete sets of copy-books for $ 3.60, 50 geographies for $ 50, 25 physiologies for $ 25, 30 grammars for $ 14, and 55 spellers for $ 9.90. How much did all the books cost him ?

24. Find the sum of two thousand three hundred one and thirty-nine hundredths, three tenths, two thousand seven hundred forty-nine ten-thousandths, and thirteen thousandths.

25. A lady bought 5 dozen buttons for $ 1.08, 2 yards of ribbon for $ .37½, 16 yards of muslin for $ 1.18¾, some thread and needles for $ .31¼, and a dress for $ 8.62½. What was the amount of her purchases ?

26. Find the sum of two and five ten-thousandths, forty-three thousandths, sixty-three and four hundred fifteen hundred-thousandths, and five hundred thirteen ten-thousandths.

27. A man bought a house for $ 4000, a store for $ 3780, merchandise for $ 12751.85, a horse for $ 185.80, a farm for $ 6175, and bank stock $ 5760.56. What did the whole cost him ?

28. Mr. Clarke bought for his house one set of parlor furniture for $ 1234.69, carpets for $ 345.97, a piano for $ 500, a mirror for $ 29.75, curtains for $ 132.19, and oil paintings for $ 8975.43. How much did he pay for all ?

SUBTRACTION.

177. **1.** From 57.25 subtract 33.1468.

57.2500
33.1468
————
24.1032

EXPLANATION. — The numbers are written so that units of the same order stand in the same column, and they are subtracted as in integers. The decimal part of the remainder is separated from the integral part by the decimal point.

The decimals may be made similar by annexing ciphers until both have the same number of places, but the ciphers may be supposed to be there even though they are not written.

Find the value of:

2. .325 — .106.

3. .4806 — .3124.

4. 3.5872 — 1.2834.

5. 5.4618 — 3.2403.

6. 17.8465 — 5.6341.

7. 315.42346 — 10.326.

8. 34.832 — 18.068193.

9. 125.4276 — 19.305.

10. 48.76 — 30.428.

11. 72.154 — 61.075.

12. 476 — 245.75.

13. 355.8 — 196.954.

14. 750 — 84.1206.

15. 647.625 — .995.

16. 1000 — .001.

17. $34.185 — $8.27.

18. $45.67 — $18.50.

19. $63.10 — $27.43.

20. $75.35 — $49.75.

21. $88.125 — $1.875.

22. $125.75 — $67.50.

23. $11.10 — $1.14.

24. $100 — $.37$\frac{1}{2}$.

25. 189.46\frac{3}{4}$ — 7.62\frac{1}{2}$.

26. 225.87\frac{1}{2}$ — 175.65\frac{3}{8}$.

27. 437.83\frac{3}{4}$ — 216.24\frac{1}{2}$.

28. A vessel sailed from Portland, Me., for New Orleans, with a cargo of 1528.375 tons of ice. On the way 94.85 tons of it melted. How much ice reached New Orleans?

29. A man bought a suit of clothes for $35.50, a hat for $3.75, and a pair of gloves for $1.87. He gave the salesman a hundred-dollar bill. How much change ought he to have received?

30. From five hundred eighty and sixty-seven ten thousandths take ninety-six and forty-nine millionths.

31. A merchant bought a tub of butter for $14.62½, paying $7.87½ in cloth, $4.58 in groceries, and the rest in money. How much money did he pay?

32. A butcher killed an ox that cost him $56.75. He retailed the meat for $54.28, sold the tallow for $4.95, and the hide for $7.65. What were his profits?

33. A merchant had, at the beginning of the year, goods worth $7600. During the year he bought goods to the amount of $6735.75, and sold to the amount of $9875.84. At the close of the year his inventory showed goods on hand worth $7026.65. How much did he make during the year?

34. In a cistern that will hold 326.5 barrels of water, there are 178.625 barrels. How much does it lack of being full?

35. A man owned sixty-nine hundredths of a township of land, and sold sixty-nine thousandths of the township. How much did he still own?

36. If I spend $45.89½ for merchandise, how much change will I receive from a fifty-dollar bill?

37. The receipts of a factory for a certain year were $1,374,837.64 and the expenses were $1,100,095.75. What were the profits?

38. A man whose income was $15,745 spent one year $12,349.97. How much did he save that year?

MULTIPLICATION.

178. 1. $\frac{3}{10} \times \frac{2}{10} = \frac{6}{100}$; $\frac{3}{100} \times \frac{2}{10} = \frac{6}{1000}$; $\frac{3}{1000} \times \frac{2}{10} = \frac{6}{10000}$.

2. How does the number of ciphers in the denominator of the product compare with the number of ciphers in the denominators of the factors?

3. How does the number of places in a decimal compare with the number of ciphers in its denominator?

4. How many places, then, will there be in the product of two decimals?

179. PRINCIPLE. — *The product of two decimals contains as many decimal places as there are decimal places in both factors.*

WRITTEN EXERCISES.

180. 1. What is the product of .417 multiplied by .34?

.417
.34
——
1668
1251
——
.14178

EXPLANATION. — The numbers may be multiplied as though they were integers. Since the multiplier contains 2 decimal places, and the multiplicand 3 decimal places, the product will contain 5 decimal places, and the decimal point is placed before the fifth figure counting from the right (Prin.).

RULE. — *Multiply as if the numbers were integers, and from the right of the product point off as many figures for decimals as there are decimal places in both factors.*

If the product does not contain as many figures as there are decimals in both factors, the deficiency must be supplied by *prefixing* ciphers.

Find the product of:

2. .25 × .32.

3. .48 × 4.8.

4. .126 × 35.

5. .043 × 6.5.

6.	$348 \times .46.$	25.	$63.18 \times 2.402.$
7.	$.0432 \times 5.4.$	26.	$51.27 \times 5.321.$
8.	$34.8 \times .74.$	27.	$24.075 \times 16\frac{1}{3}.$
9.	$.048 \times 24.$	28.	$450 \times .06.$
10.	$50 \times .008.$	29.	$.045 \times 18\frac{1}{3}.$
11.	$.095 \times 40.$	30.	$64. \times .032.$
12.	$3.24 \times 3.3.$	31.	$30.3 \times .024.$
13.	$255 \times .0007.$	32.	$.046 \times 25.$
14.	$6.75 \times 8\frac{3}{5}.$	33.	$3.826 \times 6\frac{1}{2}.$
15.	$34.5 \times 11.2.$	34.	$37.555 \times 45.64.$
16.	$8.75 \times 8.5.$	35.	$3.005 \times 25.4.$
17.	$.759 \times .032.$	36.	$214.76 \times 89.104.$
18.	$436 \times 2.75.$	37.	$.04128 \times .00025.$
19.	$3.45 \times 6.24.$	38.	$4.2008 \times 1.25.$
20.	$347 \times .085.$	39.	$34.10 \times 12.6.$
21.	$5.6 \times .056.$	40.	$185.75 \times 164\frac{3}{5}.$
22.	$3.75 \times 12\frac{1}{2}.$	41.	$.04261 \times 31245.$
23.	$35.16 \times 5\frac{5}{8}.$	42.	$87.03 \times 8.412.$
24.	$50.05 \times .045.$	43.	$14.136 \times .00045.$

44. Multiply 7.5864 by 200.

7.5864
200
———
1517.28

EXPLANATION. — Since each removal of a figure one place to the left increases its value tenfold, the removal of the decimal point one place to the right multiplies by 10, and two places by 100. The product of 7.5864×100 is therefore 758.64, and this multiplied by 2 gives the product of 7.5864×200, which is 1517.28.

45.	$5.836 \times 100.$	49. $.3856 \times 200.$	53. $42.8364 \times 3000.$
46.	$16.834 \times 100.$	50. $.4937 \times 300.$	54. $876.423 \times 4000.$
47.	$95.817 \times 1000.$	51. $5.927 \times 500.$	55. $915.976 \times 5000.$
48.	$373.186 \times 1000.$	52. $59.47 \times 600.$	56. $.813426 \times 6000.$

57. What will be the cost of 8.5 reams of paper at $3.62½ a ream?

58. How much must be paid for 35.75 bushels of corn at $.625 per bushel?

59. When land is worth $126.75 per acre, how much must be paid for a farm of 65 acres?

60. How many yards are there in 25 pieces of tapestry carpeting, if each piece contains 32.75 yards?

61. If a rolling-mill makes 95.6 tons of iron per day, how many tons will it make in 142.25 days?

62. A man bought 3.5 yards of broadcloth at $3.75 per yard, 4 yards of cashmere at $.87½ per yard, 26 yards of calico at $.06½ per yard, and 14 yards of muslin at $.07 per yard. What was the cost of the whole?

63. A grocer sold 28.5 pounds of sugar at 5½ cents a pound, and 22.6 pounds of lard at 7½ cents a pound. How much did he receive for both?

64. Mr. Ball sold 65 bushels of wheat at $1.12½ a bushel, 27.4 bushels of clover seed at $4.37½ a bushel, and 180 bushels of corn at $.62½ a bushel. How much did he get for the whole?

65. A mechanic earned $14.87½ a week for 4 weeks. The first week he spent $7.28, the second week he spent $9½, the third week he spent $6.25, and the fourth week he spent $8⅞. How much money did he save?

66. A farmer sold 40 bushels of oats at $.37½ a bushel, and 35½ bushels of potatoes at $.56 a bushel. He received in payment 25 pounds of sugar at $.05½ a pound, 4 pounds of rice at $.10 a pound, 3 gallons of molasses at $.65 a gallon, and the balance in cash. How much cash did he receive?

DIVISION.

181. 1. $.6 \times .8 = .48$; $.6 \times .08 = .048$; $.6 \times .008 = .0048$.

2. How many decimal places are there in the product of two decimals?

3. If the product and one of the factors are given, how may the number of decimal places in the other factor be found?

4. Since the dividend is the product of the divisor and quotient, if the divisor and dividend are given, how may the number of decimal places in the quotient be found?

182. PRINCIPLE. — *The quotient will contain as many decimal places as the number of decimal places in the dividend exceeds those in the divisor.*

WRITTEN EXERCISES.

183. 1. Divide .00864 by .24.

.24).00864(.036
    72
    ——
   144
   144
   ——

EXPLANATION. — The numbers are divided as if they were integers. Since the dividend contains 5 decimal places, and the divisor 2, the quotient contains $5 - 2$, or 3 decimal places (Prin.). Since there are only two figures in the quotient, a cipher is *prefixed* to make the required number of decimal places.

RULE. — *Divide as if the numbers were integers, and from the right of the quotient point off as many figures for decimals as the number of decimal places in the dividend exceeds the number of those in the divisor.*

1. If the quotient does not contain a sufficient number of decimal places, the deficiency must be supplied by *prefixing* ciphers.

2. Before commencing the division, the number of decimal places in the dividend *should be made at least equal* to the number of decimal places in the divisor.

3. When there is a remainder after using all the figures of the dividend, annex decimal ciphers and continue the division.

4. For the ordinary purposes of business, it is not necessary to carry the division further than to obtain four or five decimal figures in the quotient.

Find the quotients of:

2. $34.75 \div 25$.

3. $46.103 \div 2.14$.

4. $2.450 \div 9.8$.

5. $7.8125 \div 31.25$.

6. $272.636 \div 6.37$.

7. $.00335 \div 6.7$.

8. $6.2512 \div .37$.

9. $\$2756.25 \div \$31.5$.

10. $.05475 \div 15$.

11. $18.312 \div 24$.

12. $16.025 \div .045$.

13. $105.70 \div 3.5$.

14. $.11928 \div .056$.

15. $112.1184 \div 9.16$.

16. $9322.15 \div 6.275$.

17. $.04905 \div .327$.

18. $135.05 \div .037$.

19. $281.8585 \div 3.85$.

20. $687.50 \div .025$.

21. $\$68.875 \div \$145$.

22. $34.368 \div .013$.

23. $.014532 \div .0692$.

24. $3.72812 \div 4.07$.

25. $18712.264 \div 1.52$.

26. $.33615 \div 12.45$.

27. $62.41 \div .079$.

28. $3.1812 \div 482$.

29. $17.28 \div 1728$.

30. $1728 \div 17.28$.

31. $.00255 \div 51$.

32. $75 \div .0125$.

33. $\$135 \div \$.37\frac{1}{2}$.

34. $725.406 \div .0957$.

35. $.0021318 \div 38$.

36. Divide 568.148 by 200.

200) 568.148
————
2.84074

EXPLANATION. — Since each removal of a figure one place to the right decreases its value tenfold, the removal of the decimal point one place to the left divides by 10, and two places by 100. The quotient of $568.148 \div 100$ is, therefore, 5.68148, and this divided by 2 gives the quotient of $568.148 \div 200$, which is 2.84074.

Find the quotients of :

37. $165 \div 50$.

38. $48.250 \div 20$.

39. $382.476 \div 200$.

40. $725.61 \div 300$.

41. $59.60430 \div 600$.

42. $7.645 \div 500$.

43. $.94876 \div 400$.

44. $3725.4 \div 700$.

45. $569000 \div 800$.

46. $72.3450 \div 1000$.

47. $4624.12 \div 2000$.

48. $.51648 \div 3000$.

49. $128.7642 \div 1200$.

50. $3094.32 \div 15000$.

51. If a man earns $162 in 13.5 weeks, what are his average wages per week ?

52. At $8.25 per ton, how much hay can be bought for $45.85 ?

53. At $10.50 each, how many harrows can be bought for $178.50 ?

54. If a barrel of flour costs $5.75, how many barrels can be bought for $258.75 ?

55. At $.24 per dozen, how many dozen eggs can be bought for $30.72 ?

56. If $640.05 are paid for 75.3 tons of coal, what is the average price per ton ?

57. There are 31.5 gallons in a barrel. How many barrels are there in 2787.75 gallons ?

58. A farmer sold 22.5 bushels of wheat at $.98 a bushel, and a certain number of bushels of corn at $.625 a bushel. He received for his corn $9.20 more than he did for his wheat. How many bushels of corn did he sell ?

59. At $18.75 each, how many dressing bureaus can be bought for $506.25 ?

60. At $5.75 per ton, how many tons of range coal can be bought for $51.75 ?

SHORT PROCESSES.

WRITTEN EXERCISES.

184. To multiply by a number a little less than 100, 1000, etc.

1. Multiply 6834 by 98.

$100 \times 6834 = 683,400$
$\underline{\ 2 \times 6834 = \ 13,668}$
$98 \times 6834 = 669,732$

EXPLANATION. — 98 times a number is 100 times the number *minus* 2 times the number. Hence the number may be multiplied by 100, and 2 times the number subtracted from that product.

Find the product of:

2. 39875×99.

3. 24567×97.

4. 14815×98.

5. 42160×999.

6. 74853×998.

7. 412567×99.

8. 351428×98.

9. 524167×96.

10. 674568×997.

11. 864254×996.

185. To multiply when one part of the multiplier is a factor of another part.

1. Multiply 4256 by 315.

4256
315
$\overline{12768}$
63840
$\underline{1340640}$

EXPLANATION. — 3, the number of hundreds, is a factor of 15, which may be termed units. We first multiply the number by the 3 hundreds, and the first figure of the product is written under hundreds. The 15 units are 5 times as many units as there are hundreds, hence the product obtained by multiplying by 3 is multiplied by 5. And since the multiplier is regarded as units, the first figure is written in unit's place. The sum of the partial products is the entire product.

Find the product of:

2. 3418×63.

3. 4012×93.

4. 5683×279.

5. 2937×168.

6. 7843×213.

7. 6587×246.

8. 3826×189.

9. 8834×248.

10. 2684×312.   12. 13468×321.

11. 5168×416.   13. 24542×328.

186. To multiply by the aliquot parts of 100.

187. The parts of a number which will exactly divide it are called the **Aliquot Parts** of the number.

Thus, 5, 20, $12\frac{1}{2}$, $33\frac{1}{3}$, etc., are aliquot parts of 100.

The aliquot parts of 100 commonly used are:

$50 = \frac{1}{2}$ of 100	$20 = \frac{1}{5}$ of 100	$10 = \frac{1}{10}$ of 100
$33\frac{1}{3} = \frac{1}{3}$ of 100	$16\frac{2}{3} = \frac{1}{6}$ of 100	$8\frac{1}{3} = \frac{1}{12}$ of 100
$25 = \frac{1}{4}$ of 100	$12\frac{1}{2} = \frac{1}{8}$ of 100	$6\frac{1}{4} = \frac{1}{16}$ of 100

Other parts of 100 are:

$40 = \frac{2}{5}$ of 100	$37\frac{1}{2} = \frac{3}{8}$ of 100	$66\frac{2}{3} = \frac{2}{3}$ of 100
$60 = \frac{3}{5}$ of 100	$62\frac{1}{2} = \frac{5}{8}$ of 100	$75 = \frac{3}{4}$ of 100
$80 = \frac{4}{5}$ of 100	$87\frac{1}{2} = \frac{7}{8}$ of 100	$41\frac{2}{3} = \frac{5}{12}$ of 100

1. Multiply 3429 by $33\frac{1}{3}$.

3)342900

114300

EXPLANATION.— Since $33\frac{1}{3}$ is $\frac{1}{3}$ of 100, the number may first be multiplied by 100, and $\frac{1}{3}$ of the product found.

Multiply:

2. 3824 by 25.   7. 8592 by $12\frac{1}{2}$.   12. 4280 by 75.

3. 4218 by 50.   8. 9786 by $8\frac{1}{3}$.   13. 6474 by $66\frac{2}{3}$.

4. 5745 by 20.   9. 14352 by $37\frac{1}{2}$.   14. 8248 by $62\frac{1}{2}$.

5. 6741 by $33\frac{1}{3}$.   10. 73455 by $33\frac{1}{3}$.   15. 9120 by $87\frac{1}{2}$.

6. 8796 by $16\frac{2}{3}$.   11. 94652 by 25.   16. 7560 by $41\frac{2}{3}$.

188. To find the cost when the price by 100 or 1000 is given.

1. What will 385 pounds of coal cost, at $.33 per hundred-weight?

$ .33
3.85
$1.2705

EXPLANATION. — Since 100 pounds cost $.33, 385 pounds, which are equal to 3.85 times 100 pounds, will cost 3.85 times $.33, or $1.2705.

2. What will be the cost of 465 pounds of sugar, at $5.75 per hundred pounds?

3. What is the cost of 1235 pounds of beef, at $6.35 per hundred pounds?

4. What must be paid for 1650 pounds of coal, at $.35 per hundred-weight?

5. What will be the cost of 7955 bricks, at $8.75 per M?

NOTE. — The letters C and M are used instead of the words hundred and thousand, respectively.

6. When shingles are sold for $5.25 per M, how much must be paid for 8750?

7. What will be the cost of 5268 feet of boards, at $31.25 per M?

8. What must be paid for a load of hay, weighing 1592 pounds, when hay is being sold for $7.50 per ton (2000 pounds)?

9. What is the cost of 4235 pounds of iron, at $42.50 per ton?

10. How much will 28,750 laths cost, at $2.95 per M?

11. What will be the cost of 1678 feet of pine boards, at $19.50 per M feet?

12. How much will 15,485 pounds of plaster cost, at $1.80 per hundred pounds?

13. What will 375 pineapples cost, at $12.75 per C?

14. What will 960 cocoanuts cost, at $5.45 per C?

ACCOUNTS AND BILLS.

189. The amount which one person owes another is called a **Debt**.

190. The amount which is due to a person, or a sum paid toward discharging a debt, is called a **Credit**.

191. A party owing a debt is called a **Debtor**. A party to whom a debt is due is called a **Creditor**.

192. A record of the debts and credits between two parties is called an **Account**.

193. The difference between the amount of debt and credits is called the **Balance of an Account**.

194. A statement of the quantity and price of each article, and the value of the whole, is called a **Bill**.

A bill is *receipted* when the words *Received Payment* or *Paid* are written at the bottom, and the creditor's name is signed either by himself or by some authorized person.

195. The following abbreviations are in common use:

@,	At.	**Cr.,**	Creditor.	**Pay't,**	Payment.
%,	Account.	**Dr.,**	Debtor.	**Pd.,**	Paid.
Acc't,	Account.	**Doz.,**	Dozen.	**Per,**	By.
Bal.,	Balance.	**Hhd.,**	Hogshead.	**Rec'd,**	Received.
Bbl.,	Barrel.	**Lb.,**	Pound.	**Yd.,**	Yard.

RECEIPTED BILL.

Chicago, Ill., July 1, 1892.

1. Mr. Henry B. Sprague,

       Bought of DAVID C. BACON.

3 bbl. sugar,	647 lb.,	@ $ .04		$ 25	88
5 chests Oolong tea,	255 "	" .51		130	05
3 " black "	167 "	" .42		70	14
	Received Payment,			$ 226	07

         David C. Bacon.

196. Make out in proper form, find the footings, and receipt the following bills:

2. Mrs. H. D. Garmon bought of J. B. Hoke & Co., 25 yards of calico at 7 cents a yard, 36 yards of muslin at 8 cents a yard, and 4 pairs of hose at $ .40 a pair.

3. Mr. John Hood bought of William Cole & Co., 4 yd. of broadcloth at $ 4.25 a yard, 12 yd. of silk at $ 1.80 a yard, 7 yd. of flannel at $ .45 a yard, and 9 yd. of lace at $ .35 a yard.

4. Mr. Henry Clark bought of Edward Rill, 16 yd. of cashmere at $ 1.25 a yard, 11 yd. of cambric at 10 cents a yard, and 18 yd. of gingham at $12\frac{1}{2}$ cents a yard.

5. Mr. H. K. Martin bought of H. C. Allen, 4 pounds of coffee @ 28 cents, 18 pounds of sugar @ $5\frac{1}{2}$ cents, 6 pounds of prunes @ $12\frac{1}{2}$ cents, 2 pounds of tea @ 60 cents, and 3 pounds of rice at 10 cents.

6. Mr. D. R. West bought of Camp Bros. & Co., 2 spring bottom beds @ $ 12.50, 6 cane seat chairs @ $ 1.75, 2 cane seat rockers @ $ 4.50, 3 cottage bedsteads @ $ 7, and 1 lounge @ $ 8.75.

7. Mr. S. G. Rose bought of James Conrad, 25 yd. of silk at $ 1.80, 8 yd. of French broadcloth @ $ 4.75, 14 yd. of Merrimac prints @ 7 cents, 6 yd. of Irish linen @ $ .68$\frac{3}{4}$, and 3 tablecloths @ $ 2.25.

8. L. Roberts & Co. sold to Mrs. C. Roland, 2 doz. silver table forks @ $ 35 a dozen, 1 doz. silver tablespoons for $ 25, 2 sets of silver teaspoons @ $ 7.25 a set, and 1 silver butter dish for $ 6.

9. Mr. Robert Homer bought of A. R. Young & Co., $4\frac{1}{2}$ tons of stove coal @ $ 4.75, 7 tons of grate coal @ $ 5.25, and 4 cords of wood @ $ 4.60.

10. Mr. C. Dixon bought of H. White & Co., 18 reams of commercial note paper @ $1.40, 4500 envelopes @ $3.75 per M, 10 gross steel pens @ $.75 per gross, 50 arithmetics @ $1.25, and 20 physiologies @ $.90.

11. Mr. David Brook bought of F. Taylor, 15 sacks of flour @ $.65, 40 pounds of Rio coffee @ $.25, 18 lb. of butter @ $.28, 12 lb. of lard @ $6\frac{1}{2}$ cents, 64 lb. of ham @ 12 cents, and 10 lb. of cheese @ $12\frac{1}{2}$ cents.

12. Mr. R. B. Cooper bought of John Love, 410 bushels of corn @ $.55, 280 bushels of wheat @ $.98, 175 bushels of oats @ $.32, and $4\frac{1}{2}$ tons of hay @ $8.75.

13. Mr. J. D. Black bought of Baker & Leas, 4560 feet of hemlock @ $13.25 per M, 9725 feet of pine flooring @ $23.75 per M, 3560 feet of clear pine @ $40 per M, and 4275 feet of oak joists @ $33 per M.

14. Dell & Co. bought of Kale & Co., 25 sack coats @ $4.25, 48 vests @ $1.75, 7 doz. felt hats @ $27 per dozen, 8 doz. pairs of suspenders @ $.38 per pair, and 4 doz. pairs of gloves @ $.65 per pair.

15. Mr. H. N. Biggs bought of K. R. Butler, 2 plows @ $11.75, 1 harrow for $9.50, 2 shovels @ $1.10, and 2 steel forks @ $1.25.

16. Mr. T. R. Ranck bought of C. A. Hamlin & Co., 45 yd. of tapestry carpet @ $.67\frac{1}{2}$, 22 yd. Brussels carpet @ $1.90, and $12\frac{3}{4}$ yd. of oilcloth @ $.37\frac{1}{2}$.

REVIEW EXERCISES.

197. 1. At 19 cents a pound, how many pounds of honey can be bought for $3.99?

2. If shovels are worth $.85 apiece, how many can be bought for $22.10?

3. A cubic inch of water weighs 252.458 grains avoirdupois. How much do 231 cubic inches, or a gallon, weigh?

4. A farmer sold his corn at $ .87½ per bushel, and received for it $ 131.25. How many bushels did he sell?

5. I bought 3 loads of wood, the first containing 1.04 cords, the second 1.05 cords, and the third .946 cords. What did it cost at $ 3.50 a cord?

6. What will 465 pounds of sugar cost at $ 4.25 a hundred-weight?

7. There are 2150.42 cubic inches in a bushel. How many cubic inches are there in 10000 bushels?

8. A and B have 360 acres of land, of which A owns .37½ and B .62½. How many acres has each?

9. A man sold .26 of his wheat to one man, and .39 of it to another, and kept 70 bushels. How much had he before selling?

10. What is the product of 12 × 12 hundred-thousandths?

11. What is the quotient when 12 is divided by 12 millionths?

12. What is the quotient when 12 millionths is divided by 12 thousandths?

13. How many days must a laborer work at $ 1.12½ a day, to pay for 6 cords of wood at $ 3.37½ per cord?

14. A farmer sold 35.5 bushels of wheat at $ .93 a bushel, and a certain number of bushels of oats at $ .35 a bushel. He received for his oats $ 17.28 more than for his wheat. How many bushels of oats did he sell?

15. If a man can travel 33.68 miles in .8 of a day, how far can he travel in 7.5 days?

16. I bought a farm of 71.5 acres for $ 6220.50. What did it cost me per acre?

17. What is the value of 297,560 bricks at $ 7.62½ per thousand?

18. An architect estimates that 1,468,000 bricks will be needed for a school building. What will they cost at $ 7.75 per thousand?

19. The wheel of a bicycle is 9.13 feet around. How many times will it turn in going a mile, or 5280 feet?

20. A man owning .4725 of a vessel, sold .3 of his share. What part had he left?

21. The distance around a circle is about 3.1416 times the distance across it. If the distance across a certain circular race-course is 1710 feet, what is the distance around it?

22. Two men start from the same place at the same time and travel in opposite directions. One goes 4.31 miles an hour, the other 3.92 miles an hour. How far apart will they be in 17 hours?

23. Reduce $\dfrac{4\frac{1}{5}}{18\frac{1}{4}} \times \left(\dfrac{4}{9} + \dfrac{1}{3}\right)$ to its simplest decimal form.

24. A grocer bought 15 barrels of sugar, each containing 219 pounds, for $125, and sold it at 5 cents a pound. What was his gain?

25. If $.67\frac{1}{2}$ of a ton of hay is worth $7.50, what are 6.75 tons worth?

26. If the price of gas is $1.75 per thousand cubic feet, find the amount of a man's bill when 11,350 cubic feet have been consumed.

27. At $57.60 per acre, what are three fields worth containing, respectively, 14.6 acres, 20.25 acres, and 27.625 acres?

28. A real estate agent having 2735 acres of land to sell, sold, at different times, 183.26 acres, 412.625 acres, 640 acres, 150.875 acres, 240.5 acres, and 61.971 acres. How much remained unsold?

29. A merchant bought 150 barrels of apples for $1.87\frac{1}{2}$ a barrel. He sold seven tenths of them at $1.95 a barrel, and the remainder at $1.80 a barrel. Did he gain or lose, and how much?

30. How many rods of fence will surround a rectangular field 29.0345 rods long and 22.3265 rods wide?

31. A flour dealer bought 326 barrels of flour at $5.25 per barrel. He sold 58 barrels at a loss of $.37½ per barrel, How must he sell the rest per barrel to gain $12 on the investment?

32. Reduce $\left(\dfrac{2\frac{3}{4}}{4\frac{2}{3}} \div \dfrac{3\frac{1}{3}}{4\frac{1}{4}}\right) \times \dfrac{8}{9} + .01$ to a decimal.

33. What part of $4\frac{3}{5}$ is $\dfrac{3.5}{12\frac{8}{9}} \times \dfrac{6\frac{2}{3} - 4\frac{1}{4}}{\frac{1}{2} \times 4\frac{5}{8}}$?

34. A has $13\frac{7}{8}$ cords of wood in one pile, $15.66\frac{2}{3}$ cords in a second, $18\frac{1}{4}$ cords in a third, and $21\frac{1}{3}$ cords in a fourth. How many cords has he in all, and what is the wood worth at $4.25 per cord?

35. Twenty-three miles of a railroad, 47.95 miles long, cost $11,578.40 per mile; 12 miles cost $13,357.82 per mile, and the remainder cost $19,125.26 per mile. What was the average cost per mile of the entire road?

36. A contractor built a house for $3575. The material cost him $2150.65, and he employed 15 men for $6\frac{1}{2}$ weeks of 6 days each, at $2.10 per day. Did he gain or lose money, and how much?

37. What is the value of $\left(\dfrac{12-0.6}{2} + \dfrac{16-0.8}{4} - \dfrac{17}{2}\right) \div 18\frac{3}{4}$?

38. Mr. D. H. Noble bought of Henry Daron & Co., 9 pairs of calf boots at $4.25 a pair, 7 pairs of kip boots at $3.15 a pair, 12 pairs of ladies' kid shoes at $2.65 a pair, and 8 pairs of ladies' cloth shoes at $2.25 a pair. Make out and receipt the bill.

39. Mrs. B. D. Ross bought of Cook & Co., Philadelphia, 14 yards of silk at $1.37½ a yard, 45 yards of sheeting at 7 cents a yard, 9 handkerchiefs at 25 cents apiece, 3 pairs of kid gloves at $1.12½ a pair, and 5 neckties at 50 cents each. Make out and receipt this bill as clerk for Cook & Co.

DENOMINATE NUMBERS.

198. A concrete number in which the unit of measure is established by law or custom is called a **Denominate Number.**

Thus, 7 dollars, 2 feet, 4 inches, 5 hours, 8 quarts, 6 pounds, are denominate numbers.

199. A denominate number which is composed of units of one denomination only is called a **Simple Denominate Number.**

Thus, 5 ounces, 7 yards, 3 miles, 6 hours, 10 pounds, 12 quarts, are simple denominate numbers.

200. A denominate number which is composed of units of two or more denominations that are related to each other, is called a **Compound Denominate Number.**

Thus, 3 yards, 2 feet, 4 inches, is a compound denominate number. So also is 1 year, 5 months, 3 days.

201. A unit of measure, from which other units of the same kind may be derived, is called a **Standard Unit.**

Thus, the yard is the standard unit of length, because the other units are derived from it.

202. The ratio by which numbers increase and decrease is called a **Scale.**

Scales are either *uniform* or *varying*.

Thus, in United States currency the scale is uniform, being *decimal;* in Linear measure it is varying, for 12 inches equal one foot, 3 feet one yard, etc.

REDUCTION.

LINEAR MEASURES.

203. That which has length only is called a **Line.**

Thus, the distance between two objects or places is a line.

204. Measures that are used in measuring length only are called **Linear Measures.**

NOTE. — The tables of Denominate Numbers will be found on page 418 and the subsequent pages.

1. How many inches are there in 5 ft. ?   In 7 ft. ?

2. How many feet are there in 5 yd. ?   In 7 yd. ?

3. How many yards are there in 2 rd. ?   In 4 rd. ?

4. How many feet are there in 2 rd. ?   In 4 rd. ?

5. How many rods are there in 2 mi. ?   In 3 mi. ?   In 10 mi. ?   In 30 mi. ?   In 100 mi. ?

6. How many inches are there in 2 ft. 6 in. ?   In 3 ft. 4 in. ?   In 5 ft. ?   In 5 ft. 2 in. ?

7. How many feet are there in 2 yd. 2 ft. ?   In 3 yd. 2 ft. ?   In 10 yd. ?   In 10 rd. ?

8. How many yards are there in 2 rd. 3 yd. ?   In 4 rd. 2 yd. ?   In 10 rd. 2 yd. ?   In 1 mi. ?

9. How many rods are there in 1 mi. 80 rd. ?   In 2 mi. 60 rd. ?   In 5 mi. 80 rd. ?

10. How many inches are there in $\frac{1}{3}$ ft. ?   In $\frac{2}{3}$ ft. ?   In $\frac{1}{2}$ ft. ?   In $\frac{3}{4}$ ft. ?   In $\frac{7}{8}$ ft. ?

205. The process of changing a denominate number from one denomination to another without altering its value is called **Reduction.**

206. The process of changing a denominate number to an equivalent number of a *lower* denomination is called **Reduction to Lower Denominations** or **Reduction Descending.**

WRITTEN EXERCISES.

$$\begin{array}{r} 5 \\ 3 \\ \hline 15 \\ 2 \\ \hline 17 \\ 12 \\ \hline 204 \\ 8 \\ \hline 212 \end{array}$$

1. Reduce 5 yd. 2 ft. 8 in. to inches.

EXPLANATION. — Since there are 3 feet in 1 yard, in 5 yards there are 5 times 3 feet = 15 feet, and 15 feet + 2 feet = 17 feet.

Since there are 12 inches in 1 foot, in 17 feet there are 17 times 12 inches = 204 inches, and 204 inches + 8 inches = 212 inches.

Hence 5 yd. 2 ft. 8 in. = 212 inches.

RULE. — *Multiply the number of the highest denomination given, by the number indicating how many units of the next lower denomination are equal to one of the higher, and to the product add the number given of this lower denomination.*

Proceed in like manner with this and each successive result thus obtained, until the number is reduced to the required denomination.

Reduce to feet:

2. 4 rd. 2 yd. 2 ft.   **6.** 30 rd. 6 ft.

3. 6 rd. 3 yd. 1 ft.   **7.** 2 mi. 15 rd. 8 ft.

4. 5 rd. 4 yd. 2 ft.   **8.** 3 mi. 25 rd. 12 ft.

5. 13 rd. 5 yd. 2 ft.   **9.** 5 mi. 100 rd. 15 ft.

Reduce to inches:

10. 2 yd. 2 ft. 2 in.   **13.** 25 rd. 12 ft. 4 in.

11. 3 yd. 1 ft. 4 in.   **14.** 3 mi. 40 rd. 8 ft. 7 in.

12. 5 yd. 2 ft. 6 in.   **15.** 5 mi. 50 rd. 5 yd. 3 ft. 4 in.

16. Reduce $\frac{3}{7}$ of a rod to units of lower denominations.

SOLUTION.

$\frac{3}{7}$ of a rod = $\frac{3}{7}$ of $1\frac{1}{2}$ yd. = $\frac{33}{14}$ yd. = $2\frac{5}{14}$ yd.

$\frac{5}{14}$ of a yd. = $\frac{5}{14}$ of 3 ft. = $\frac{15}{14}$ ft. = $1\frac{1}{14}$ ft.

$\frac{1}{14}$ of a ft. = $\frac{1}{14}$ of 12 in. = $\frac{12}{14}$ in.

∴ $\frac{3}{7}$ of a rod = 2 yd. 1 ft. $\frac{12}{14}$ in.

Reduce to units of lower denominations:

17. $\frac{2}{5}$ rd.   **19.** $\frac{5}{7}$ rd.   **21.** $\frac{1}{3}$ mi.   **23.** $\frac{5}{9}$ mi.

18. $\frac{3}{8}$ rd.   **20.** $\frac{9}{10}$ rd.   **22.** $\frac{3}{7}$ mi.   **24.** $\frac{7}{12}$ mi.

25. Reduce .885 of a yd. to feet and inches.

SOLUTION.

.885 of a yd. = .885 of 3 ft. = 2.655 ft.
.655 of a ft. = .655 of 12 in. = 7.860 in.
∴ .885 of a yd. = 2 ft. 7.86 in.

Reduce to units of lower denominations:

26. .75 yd.   **28.** .625 yd.   **30.** .375 rd.   **32.** .725 mi.
27. .95 yd.   **29.** .875 yd.   **31.** .645 rd.   **33.** .975 mi.

207. **1.** How many feet are there in 48 in. ?   In 72 in. ?
  2. How many yards are there in 30 ft. ?   In 48 ft. ?
  3. How many rods are there in 11 yd. ?   In 22 yd. ?
  4. How many rods are there in 33 ft. ?   In 66 ft. ?
  5. How many miles are there in 640 rd. ?   In 960 rd. ?
  6. What part of a rod are $8\frac{1}{4}$ ft. ? $4\frac{1}{8}$ ft. ? $1\frac{1}{2}$ ft. ?

208. The process of changing a denominate number to an equivalent number of a higher denomination is called **Reduction to Higher Denominations** or **Reduction Ascending.**

WRITTEN EXERCISES.

1. Reduce 641558 in. to miles, etc.

12	641558 in
3	53463 ft. + 2 in.
$5\frac{1}{2}$	17821 yd. + 0 ft.
	2
11	35642 [or 1 yd.
320	3240 rd. + 2 half-yards,
	10 mi. + 40 rd.

Ans. 10 mi. 40 rd. 1 yd. 2 in.

EXPLANATION. — Since there are 12 inches in 1 ft., in 641558 inches there are as many feet as 12 in. are contained times in 641558 in., or 53463 ft. and 2 in.

Since there are 3 ft. in 1 yd., in 53463 ft. there are as many yards as 3 ft. are contained times in 53463 ft., or 17821 yd.

Since there are $5\frac{1}{2}$ yd. in 1 rd., in 17821 yd. there are as many rods as $5\frac{1}{2}$ yd. are contained times in 17821 yd., or what is the same thing, as many times as 11 half-yards are contained times in 35642 half-yards, or 3240 rd. and 2 half-yards, or 1 yd. remaining.

Since there are 320 rd. in 1 mi., in 3240 rd. there are as many miles as 320 rd. are contained times in 3240 rd., or 10 mi. and 40 rd.

∴ 641558 in. = 10 mi. 40 rd. 1 yd. 2 in.

RULE. — *Divide the given number by the number indicating how many units of the given denomination make one of the next higher denomination.*

Proceed in like manner with this, and each successive quotient, till the whole is reduced to the required denomination.

The last quotient, with the remainders, if any, annexed, will be the required answer.

Reduce to higher denominations :

2. 1320 in.	**7.** 88792 in.	**12.** 99999 yd.
3. 4254 in.	**8.** 96450 in.	**13.** 425644 in.
4. 7560 ft.	**9.** 75680 ft.	**14.** 586100 in.
5. 16890 yd.	**10.** 97480 yd.	**15.** 76840 ft.
6. 42560 yd.	**11.** 98764 ft.	**16.** 876400 in.

17. Reduce $\frac{5}{16}$ of a ft. to the fraction of a mile.

SOLUTION.

1 ft. $= \frac{1}{3}$ of a yd. $\quad \therefore \frac{5}{16}$ ft. $= \frac{5}{16}$ of $\frac{1}{3}$ yd. $= \frac{5}{48}$ yd.

1 yd. $= \frac{2}{11}$ of a rd. $\quad \therefore \frac{5}{48}$ yd. $= \frac{5}{48}$ of $\frac{2}{11}$ rd. $= \frac{5}{264}$ rd.

1 rd. $= \frac{1}{320}$ of a mi. $\quad \therefore \frac{5}{264}$ rd. $= \frac{5}{264}$ of $\frac{1}{320}$ mi. $= \frac{1}{16896}$ mi.

Or,

1 ft. $= \frac{1}{5280}$ of a mi. $\quad \therefore \frac{5}{16}$ ft. $= \frac{5}{16}$ of $\frac{1}{5280}$ mi. $= \frac{1}{16896}$ mi.

Reduce to the fraction of a rod :

18. $\frac{3}{4}$ ft.	**20.** .635 ft.	**22.** $\frac{7}{18}$ in.
19. $\frac{5}{8}$ ft.	**21.** $\frac{11}{12}$ in.	**23.** .375 in.

Reduce to the fraction of a mile :

24. $\frac{8}{9}$ rd.	**26.** .44 rd.	**28.** $\frac{4}{15}$ ft.
25. $\frac{5}{76}$ rd.	**27.** $\frac{3}{8}$ ft.	**29.** .35 ft.

30. Reduce 3 yd. 2 ft. 6 in. to the decimal of a rod.

12|6	in.
3|2.5	ft.
5½|3.8333+	yd.
.6969+	rd.

EXPLANATION.—Since there are 12 in. in 1 ft., $\frac{1}{12}$ of the number of inches equals the number of feet. $\frac{1}{12}$ of 6 equals .5 ; therefore there are 2.5 ft. Since there are 3 ft. in 1 yd., $\frac{1}{3}$ of the number of feet equals the number of yards. $\frac{1}{3}$ of 2.5 is .8333 + ; therefore there are 3.8333 + yd., etc.

Reduce to the decimal of a rod :

31. 3 yd. 2 ft. 8 in. **32.** 4 yd. 1 ft. 6 in. **33.** 2 yd. 2 ft. 5 in.

Express as rods and decimals of a rod :

34. 4 rd. 3 yd. 1 ft. 5 in. **35.** 8 rd. 1 yd. 2 ft. 9 in.

SURFACE MEASURES.

209. Anything that has only length and breadth is called a **Surface**.

Thus, this page, the floor, or the outside of anything is a surface.

210. The difference in the direction of two lines that meet is called an **Angle**.

ANGLE.

211. A figure that is bounded by four equal straight sides and has four equal angles is called a **Square**.

A *square inch* is a square each of whose sides is *one inch* long ; a *square foot* is a square each of whose sides is *one foot* long.

The angles of a square are called *right angles*.

ONE SQUARE INCH.

SQUARE.

212. A figure that has four straight sides and four right angles is called a **Rectangle**.

It will be seen that a square is a rectangle whose four sides are equal each to each.

RECTANGLE.

213. The number of square units in the surface of anything is called its **Area.**

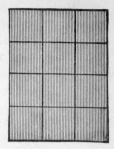

Thus, if a rectangle is 4 inches long and 3 inches wide, the area will be 12 square inches.

For it may be divided into 4 rows, each containing 3 square *inches* or *units*, and the entire area will be 12 square inches.

The method of computing the area of figures that are not rectangular is given in MENSURATION.

214. PRINCIPLE. — *The area of a rectangle is equal to the product of the numbers that express its length and breadth.*

The length and breadth must be expressed in units of the same denomination.

1. How many square inches are there in the surface of a rectangle that is 6 in. long and 4 in. wide? In one 8 in. long and 5 in. wide? In one 7 in. long and 6 in. wide?

2. How many square feet are there in the surface of a rectangle 9 ft. by 5 ft.? In one 8 ft. by 7 ft.? In one 10 ft. by 8 ft.?

3. How many square inches are there in a square whose sides are 5 in.? 6 in.? 8 in.? 12 in., or 1 ft.? How many square inches, then, are there in a square foot?

4. How many square feet are there in a square whose sides are 2 ft.? 3 ft., or 1 yd.? How many square feet are there, then, in a square yard?

5. How many square yards are there in a square whose sides are 3 yd.? 4 yd.? 5 yd.? 5½ yd., or a rod? How many square yards are there in a square rod?

6. How many square rods are there in a rectangle 8 rd. by 6 rd.? 10 rd. by 12 rd.? 10 rd. by 16 rd.? A rectangle that contains 160 square rods is called an *Acre.*

7. How many rods are there in a mile? How many square rods are there in a square whose sides are each a mile, or how many square rods are there in a sq. mi.?

8. Since there are 160 sq. rd. in an acre, how many acres are there in a square mile?

9. Write out a table of square measures.

WRITTEN EXERCISES.

Reduce to square inches:

1. 4 sq. yd. 5 sq. ft. **6.** 120 sq. rd. 120 sq. in.

2. 9 sq. yd. 3 sq. ft. **7.** 5 A. 20 sq. yd.

3. 20 sq. yd. 4 sq. ft. **8.** 8 A. 45 sq. rd.

4. 8 sq. rd. 4 sq. yd. **9.** 30 A. 5 sq. rd.

5. 12 sq. rd. 7 sq. ft. **10.** 2 sq. mi. 80 sq. rd.

Reduce to higher denominations:

11. 7460 sq. in.   **14.** 12340 sq. ft.   **17.** 102400 sq. rd.

12. 6720 sq. in.   **15.** 7580 sq. yd.   **18.** 387690 sq. rd.

13. 8000 sq. in.   **16.** 9678 sq. yd.   **19.** 3968479 sq. ft.

Reduce to units of lower denominations:

20. $\frac{5}{8}$ sq. rd. **22.** $\frac{6}{7}$ sq. rd.   **24.** $\frac{7}{12}$ sq. yd.   **26.** $\frac{6}{25}$ sq. rd.

21. .025 A.   **23.** .545 sq. rd.   **25.** .875 sq. ft.   **27.** .495 A.

28. Reduce $\frac{5}{7}$ of a sq. yd. to the fraction of a sq. rd.

SOLUTION.   1 sq. rd. $= 30\frac{1}{4}$, or $\frac{121}{4}$ sq. yd.

1 sq. yd. $= \frac{4}{121}$ sq. rd.

$\frac{5}{7}$ sq. yd. $= \frac{5}{7}$ of $\frac{4}{121}$ sq. rd. $= \frac{20}{847}$ sq. rd.

29. Reduce $\frac{5}{6}$ of a sq. ft. to the fraction of a sq. rd.

30. Reduce $\frac{8}{9}$ of a sq. in. to the fraction of a sq. yd.

31. Reduce .65 of a sq. yd. to the fraction of an A.

32. Reduce 5 sq. ft. 100 sq. in. to the decimal of a sq. yd.

MEASURES OF VOLUME.

215. Anything which has length, breadth, and thickness is called a **Solid**.

216. A solid having six equal square sides or faces is called a **Cube**.

A cube whose sides or faces are each a square inch is called a **Cubic Inch**. One whose sides are each a square foot is called a **Cubic Foot**. One whose sides are each a square yard is called a **Cubic Yard**.

217. The number of solid units any body contains is its **Solid Contents** or **Volume**.

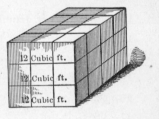

Thus, if a solid is 4 ft. long, 3 ft. wide, and 3 ft. thick, its solid contents or volume is 36 cubic feet. For it may be divided into 3 blocks, each containing 12 cubic feet. The number of cubic feet in each block is equal to the product of the numbers expressing the length and breadth of the solid, and the number of blocks is equal to the number of units of thickness. Therefore,

218. Principle. — *The volume of any rectangular solid is equal to the product of the numbers expressing its length, breadth, and thickness.*

The length, breadth, and thickness must be expressed in units of the same denomination.

1. How many cubic inches are there in a rectangular solid 3 in. long, 2 in. wide, and 2 in. thick?

2. How many cubic inches are there in a rectangular solid 1 ft. long, 1 ft. wide, and 1 ft. thick, or a cube whose edge is 1 ft. ?

3. How many cubic feet are there in a cube whose edge is 1 yd. ?

4. A cord of wood is 8 ft. long, 4 ft. wide, and 4 ft. high. How many cubic feet does it contain ?

5. Write a table of cubic measures.

WRITTEN EXERCISES.

Reduce to cubic inches :

1. 15 cu. ft. 120 cu. in.

2. 32 cu. ft. 114 cu. in.

3. 40 cu. yd. 18 cu. ft.

4. 60 cu. yd. 25 cu. ft.

5. 80 cu. yd. 16 cu. ft.

6. 2 C. 8 cu. ft.

7. 5 C. 13 cu. ft.

8. 15 cu. ft. 1115 cu. in.

Reduce to units of higher denominations :

9. 148760 cu. in.

10. 96780 cu. in.

11. 69875 cu. in.

12. 724570 cu. in.

13. 426790 cu. in.

14. 6037860 cu. in.

15. Reduce $\frac{7}{8}$ of a cu. yd. to units of lower denominations.

16. Reduce $\frac{5}{6}$ of a cu. ft. to cubic inches.

17. Reduce $\frac{3}{4}$ of a cu. yd. to cubic feet and inches.

18. Reduce .675 of a cu. ft. to cubic inches.

19. Reduce $\frac{3}{5}$ of a cu. ft. to a fraction of a cubic yard.

20. Reduce 8 cu. ft. 240 cu. in. to the decimal of a cubic yard.

21. A man bought a block of marble 4 ft. 9 in. long, 2 ft. 7 in. wide, and 2 ft. $5\frac{1}{2}$ in. thick. How much did he pay for it at the rate of $ 15.80 per cubic yard ?

SURVEYORS' MEASURES.

SURVEYORS' LINEAR MEASURE.

219. Surveyors, in measuring, use a chain consisting of 100 links, its length being 4 rods, or 66 feet.

1. Since a chain contains a hundred links, how many links make a rod ?

2. How many rods make a mile ?   How many chains ?

3. How many inches are there in a chain, or 66 ft. ?

4. Since there are 100 links in a chain, what is the length of each link ?

5. Write a table of surveyors' linear measures.

6. How many links in 2 rd. ?   In 3 rd. ?   In 4 rd. ?

7. How many ch. in 20 rd. ?   In 32 rd. ?   In 40 rd. ?

WRITTEN EXERCISES.

Reduce to links :

1. 40 rd. 15 l. | **5.** 25 ch. 3 rd. 20 l.

2. 3 rd. 12½ l. | **6.** 40 ch. 60 l.

3. 5 rd. 15 l. | **7.** 75 ch. 75 l.

4. 7 ch. 2 rd. 14 l. | **8.** 12 mi. 16 ch. 20 l.

Reduce to units of lower denominations :

9. $\frac{3}{8}$ ch. | **11.** $\frac{3}{5}$ rd. | **13.** .675 mi.

10. $\frac{5}{7}$ mi. | **12.** $\frac{4}{5}$ ch. | **14.** .595 ch.

Reduce to units of higher denominations :

15. 792 in. | **17.** 7685 l. | **19.** 76489 in.

16. 876 l. | **18.** 8436 l. | **20.** 123456 in.

21. Reduce $\frac{3}{8}$ of a chain to the fraction of a mile.

22. Reduce $\frac{5}{7}$ of a chain to links.

23. Reduce 28 links to a fraction of a chain.

Surveyors' Square Measure.

220. 1. How many links are there in a rod?   How many square links are there in a square rod?

2. How many rods are there in a chain?   How many square rods are there in a square chain?

3. How many rods are there in an acre?   How many square chains are there in an acre?

4. Write a table of surveyors' square measures.

WRITTEN EXERCISES.

Reduce to units of lower denominations:

1. 5 sq. ch.
2. 2 acres 8 sq. ch.
3. ⅝ of a chain.
4. 240 acres 15 sq. ch.
5. 3 sq. mi. 18 A. 15 sq. ch.
6. .645 of an acre.

Reduce to units of higher denominations:

7. 890 sq. ch.
8. 960 sq. rd.
9. 1875 sq. l.
10. 1920 sq. ch.
11. 2430 sq. l.
12. 3000 sq. ch.
13. 3375 sq. l.
14. 7500 sq. rd.
15. 8640 sq. l.

MEASURES OF CAPACITY.

Liquid Measure.

221. 1. How many gills are there in 7 pt.?   In 10 pt.?

2. How many gills are there in 5 qt.?   In 8 qt.?

3. How many pints are there in 8 qt.?   In 10 qt.?

4. How many quarts are there in 50 pt.?   In 68 pt.?

WRITTEN EXERCISES.

Reduce to units of lower denominations:

1. 25 gal. 3 qt. 1 pt.
2. 27 gal. 2 qt. 1 pt.
3. 30 gal. 3 qt. 2 gi.
4. ⅜ gal.
5. 15 gal. 3 qt. 1 pt. 2 gi.
6. 45 gal. 2 qt. 1 pt. 3 gi.
7. .375 gal.
8. 5/7 gal.

Reduce to units of higher denominations:

9. 196 pt. 12. 1980 gi. 15. 14620 gi.
10. 428 gi. 13. 1286 qt. 16. 15408 pt.
11. 680 qt. 14. 1648 pt. 17. 25600 gi.
18. Reduce $\frac{7}{10}$ of a pint to the fraction of a gallon.
19. Reduce $\frac{3}{8}$ of a gill to the fraction of a gallon.
20. Reduce 1 pt. 2 gi. to the decimal of a gallon.

DRY MEASURE.

222. 1. How many pints are there in 10 qt.? In 12 qt.?

2. How many quarts are there in 8 pk.? In 10 pk.?

3. How many quarts are there in a bushel? How many pints? In 3 bushels how many quarts? How many pints?

4. How many pecks are there in 33 qt.? In 41 qt.?

5. How many pecks are there in 18 pt.? In 24 pt.?

6. How many bushels are there in 20 pk.? In 25 pk.?

WRITTEN EXERCISES.

Reduce to pints:

1. 3 pk. 6 qt. 1 pt. 5. 2 bu. 3 pk. 5 qt. 1 pt.
2. 5 pk. 5 qt. 1 pt. 6. 6 bu. 2 pk. 3 qt. 1 pt.
3. 4 bu. 3 pk. 5 qt. 7. 15 bu. 3 qt. 1$\frac{1}{2}$ pt.
4. $\frac{2}{5}$ bu. 8. .625 pk.

Reduce to units of higher denominations:

9. 2144 qt. 12. 4640 pt. 15. 3930 gi.
10. 3360 qt. 13. 3760 pt. 16. 7870 pt.
11. 5500 qt. 14. 4800 qt. 17. 8000 gi.
18. Reduce $\frac{3}{10}$ of a pint to the fraction of a bushel.
19. Reduce $\frac{5}{7}$ of a quart to the fraction of a bushel.
20. Reduce 3 pk. 7 qt. to the decimal of a bushel.

MEASURES OF WEIGHT.

223. The measure of the force which attracts bodies to the earth is called **Weight**.

AVOIRDUPOIS WEIGHT.

224. 1. How many ounces are there in 5 lb. ? In 8 lb. ?

2. How many pounds are there in 6 cwt. ? In 8 cwt. ?

3. How many pounds are there in 3 tons ? In 5 tons ?

4. How many cwt. are there in 5 tons 3 hundredweight ?

5. How many pounds are there in 6 T. 8 cwt. 8 lb. ?

6. How many pounds are there in 48 oz. ? In 64 oz. ?

7. How many tons are there in 60 cwt. ? In 100 cwt. ?

WRITTEN EXERCISES.

Reduce to units of lower denominations :

1. 4 cwt. 25 lb. 12 oz.
2. 3 cwt. 76 lb. 8 oz.
3. 2 cwt. 18 lb. 9 oz.
4. $\frac{3}{8}$ of a ton.
5. 7 cwt. 16 lb. 4 oz.
6. 3 T. 15 cwt. 8 lb. 2 oz.
7. 5 T. 10 cwt. 24 lb. 8 oz.
8. .675 of a cwt.

Reduce to units of higher denominations :

9. 1400 oz.
10. 1056 oz.
11. 2080 oz.
12. 4260 lb.
13. 7525 lb.
14. 8123 lb.
15. 14784 oz.
16. 36450 lb.
17. 987696 oz.

18. Reduce $\frac{5}{7}$ of an ounce to the fraction of a hundredweight.

19. Reduce $\frac{8}{9}$ of a pound to the fraction of a ton.

20. Reduce 5 lb. 8 oz. to the decimal of a ton.

21. Reduce .725 of a pound to the fraction of a ton.

TROY WEIGHT.

225. 1. How many grains are there in 2 pwt.? In 3 pwt.? In 2 pwt. 10 gr.? In 3 pwt. 5 gr.? In 4 pwt. 4 gr.?

2. How many pennyweights are there in 4 oz.? In 5 oz.? In 6 oz.? In 5 oz. 6 pwt.? In 4 oz. 10 pwt.?

3. How many ounces are there in 2 lb.? In 3 lb.? In 3 lb. 2 oz.? In 5 lb. 8 oz.? In 10 lb. 7 oz.?

4. How many ounces are there in 1 lb.? How many pennyweights? How many grains?

5. How many ounces are there in $\frac{3}{4}$ lb.? In $\frac{5}{6}$ lb.?

6. How many ounces and pennyweights are there in $\frac{5}{8}$ lb.? In $\frac{7}{8}$ lb.?

7. How many pounds are there in 48 oz.? In 72 oz.?

WRITTEN EXERCISES.

Reduce to units of lower denominations:

1. 3 oz. 18 pwt. 20 gr.

2. 7 oz. 12 pwt. 10 gr.

3. 10 oz. 16 pwt. 12 gr.

4. $\frac{3}{5}$ of a pound.

5. 8 lb. 9 oz. 15 pwt. 18 gr.

6. 45 lb. 7 oz. 13 pwt. 15 gr.

7. .875 of a lb.

8. $\frac{5}{7}$ of an ounce.

Reduce to units of higher denominations:

9. 1940 gr.

10. 2560 gr.

11. 1276 pwt.

12. 4460 pwt.

13. 14520 gr.

14. 24676 pwt.

15. 7896 oz.

16. 9678 pwt.

17. 34560 gr.

18. Reduce $\frac{3}{8}$ of a pwt. to the fraction of a pound.

19. Reduce .395 of a grain to the fraction of an ounce.

20. Reduce 3 oz. 5 pwt. to the decimal of a pound.

APOTHECARIES' WEIGHT.

226. 1. How many grains are there in 3 ℈ ? In 5 ℈ ?
2. How many scruples are there in 8 ʒ ? In 10 ʒ 1 ℈ ?
3. How many drams are there in 5 ℥ ? In 8 ℥ 6 ʒ ?
4. How many drams are there in 1 ℔ ? In 2 ℔ ?
5. How many ounces are there in 4 ℔ ? In 8 ℔ 4 ℥ ?
6. How many drams are there in 18 ℈ ? In 30 ℈ ?

WRITTEN EXERCISES.

Reduce to grains:

1. 7 ʒ 2 ℈ 15 gr.
2. 6 ℥ 5 ʒ 2 ℈.
3. 15 ℔ 5 ℥ 2 3 4 ℈.
4. 24 ℔ 6 ℥ 2 ʒ 15 gr.

Reduce to units of higher denominations:

5. 1239 ʒ.
6. 4260 ℈.
7. 3648 ʒ.
8. 8260 ℈.
9. 12560 gr.
10. 92375 gr.

227. Comparison of common weights and measures.

1 pound Troy or Apothecaries' weight contains . . . 5760 gr.
1 pound Avoirdupois weight contains . . . . . . 7000 gr.
A bushel (32 qt.) contains . . . . 2150.4 cu. in.
A quart dry measure contains . . . . 67¼ cu. in.
A gallon liquid measure contains . . . . 231 cu. in.
A quart liquid measure contains . . . . 57¾ cu. in.

1. A druggist bought 5 pounds of opium by Avoirdupois weight at $8 a pound, and sold it by Apothecaries' weight at $1 per ounce. How much did he gain ?

2. A miner sold to a broker 2 pounds of gold dust at $220 per pound Avoirdupois, and the broker sold it at $16 per ounce Troy. Did he gain or lose, and how much ?

3. What part of a pound Avoirdupois is a pound Troy ?

4. A boy buys chestnuts at $1.60 per bu., and sells them at $.10 per quart liquid measure. How much is his gain per bushel ?

MEASURES OF TIME.

228. **1.** How many seconds are there in 5 min.? In 6 min.? In 8 min.? In 10 min. 20 sec.? In 5 min. 35 sec.?

2. How many minutes are there in 3 hr.? In 5 hr.? In 6 hr.? In 6 hr. 30 min.? In 8 hr. 20 min.? In ½ hr.?

3. How many hours are there in 2 da.? In 3 da.? In 5 da.? In 2 da. 5 hr.? In 3 da. 10 hr.? In ½ da.?

4. How many days are there in 5 wk.? In 8 wk.? In 6 wk.? In 6 wk. 5 da.? In 5 wk. 5 da.? In $\frac{2}{7}$ wk.? In $\frac{3}{7}$ wk.? In $\frac{2}{3}$ wk.?

5. How many days are there in two calendar years? In ½ yr.? In 2 leap years? In ½ of a leap year? What years are leap years?

6. How many minutes are there in 120 sec.? In 180 sec.?

7. How many hours are there in 120 min.? In 240 min.? In 140 min.? In 190 min.? In 270 min.?

8. How many days are there in 48 hr.? In 72 hr.? In 96 hr.? In 56 hr.? In 80 hr.? In 100 hr.?

WRITTEN EXERCISES.

Reduce to units of lower denominations:

1. 5 hr. 15 min. 12 sec.　　**5.** 4 wk. 2 da.

2. 6 hr. 27 min. 38 sec.　　**6.** 2 wk. 12 hr.

3. 2 wk. 5 da. 13 hr.　　**7.** 5 wk. 6 da. 10 hr.

4. $\frac{5}{7}$ of a day.　　**8.** .785 of a day.

Reduce to units of higher denominations:

9. 1460 min.　　**12.** 8000 hr.　　**15.** 486950 sec.

10. 3648 hr.　　**13.** 12000 hr.　　**16.** 867896 sec.

11. 7432 hr.　　**14.** 65460 min.　　**17.** 1153800 sec.

18. Reduce $\frac{2}{5}$ of a minute to the fraction of a day.

CIRCULAR OR ANGULAR MEASURE.

EXERCISES.

229. 1. How many minutes are there in 5°? In 7°?

2. How many seconds are there in 3'? In 5'? In 6'?

3. How many degrees are there in ¼ cir.? In ½ cir.?

4. How many seconds are there in 34° 12' 43"?

5. Reduce 468560 sec. to higher denominations.

6. Reduce 195600 sec. to signs.

7. Reduce 35° 41' 18" to seconds; also 18° 37' 14".

Reduce to higher denominations:

8. 489600".	10. 248300".	12. 486300".
9. 381400".	11. 319400".	13. 389600".

MEASURES OF VALUE.

ENGLISH MONEY.

230. 1. How many farthings are there in a penny? In 8 pence? In 10 pence? In 15 pence? In 20 pence?

2. How many pence are there in 2 shillings? In 5 shillings? In 6 s. 3 d.? In 5 s. 10 d.? In 8 s. 4 d.?

3. How many shillings are there in 3 pounds? In 5 pounds? In £3 5s.? In £4 8s.? In £5 10s.?

4. How many pence are there in £1? In £½? In £¼?

5. How many pence are there in 40 far.? In 48 far.?

6. How many shillings are there in 48 d.? In 60 d.?

WRITTEN EXERCISES.

Reduce to units of lower denominations:

1. £2 10s. 6d.	6. £45 3s. 9¾d.
2. £13 5s. 5¾d.	7. £75 to farthings.
3. £14 6s. 5¼d.	8. ⅜ of a sovereign.
4. £20 12s. 6¾d.	9. .65 of a pound.
5. £35 6s. 8¼d.	10. ³⁄₇ of a guinea.

Reduce to units of higher denominations:

11. 34567 far.　　14. 35968 far.　　17. 48596 far.

12. 21586 d.　　15. 16500 d.　　18. 34856 d.

13. 3846 far.　　16. 47384 d.　　19. 12000 d.

20. Reduce 3 s. 6 d. to the decimal of a pound.

21. Reduce 5 s. 8 d. to the decimal of a pound.

22. Express £ 3 6 s. 5 d. as pounds and decimals of a pound.

23. Express £ 5 8 s. 4 d. as pounds and decimals of a pound.

Find the value of the following in U. S. money:

24. £ 25 18 s. 6 d.

Solution.—　£25 18 s. 6 d. = £25.925.

£1 = \$4.8665.

∴ £25.925 = \$4.8665 × 25.925 = 126.164.

25. £ 31　6 s. 5 d.　　28. £ 51 6 s.　　31. £ 10 6 s. 5 d.

26. £ 24　8 s. 3 d.　　29. £ 35 8 s. 8 d.　　32. £ 35 8 s. 2 d.

27. £ 29 15 s. 6 d.　　30. £ 18 9 s. 4 d.　　33. £ 15 7 s. 4 d.

Find the value of the following in English money:

34. \$ 395.18.　36. \$ 573.25.　38. \$ 237.16.　40. \$ 324.25.

35. \$ 246.93.　37. \$ 615.86.　39. \$ 426.95.　41. \$ 1000.

MISCELLANEOUS TABLES.

231. 1. How many are 5 dozen? 8 dozen? 10 dozen?

2. How many are 4 score? 3 score? 3 score and 10?

3. How many is a gross? How many are 2 gross? 3 gross? How many is a great gross?

4. How many sheets are there in 3 quires? In 4 quires?

5. How many quires are there in 3 reams? In 5 reams?

6. How many reams are there in 3 bundles?

7. How many knives are there in 6 sets? In 8 sets?

8. How many dozen are there in 60 things? In 72?

ADDITION.

232. The processes of adding, subtracting, multiplying, and dividing compound denominate numbers are based upon the same principles as those governing similar operations in simple numbers.

The only difference between the processes is caused by compound numbers having a *varying scale*, while simple numbers have a *uniform decimal scale*.

WRITTEN EXERCISES.

1. What is the sum of 130 rd. 5 yd. 1 ft. 6 in., 215 rd. 2 ft. 8 in., 304 rd. 4 yd. 11 in. ?

	rd.	yd.	ft.	in.
	130	5	1	6
	215	0	2	8
	304	· 4	0	11
2 mi.	10	4½	2	1
		½=1		6
2 mi.	10	5	0	7

EXPLANATION. — The numbers should be written as in simple addition, so that units of the same denomination stand in the same column, and for convenience we begin at the right to add.

The sum of the inches is 25 in., which is equal to 2 ft. 1 in. We write the 1 under the inches and add the 2 ft. to the feet. The sum of the feet is 5 ft., or 1 yd. 2 ft. We write the 2 as feet in the sum and add the 1 yd. to the yards.

The sum of the yards is 10 yd., or 1 rd. 4½ yd. We write the 4½ yd. as yards in the sum, and add the 1 rd. to the rods. The sum of the rods is 650 rd., or 2 mi. 10 rd., which we write as miles and rods in the sum.

Therefore the sum is 2 mi. 10 rd. 4½ yd. 2 ft. 1 in. Or, since ½ yd. equals 1 ft. 6 in., the sum may be expressed as 2 mi. 10 rd. 5 yd. 7 in.

2. Find the sum of 18 lb. 10 oz. 14 pwt. 20 gr., 28 lb. 6 oz. 15 pwt. 15 gr., 36 lb. 4 oz. 12 pwt. 16 gr.

3. Find the sum of 12 bu. 3 pk. 7 qt., 25 bu. 5 qt., 8 bu. 2 pk. 1 pt., 48 bu. 3 pk., 42 bu. 1 pk. 2 qt., 48 bu. 3 pk. 6 qt.

4. Find the sum of 18 T. 12 cwt. 50 lb. 15 oz., 25 T. 12 cwt. 19 lb. 13 oz., 15 T. 14 cwt. 35 lb. 9 oz., 20 T. 18 cwt.

5. Find the sum of 14 gal. 3 qt. 1 pt. 3 gi., 15 gal. 2 qt. 1 pt. 2 gi., 11 gal. 2 qt. 2 gi., 16 gal. 1 pt., 30 gal. 3 qt. 2 gi.

6. What is the sum of 28 ℔ 7 ℥ 5 ʒ 2 ℈ 15 gr., 25 ℔ 10 ℥ 4 ʒ 1 ℈ 15 gr., 19 ℔ 9 ℥ 5 ʒ 1 ℈ 23 gr., 27 ℔ 8 ℥ 3 ʒ 2 ℈ 17 gr., 24 ℔ 7 ℥ 2 ʒ 1 ℈ 18 gr. ?

7. Find the sum of 9 mi. 212 rd. 2 yd. 2 ft. 8 in., 10 mi. 185 rd. 3 yd. 9 in., 15 mi. 76 rd. 1 yd. 3 ft. 5 in., 20 mi. 200 rd. 4 yd. 6 in., 36 mi. 126 rd. 5 yd. 2 ft. 10 in.

8. Find the sum of 132 sq. rd. 20 sq. yd. 8 sq. ft. 72 sq. in., 12 sq. rd. 15 sq. yd. 7 sq. ft. 80 sq. in., 18 sq. yd. 6 sq. ft. 86 sq. in.

9. What is the sum of £45 5s. 3¾d., £36 8s. 5½d., £65 15s. 7¼d., £52 13s. 9¾d., £120 10s. 8d. ?

10. Find the sum of 142 cu. yd. 18 cu. ft. 1229 cu. in., 275 cu. yd. 25 cu. ft. 1076 cu. in., 382 cu. yd. 17 cu. ft. 1521 cu. in., 420 cu. yd. 20 cu. ft. 1507 cu. in.

11. New York is 74° 3' west longitude, and Paris, France, is 2° 20' east. What is the difference in longitude between the two cities ?

SUGGESTION. — To find the difference in longitude between two places, one of which is east and the other west longitude, we add their respective longitudes.

12. Find the sum of ³⁄₇ mi., .35 rd., and 2⅜ rd.

SOLUTION.

	rd.	ft.	in.
³⁄₇ mi. =	137	2	4²⁄₇
.35 rd. =		5	9³⁄₁₀
2⅜ rd. =	2	6	2¼
	139	14	3¹¹⁷⁄₁₄₀

13. Find the sum of 10 wk. 4 da. 5¼ hr., 2 wk. 5¾ da., 9 wk. 3 da. 18 hr. 12⅔ min., 6 da. 15 hr. 15 min.

14. What is the sum of £.35, £2.875, and £6 8s. 6d. ?

15. What is the sum of ⅔ T., ⁴⁄₉ cwt., and ¾ lb. ?

SUBTRACTION.

WRITTEN EXERCISES.

233. 1. From 127 rd. 3 yd. 1 ft. 7 in., subtract 100 rd. 4 yd. 2 ft. 9 in.

rd.	yd.	ft.	in.
127	3	1	7
100	4	2	9
26	$3\frac{1}{2}$	1	10
	$\frac{1}{2}=1$		6
26	4	0	4

EXPLANATION. — The numbers should be written as in simple subtraction, so that units of the same order stand in the same column, and, for convenience, we should begin at the right to subtract.

Since 9 in. cannot be subtracted from 7 in., we add to 7 in. a unit of the next higher order, making 1 ft. 7 in., or 19 in. Then 9 in. taken from 19 in. leave 10 in., which we write as inches in the remainder. Inasmuch as 1 ft. was added to 7 in., there are no feet remaining in the minuend.

Since we cannot subtract 2 ft. from 0 ft., we add to 0 ft. a unit of the next higher order, making 3 ft. Then 2 ft. taken from 3 ft. leave 1 ft., which we write as the feet of the remainder.

Since 4 yd. cannot be subtracted from 2 yd., we add to 2 yd. a unit of the next higher order and proceed as before. The remainder is 26 rd. 4 yd. 0 ft. 4 in.

2. From 16 lb. 10 oz. 16 pwt. 18 gr., take 12 lb. 11 oz. 17 pwt. 15 gr.

3. From £25 4s., take £20 8s. 10d.

4. From 5 ℔ 7 ℨ, take 3 ℔ 10 ℨ 5 ℈ 1 ℈ 15 gr.

5. From 2 hhd. 20 gal. 3 qt., take 1 hhd. 60 gal. 3 qt. 1 pt.

6. From 4 mi. 126 rd. 4 yd. 6 in., take 2 mi. 140 rd. 3 yd. 2 ft. 8 in.

7. From a barrel containing 36 gal. 3 qt. 1 pt. of vinegar, there were sold 27 gal. 1 qt. 1 pt. 2 gi. How much remained unsold ?

8. One train left Albany at 7 o'clock 35 min. A.M., and another at 11 o'clock 15 min. A.M. How long after the first did the second start ?

9. From $\frac{3}{4}$ bbl. take $7\frac{3}{5}$ gal.

SOLUTION.

	gal.	qt.	pt.	gi.
$\frac{3}{4}$ bbl. =	23	2	1	
$7\frac{3}{5}$ gal. =	7	2	0	$3\frac{1}{5}$
	16	0	0	$\frac{4}{5}$

10. From £ $\frac{11}{30}$, take $5 s$. $2 d$. 3 far.

11. From $\frac{4}{9}$ mi., take 120.65 rd.

12. From $\frac{7}{8}$ wk., take $\frac{4}{15}$ da.

13. From 15.576 bu., take 3.65 pk.

14. From .9 mi., take 120 rd. 4 yd. 2 ft.

15. Baltimore is 76° 37' west longitude, and San Francisco is 122° 26$\frac{1}{4}$' west longitude. What is their difference in longitude ?

SUGGESTION. — To find the difference in longitude between two places both of which are east, or both west, we subtract the less from the greater.

16. How long was it from Jan. 10, 1841, to May 7, 1853 ?

yr.	mo.	da.
1853	5	7
1841	1	10
12	3	27

EXPLANATION. — Since the later date expresses the greater period of time, we write it as the minuend, and the earlier date as the subtrahend, giving the month its number instead of the name. We then subtract as in denominate numbers, considering 30 days 1 month, and 12 months one year. The remainder will be the time as correct as it can be expressed in months and days.

17. A certain person was born June 24, 1859. How old was he Sept. 9, 1891 ?

18. How many years, months, and days is it from the day of your birth, or, how old are you ?

19. A note dated May 6, 1885, was paid Nov. 4, 1890. How long did it run before it was paid ?

20. A man was born Feb. 29, 1844, and died Mar. 15, 1880. How many birthdays did he have, and what was his age ?

MULTIPLICATION.

WRITTEN EXERCISES.

234. 1. How much is 5 times 147 rd. 4 yd. 2 ft. 8 in.?

```
rd.  yd.  ft.  in.
147   4    2    8
               5
2 mi. 99  2    1    4
```

EXPLANATION. — We write the numbers as in simple numbers, and for convenience begin at the right to multiply.

5 times 8 in. are 40 in., or 3 ft. 4 in. We write the 4 in. as inches in the product, and reserve the 3 ft. to add to the product of feet.

5 times 2 ft. are 10 ft.; 10 ft. + 3 ft. reserved equal 13 ft., or 4 yd. 1 ft. We write the 1 ft. in the product, and reserve the 4 yd. to add to the product of yards.

5 times 4 yd. equal 20 yd.; 20 yd. + 4 yd. reserved equal 24 yd., or 4 rd. 2 yd. We write the 2 yd. in the product, and reserve the rods to add to the product of rods.

5 times 147 rd. are 735 rd.; 735 rd. + 4 rd. reserved equal 739 rd., or 2 mi. 99 rd., which we write in the product.

Therefore the product is 2 mi. 99 rd. 2 yd. 1 ft. 4 in.

2. Multiply 12 bu. 3 pk. 2 qt. 1 pt. by 8.

3. Multiply 7 lb. 8 oz. 15 pwt. 18 gr. by 15.

4. Multiply £4 8 s. 6 d. by 5.

5. Multiply 3 cwt. 10 lb. 9 oz. by 12.

6. Multiply 38 gal. 3 qt. 1 pt. 2 gi. by 10.

7. How much wheat can be put into 18 sacks, if each sack holds 1 bu. 3 pk. 7 qt. 1 pt.?

8. A solar year consists of 365 da. 5 hr. 48 min. 49.7 sec. How much time is there in 20 solar years?

9. If one silver spoon weighs 3 oz. 10 pwt. 15 gr., what will be the weight of two sets of 6 spoons each?

10. How many bushels of corn will a field of 14 acres produce, if it produces 28 bu. 3 pk. 5 qt. 1 pt. to the acre?

11. If one load of wood measures 112 cu. ft. 432 cu. in., how much will 25 loads of the same size measure?

DIVISION.

WRITTEN EXERCISES.

235. **1.** Divide 27 bu. 3 pk. 5 qt. 1 pt. into 6 equal parts.

6)27 bu. 3 pk. 5 qt. 1 pt.
   4   2   4   1⅚

EXPLANATION. — Since the quantity is to be divided into 6 equal parts, each part will contain *one sixth* of the quantity.

One sixth of 27 bu. is 4 bu., with a remainder of 3 bu. We write the 4 bu. in the quotient and add the 3 bu. remaining to the number of the next lower denomination, making 15 pk.

One sixth of 15 pk. is 2 pk., with 3 pk. remaining. We write the 2 pk. in the quotient, and add the 3 pk. remaining to the number of the next lower denomination, making 29 qt.

One sixth of 29 qt. is 4 qt., with 5 qt. remaining. We write the 4 qt. in the quotient, and add the 5 qt. to the number of the next lower denomination, making 11 pt.

One sixth of 11 pt. is 1⅚ pt., which we write in the quotient.

Therefore the quotient is 4 bu. 2 pk. 4 qt. 1⅚ pt.

2. Divide 70 lb. 10 oz. 14 pwt. 12 gr. by 6.

3. Divide 112 T. 16 cwt. 66 lb. by 7.

4. Divide 117 hhd. 33 gal. 2 qt. 1 pt. 2 gi. by 9.

5. Divide 153 mi. 313 rd. 3 yd. 2 ft. by 11.

6. Divide 103 C. 12 cu. ft. 632 cu. in. by 10.

7. If 15 bars of silver weigh 39 lb. 8 oz. 16 pwt., what is the average weight of a bar ?

8. If 6 men build 124 rd. 2 ft. 6 in. of wall in 17 days, how much do they build in one day ?

9. A man traveled 348 mi. 52 rd. in 28 days. How far, on an average, did he travel per day ?

10. The entire weight of 41 hhd. of sugar is 19 T. 6 cwt. 22 lb. What is the average weight of a hhd. ?

11. If a ship sailed 64° 59' 3" in 29 days, how far did she sail on an average per day ?

12. If 31 cwt. 18 lb. of tea are put up in packages, each containing 3 lb. 8 oz., how many packages will there be?

31 cwt. 18 lb. = 49888 oz.

3 lb. 8 oz. = 56 oz.

49888 oz. ÷ 56 oz. = 890$\frac{8}{7}$, the number of packages.

13. Divide £36 13s. 3d. by £5 4s. 9d.

14. Divide 2 lb. 7 oz. 19 pwt. by 5 oz. 6 pwt. 12 gr.

15. Divide 40 T. 16 cwt. 11 lb. 4 oz. by 2 T. 14 cwt. 10 lb. 12 oz.

16. How long will 9 bu. 1 pk. 4 qt. of oats last a horse if he eats 1 pk. 4 qt. per day?

17. How many sacks will it require to contain 39 bu. 2 pk. 6 qt. of wheat, if each sack holds 1 bu. 3 pk. 7$\frac{1}{2}$ qt.?

18. If one bale of hay weighs 5 cwt. 25 lb., how many bales will it take to weigh 2 T. 7 cwt. 25 lb.?

19. A man traveled 3 mi. 20 rd. 4 yd. in one hour. In what time could he travel 240 miles, traveling at the same rate?

20. A man bought 60 cwt. 85 lb. of sugar at 4 cts. a pound. He sold $\frac{1}{9}$ of it at 5 cts. a pound, $\frac{1}{8}$ of it at 5$\frac{1}{2}$ cts. a pound, and the remainder at cost. How much did he gain?

21. How many fence pickets, 2 ft. 4 in. long and 2 in. wide, can be made from 8 boards, each 11 ft. 8 in. long and 8 in. wide?

22. How many medals, each weighing 5 oz. 13 pwt. 21 gr., can be made from a bar of gold, which weighs 88 lb. 8 oz. 14 pwt. 15 gr.?

23. A man owned a pile of wood containing 40 cords. If it was 4 ft. wide and 8 ft. high, what was its length?

REVIEW EXERCISES.

236. 1. What will be the cost of 8 lb. 6 oz. of lard at 10 cents per pound ?

2. How much will 2 pk. 3 qt. of beans cost at 12 cents a quart ?

3. How many quart boxes will 2 bu. 3 pk. 5 qt. of strawberries fill ?

4. A dealer sold 1 bu. 5 qt. of chestnuts at 5 cents a pint.   How much did he get for them ?

5. How many bushels of potatoes, at $.45 a bushel, must be given for 5 gal. 3 qt. of syrup at 15 cents a quart ?

6. How many square yards are there in a lot 75 feet long and 60 feet wide ?

7. The area of a blackboard $3\frac{3}{4}$ feet wide is $112\frac{1}{2}$ sq. ft. What is its length ?

8. The diameter of the earth is 7912 miles.   How many feet is it ?

9. How high is a horse that measures 15 hands ?

10. A farm is 67 ch. 83 l. long.   How many rods long is it ?

11. How many inches are there in 59 ch. 75 l. ?

12. A pasture containing 10 acres had a width of 20 rods. How long was it ?

13. What is the difference between 10 square feet and 10 feet square ?   Illustrate this by drawings ?

14. What will be the expense of painting a roof 48 feet long and 22 feet wide at $.30 a square yard ?

15. How much will 8 barrels of flour cost, at the rate of $3\frac{1}{2}$ cents a pound ?

16. How many bars of iron, each weighing 41 lb. 10⅔ oz., will it take to weigh a ton?

17. How many times will a wheel 12 ft. 4 in. in circumference revolve in going 10 miles?

18. Milton was born Dec. 9, 1608, and died Nov. 8, 1675. What was his age at the time of his death?

19. From a pile of wood containing 120 cords, there were sold at one time 48 C. 96 cu. ft., and at another time 36 C. 28 cu. ft. How much remained?

20. A man who owned 300 acres of land, sold 120 A. 29 sq. rd. 27 sq. yd. 6 sq. ft. How much remained unsold?

21. Reduce ⅕ of a bushel to lower denominations.

22. Reduce ⁴⁄₉ of a scruple to the fraction of a pound.

23. Reduce ⁹⁄₁₁ of an acre to lower denominations

24. What is the difference between 6 dozen dozen and a half a dozen dozen?

25. Express .65 of a pint as a decimal of a bushel.

26. How many times must a man dip with a dipper holding 1 qt. 1 pt. so that he may empty a cask containing 31½ gal.?

27. How many barrels of sugar, each containing 2 cwt. 35 lb., are there in 3 T. 4 cwt. 18 lb.?

28. Express .375 of a week as a fraction of a year.

29. What part of 5 gal. 3 qt. 1 pt. are 2 gal. 1 qt. 1 pt.?

30. Reduce 4 hr. 15 min. to the decimal of a day.

31. Reduce .1845 of a gill to the decimal of a gal.

32. What part of 9 inches square are 9 square inches?

33. From .625 lb. Troy take 5.25 oz. Troy.

34. What is the length of a fence inclosing a square field, each side of which is 25 rd. 3 yd. 2⅔ ft. long?

35. If a hogshead of sugar weighs 5 cwt. 24 lb. 4 oz., what will 8 hhd. be worth at $4\frac{1}{2}$ ct. per pound?

36. How many cups, holding one half pint each, can be filled from a coffee urn holding 2 gal. 3 qt. $1\frac{1}{2}$ pt.?

37. If the weight of a bushel of wheat is 60 lb., how many bags that hold 2 bu. each will be required to sack 3 T. 4 cwt. 20 lb. of wheat?

38. Which is the heavier, and how much, a pound of lead or a pound of gold?

39. Which is the heavier, and how much, an ounce of feathers or an ounce of silver?

40. An iron block weighed 115 pounds Avoirdupois weight. How much would it have weighed by Troy weight?

41. How many steel rails 30 ft. long are needed to build 5 miles of railroad?

42. If a horse travels on an average a mile in 10 min. 15 sec., how far does he go in 6 hr.?

43. I have a rectangular farm 230 rods long and 180 rods wide which is worth $75 per acre. What is the value of the farm?

44. Find the sum of $\frac{7}{8}$ mi., $\frac{1}{3}$ rd., $\frac{5}{6}$ ft.

45. What part of a mile is $\frac{2}{3}$ of 6 rd. 3 yd. 2 in.?

46. Find the value in U. S. money of the contents of a purse containing 35 sovereigns, 27 half-sovereigns, 13 crowns, 41 half-crowns, a guinea, and a shilling.

47. A farmer sowed 4 bu. 1 pk. 1 qt. of seed, and harvested from it 110 bu. 3 pk. 5 qt. How much did he raise from a bushel of seed?

48. What will be the cost of 3 T. 6 cwt. 27 lb. of coal at $4.75 a ton?

49. A merchant's profits in $7\frac{1}{2}$ months were $1675. At this rate, what would be his profits in a year?

50. A train running from Philadelphia to New York, a distance of 90 miles, makes the whole distance in 1 hr. 35 min. What is its rate per hour?

51. If a cubic foot of ice weighs $57\frac{3}{8}$ pounds, how many cubic feet of ice will it take to weigh a ton?

52. Washington is $77°\,2'\,48''$ west longitude, and Albany is $73°\,44'\,53''$ west longitude. What is the difference in longitude between these two places?

53. Paris is $2°\,20'\,22''$ east of Greenwich, and New York is $74°\,3''$ west. What is their difference in longitude?

54. What will be the cost of fencing a rectangular lot 18 rods by 24 rods at $18\frac{3}{4}$ cents a foot?

55. How much fertilizer will be needed for 5 A. 96 sq. rd. of land, allowing 3 bu. 1 pk. 3 qt. to an acre?

56. The area of a rectangular field is 60 A. 130 sq. rd., and one side is 20.25 chains. What is the length of the other side?

57. How many days, of 10 hours each, will it take to count a million at the rate of 100 a minute?

58. What will be the cost of 5 reams 15 quires and 20 sheets of paper at $3.60 a ream?

59. How many barrels of flour, at $4.75 per barrel, must be given for 3 T. 5 cwt. of coal at $6.50 per ton?

60. A druggist purchased $9\frac{3}{4}$ ounces of quinine at $.40 an ounce Avoirdupois, and sold it at $.60 an ounce Troy. How much did he gain?

61. How many silver spoons, each weighing 2 oz. 5 pwt., can be made from a bar of silver weighing 6 lb. 4 oz. 10 pwt.?

62. I wish to have 6 reams 15 quires 20 sheets of paper printed for one fourth sheet posters. How many can I get, and what will they cost at $5.75 per M?

63. If I burn a pint of kerosene every night, what will a three weeks' supply cost me at 15 cents a gallon?

64. What is the value in U. S. money of 1000 francs?

65. A man retails oil at 10 cts. a pint. What is his profit on 3 bbl., of 31½ gal. each, which cost $.65 a gallon?

66. What will 12 horses cost in U. S. money, if 5 horses cost £175 10s. 6d.?

67. A milkman sold one morning 220 qt. of milk at 6 cts. a quart. His measure lacked ⅕ of a gill of holding a full quart. What was the actual worth of the milk sold?

68. How many powders, of 6 grains each, can be made from one fourth of an ounce of medicine?

69. A physician's prescription calls for ʒvij, ℈ij of calomel. How many pills, of 5 grains each, can be made from the prescribed quantity?

70. If a grocer's scales give only 15¾ oz. for a pound, of how much money does he defraud his customers in the sale of 5 bbl. of sugar, each weighing 2 cwt. 10 lb. 12 oz., true weight, at 5 cents a pound?

71. A man sold 8 bu. 3 pk. 4 qt. of cranberries at $3½ a bushel, and took his pay in flour at 3½ cents a pound. How many barrels of flour did he receive?

72. A man purchased 54 cwt. 85 lb. of sugar at 4 cts. a pound. He sold ½ of it at 5 cts. a pound, ⅓ of it at 5½ cts. a pound, and the rest at cost. How much did he gain?

73. How many silver coins, each weighing 412½ gr., can be coined from a bar of silver weighing 8 lb. 4 oz. Avoirdupois?

74. I wish to put 116 bu. 1 pk. 4 qt. of grain into bags that shall contain 2 bu. 1 pk. 4 qt. each. How many bags will be required?

LONGITUDE AND TIME.

237. **1.** Where does the sun appear to rise?

2. How often does it appear to rise in the east?

3. Through how many degrees of space does it appear to pass in this daily motion? *Ans.* 360°.

4. Since it seems to travel 360° in one day, or 24 hours, how great will be its apparent motion in 1 hour?

5. If the earth moves 15° in one hour, how far will it move in 1 minute?

6. If it moves ¼ of a degree or 15′ of distance in one minute of time, how far will it move in 1 second of time?

7. How does the number of degrees passed over compare with the number of hours? The number of minutes of space with the number of minutes of time? The number of seconds of space with the number of seconds of time?

8. When it is sunrise at any place, how long will it be before it is sunrise at a place 15° west of that place? 30° west? 45° west?

9. When it is sunrise at any place, how long before was it sunrise at a place 15° east of that place? 30° east?

10. When it is noon at any place, what time is it at a place 15° west? 15° east? 30° west? 30° east?

11. If I travel eastward, will my watch become too slow or too fast? If I travel westward, will my watch be too slow or too fast?

12. What places have noon at the same time? Midnight at the same time?

238. A **Meridian** is an imaginary line passing from the North Pole to the South Pole, through any place.

239. The distance east or west from a given meridian is called **Longitude**.

The meridians from which longitude is commonly reckoned are those which pass through Washington, D.C., and Greenwich, England.

RELATIONS BETWEEN LONGITUDE AND TIME.

Two places distant from each other

15° of longitude differ	1 hour	in time.
15′ " " "	1 minute " "
15″ " " "	1 second " "
1° " " "	4 minutes " "
1′ " " "	4 seconds " "

WRITTEN EXERCISES.

240. To find the difference in time between two places when the difference in longitude is given.

1. Two places are 35° 12′ 15″ apart. What is the difference in time between them?

15)35° 12′ 15″   EXPLANATION.—Since places distant from each
  2 20 49   other 15° of longitude differ 1 hr. in time, 15′ of
               longitude 1 min. in time, and 15″ of longitude 1 sec.
in time, $\frac{1}{15}$ of 35° 12′ 15″, is the difference in hours, minutes, and seconds of time.   Therefore, the difference in time is 2 hr. 20 min. 49 sec.

2. The difference in longitude between two places is 46° 15′ 30″. What is the difference in time?

3. Washington is 77° 2′ 48″ west from Greenwich. What is the difference in time between the two places?

4. New York is 74° 3″ west longitude, and Chicago is 87° 38′ west. What is their difference in time?

5. The longitude of Philadelphia is 75° 10′ west from Greenwich, and that of San Francisco 122° 26′ 15″ west from Greenwich. What time is it at San Francisco when it is noon at Philadelphia?

6. Boston is 5° 59′ 18″ east from Washington. What time is it at Washington when it is noon at Boston?

7. The longitude of Albany is 73° 44′ 53″ west from Greenwich, and that of St. Paul is 93° 4′ 55″ west from Greenwich. How much earlier does the sun rise at Albany than at St. Paul?

8. The longitude of Berlin is 13° 23′ 43″ east from Greenwich, and that of Cincinnati 84° 26′ west from Greenwich. What is their difference in time?

9. Paris is 2° 20′ 22″ east from Greenwich. Will a traveler's watch be slow or fast, and how much, when he goes from Greenwich to Paris?

10. Pekin in China is 116° 27′ 30″ east longitude, and Washington is 77° west longitude. When it is midnight on December 31st at Washington, what time will it be at Pekin?

241. To find the difference in longitude between two places when the difference in time is given.

1. The difference in time between two places is 2 hr. 20 min. 49 sec. What is their difference in longitude?

2 hr. 20 min. 49 sec.   EXPLANATION. — Since there are 15 times
        15   as many degrees, minutes, and seconds of
—————————————   longitude, as there are hours, minutes, and
35   12   15   seconds of time, 15 times 2 hr. 20 min. 49
sec., is the difference in degrees, minutes, and seconds of longitude.
Therefore, the difference in longitude is 35° 12′ 15″.

2. The difference in time between two places is **3 hr. 16 min. 23 sec.** What is their difference in longitude?

3. The difference in time between Boston and New Orleans is 1 hr. 16 min. 14 sec. What is their difference in longitude?

4. The difference in time between New York and St. Louis is 1 hr. 2 min. 20 sec. What is the difference in their longitude?

5. Two persons observed the occultation of a certain star by the moon, one seeing it at 9 P.M., and the other at 10½ P.M. What was the difference in their longitude?

6. The difference in time between Savannah, Ga., and Portland, Me., is 43 min. 32 sec. What is their difference in longitude?

7. The difference in time between London and New York is 4 hr. 55 min. 37⅔ sec. What is their difference in longitude?

8. When it is 12 o'clock M. at Rochester, N.Y., it is 9 hr. 1 min. 47 sec. A.M. at San Francisco. The longitude of Rochester is 77° 51′ west from Greenwich. What is the longitude of San Francisco?

9. When it is noon at Greenwich it is 6 hr. 52 min. 40 sec. A.M. at Harrisburg, Penn. What is the longitude of Harrisburg?

10. A traveler found on arriving at his destination that his watch was 1 hr. 35 min. too slow. In which direction had he been traveling? How far had he traveled?

11. When it is noon at Philadelphia it is 10 min. past 5 o'clock P.M. at Paris. What is the longitude of Paris, the longitude of Philadelphia being 75° 10′?

PRACTICAL MEASUREMENTS.

242. The method of computing the area of a *rectangle* and a *square* was learned in Art. 214, but there are other surfaces whose area can be readily found.

243. When a straight line meets another straight line forming two equal angles, each angle is called a **Right Angle.**

Two Right Angles

When two lines form right angles, they are said to be perpendicular to each other.

244. An angle smaller than a right angle is called an **Acute Angle.**

Acute Angle

245. An angle larger than a right angle is called an **Obtuse Angle.**

Obtuse Angle

246. Lines which are equidistant throughout their entire length are called **Parallel Lines.**

Parallel Lines

247. A figure having four straight sides and its opposite sides parallel is called a **Parallelogram.**

Parallelogram

1. When the angles of a parallelogram are right angles, it is called a **Rectangle.**
2. The side upon which a figure is assumed to stand is called the **Base.**

Rectangle

3. The perpendicular distance between the base of a figure and the highest point opposite it is the **Altitude.**
4. The straight line joining the opposite angles of a parallelogram is called its **Diagonal.**

205

248. **The measurement of rectangles.** (See § 214.)

Find the area of a rectangular figure

1. 15 rd. by 12 rd.
2. 36 rd. by 24 rd.
3. 45 ft. by 36 ft.
4. 400 ft. by 80 ft.

5. 37.5 yd. by 8.3 yd.
6. 367 in. by 4.12 in.
7. 384 ft. by 21.6 ft.
8. 81.2 mi. by 53.2 mi.

9. A gable roof was 43 ft. by 26. How many square feet of tin will be required to cover it?

10. A lot was 18 rods long and 8 rods wide. What part of an acre did it contain?

11. What was the value of the above lot at $342.50 per acre?

12. How many acres are there in a square farm, each of whose sides is 20 chains?

13. A rectangular piece of land is 160 rods long and 120 rods wide. How many acres does it contain?

14. A man bought a rectangular farm 40 ch. long and 35 ch. wide, at $85 an acre. What did the farm cost?

15. The area of a certain rectangular garden is 840 square yards, and its length is 35 yards. How wide is it?

16. A rectangular field containing 8 acres is 32 rods wide. How long is it?

17. A rectangular mirror has an area of 2520 sq. in. If its width is $3\frac{1}{2}$ ft., what is its length?

18. A city lot containing 1610 sq. yd. has a front of $80\frac{1}{2}$ ft. What is its depth?

19. A rectangular farm containing 100 acres is 80 rods wide. How long is it?

249. The measurement of parallelograms.

It is apparent that the parallelogram $ABCD =$ the rectangle $EFCD$; that the base $AB =$ the base EF, and that the altitude of each is DE. Hence a parallelogram is equivalent to a rectangle having the same base and altitude.

250. Principle. — *The area of a parallelogram is equal to the product of the numbers expressing its base and altitude.*

The base and altitude must be expressed in units of the same denomination.

Find the area of the following parallelograms:

1. Base 46 ft., alt. 10 ft.
2. Base 52 ft., alt. 12 ft.
3. Base 47 ft., alt. 15 ft.
4. Base 265 ft., alt. 119 ft.
5. Base 388 ft., alt. 125 ft.
6. Base 175 ft., alt. 5 rd.
7. Base 12 rd., alt. 45 yd.
8. Base 275 rd., alt. 170 rd.

9. The area of a parallelogram is 1628 sq. ft. Its length is 74 ft. What is its altitude ?

10. The area of a parallelogram is 3404 sq. ft. It has an altitude of 37 feet. What is its length ?

11. I have a lot in the form of a parallelogram containing one acre. The distance between two of its parallel sides is 12 rods. What is its length ?

12. The area of a field is $3\frac{1}{2}$ acres. It is in the form of a parallelogram, and its length is 80 rods. How wide is it ?

13. There is a farm in the form of a parallelogram containing 132 acres. The perpendicular distance between the sides is 132 rods. What is its length ?

251. To find the area of a triangle.

252. A figure having three sides and three angles is called a **Triangle**.

The point where the sides which form an angle meet is called the **Vertex**.

We have just learned that the area of a parallelogram is equal to the product of the numbers
expressing its base and altitude. It is evident
that a diagonal of a parallelogram divides it into
two equal triangles. Hence,

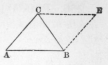

253. PRINCIPLE. — *The area of a triangle is one half the
product of the numbers expressing its base and altitude.*

Find the area of the following triangles:

1. Base 30 ft., alt. 12 ft.　　4. Base 54 ft., alt. 43 ft.

2. Base 45 ft., alt. 30 ft.　　5. Base 67 ft., alt. 55 ft.

3. Base 37 ft., alt. 28 ft.　　6. Base 40 ft., alt. 25 ft.

7. The base of a triangular field is 360 yards, and the
altitude is 615 feet. How many acres does it contain?

8. What will be the cost of a triangular piece of land
whose base is 18.36 ch., and the altitude 10.54 ch., at $70
per acre?

9. How many square feet of boards will be required to
cover the gables of a house that is 28 ft. wide, the ridge of
the roof of the house being 13 ft. higher than the foot of
the rafters?

254. To find the area of a trapezoid.

255. A figure having four sides, two of which are parallel,
is called a **Trapezoid.**

It is evident that any trapezoid may be divided into two triangles
by a line; as, *AC.* The area of one triangle is the
product of one half the length of one of the parallel
sides, as *AD,* multiplied by the altitude *CE,* and
the area of the other triangle is the product of one
half the length of the other parallel side, as *CB,*
multiplied by the altitude *CE.* Therefore,

256. Principle. — *The area of a trapezoid is equal to the length of one half the sum of the parallel sides multiplied by the altitude.*

Find the area of the following trapezoids:

1. Altitude 10 ft., parallel sides 15 ft. and 11 ft.

2. Altitude 12 ft., parallel sides 16 ft. and 14 ft.

3. Altitude 18 ft., parallel sides 20 ft. and 18 ft.

4. Altitude 25 ft., parallel sides 28 ft. and 23 ft.

5. Altitude 46 ft., parallel sides 54 ft. and 39 ft.

6. There is a field in the form of a trapezoid whose altitude is 32 rd., and whose parallel sides are 42 rd. and 50 rd. long, respectively. How many acres are there in the field?

7. A field in the form of a trapezoid, which has an altitude of 40 rd. and whose parallel sides are 52 rd. and 58 rd., respectively, contains how many acres?

8. A farm in the form of a trapezoid has its parallel sides 64 ch. and 76 ch. in length. The perpendicular distance between them is 192 rods. How large is the farm?

9. There is a field in the form of a trapezoid which has an altitude of 180 rd. The parallel sides are 96 rd. and 108 rd. long, respectively. How many acres are there in the field?

10. One side of a field is 38 chains long, the side parallel to it is 28 chains long, and the perpendicular distance between them is 25 chains. How many acres are there in the field?

11. What are the square contents of a walk, in the form of a trapezoid, 20 ft. long and 3 ft. wide at one end and 5 ft. at the other?

257. To find the circumference or diameter of a circle.

A plane figure, bounded by a curved line, every point of which is equally distant from a point within, called the center, is a **Circle**.

1. The line which bounds a circle is called its **Circumference**.

2. The straight line drawn from the center of the circle to the circumference is called the **Radius**.

3. A straight line drawn through the center of a circle, terminating at both ends in the circumference, is called the **Diameter**.

4. A radius is one half a diameter.

258. PRINCIPLE. —*The circumference of a circle is about* $3\frac{1}{7}$ *times the diameter; or more accurately,* 3.1416 *times the diameter.*

Find the approximate circumferences of circles having the following diameters:

1. 35 ft. **3.** 63 ft. **5.** 84 ft. **7.** 98 ft. **9.** 126 ft.

2. 77 ft. **4.** 49 ft. **6.** 56 ft. **8.** 105 ft. **10.** 168 ft.

Find the more accurate circumferences of the following circles:

11. Diameter 15 ft.   **16.** Diameter 35 ft.

12. Diameter 20 ft.   **17.** Radius 8 ft.

13. Diameter 24 ft.   **18.** Radius $12\frac{1}{2}$ ft.

14. Diameter 19 ft.   **19.** Radius $15\frac{1}{2}$ ft.

15. Diameter 29 ft.   **20.** Radius $22\frac{1}{2}$ ft.

21. What is the diameter of a circle whose circumference is 37.6992 ft.

SOLUTION. — 37.6992 ft. ÷ 3.1416 = 12 ft., the diameter.

Find the diameters of circles having the following circumferences:

22. 14.3 ft.   24. 318 ft.   26. 670 ft.   28. 1200 rd.
23. 164 ft.   25. 426 ft.   27. 955.5 rd.   29. 1676 rd.

259. To find the area of a circle.

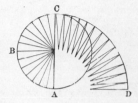

From the accompanying figure, it is evident that a circle may be regarded as composed of a large number of triangles, the sum of whose bases forms the circumference of the circle, and whose altitude is the radius of the circle. Hence,

260. PRINCIPLE. — *The area of a circle is equal to the circumference, multiplied by half the radius.*

Find the area of the following circles:

1. Circum. 50 ft., diam. 15.915 ft.   6. Circum. 869 rd.
2. Circum. 60 ft., diam. 19.098 ft.   7. Circum. 728 rd.
3. Circum. 37.6992 ft., diam. 12 ft.   8. Diam. 240 rd.
4. Circum. 314.16 ft., diam. 100 ft.   9. Diam. 125 ft.
5. Circum. 640 ft., diam. 203.7 ft.   10. Diam. 364 rd.

11. What is the area of a circular field, whose circumference is 320 rd., and whose diameter is 101.856 rd.?

12. The circumference of a circular field is 436 rd. How many acres does it contain?

261. To find the cost of plastering, painting, and kalsomining.

Plastering, painting, and kalsomining are usually computed by the square yard.

Allowances are sometimes made for the whole or part of the area of openings, and for baseboards, but custom varies so greatly that a written contract regarding the allowances should be made to avoid complications at the time of settlement. In the examples given, the plastering is considered to extend only to the baseboard.

1. Find the cost of plastering a room 18 ft. by 16 ft. and 12 ft. high, at 35¢ per sq. yd. — no allowance for openings.

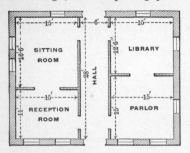

EXPLANATION. — This diagram shows the plan of the rooms on the first floor of a two-story brick house. The dimensions are as follows:

House. — 40 ft. long, 31 ft. wide, and 25 feet high.

Rooms. — As shown in diagram, and of the uniform height of 10 feet.

Doors. — Front, 5 ft. by 8½ ft.; the doors between the parlor and library, and between the reception-room and sitting-room, each 6 ft. by 8 ft.; all others 3 ft. by 7 ft.

Windows. — Front 3½ ft. by 8 ft.; all others 3 ft. by 6 ft.

Baseboards. — Uniformly 9 in. wide.

Second Floor. — Similar to first floor, except no outside doors.

2. Find the cost of plastering the reception-room, walls, and ceiling, at 30¢ a sq. yd., deducting for one half the area of the openings.

3. What will it cost to plaster the walls and ceiling of the sitting-room, at 35¢ a sq. yd., making full deduction for openings?

4. What will be the cost of plastering the walls and ceiling of the library, at 30¢ a sq. yd., deducting for one half the area of the openings?

5. What will be the cost of plastering the walls and ceiling of the parlor on the terms given for plastering the library?

6. Find the cost of kalsomining the ceilings, including the hall, at 8¢ a sq. yd.

7. What will be the total cost of painting the outside brick work of the house, 2 coats, each 8½¢ a sq. yd., deducting for doors and windows?

262. To find the cost of carpeting.

Carpets are commonly either 1 yd. or $\frac{3}{4}$ yd. in width, but matting, oilcloth, and other materials are of various widths.

1. In matching the patterns in carpets there is usually some waste.

2. Sometimes carpets are necessarily made a little too wide and are *turned under*, consequently in computing the cost of carpets the number of strips of carpet must be found.

3. When borders are put around carpets the corners must be counted twice because one half of each corner is wasted in making.

1. A room 36 ft. long and 18 ft. wide is carpeted with ingrain carpet 1 yd. wide without waste in matching. What will be the cost of the carpet at $.85 per lineal yard?

2. If the floor is covered by paper lining at 10¢ per sq. yd., and 5 cents per lineal yd. is charged for laying the carpet, what will be the entire cost of carpeting the room?

3. How many yards of carpet, a yard wide, will be required for a room 24 ft. long and 17 ft. wide, if the strips run lengthwise and there is no waste in matching?

4. What will the carpet cost, at $1.75 per lineal yard, and what will be the entire cost if the floor is first covered with paper lining, at 9¢ per sq. yard?

5. Find the cost of a carpet 27 inches wide, at $1.60 per lineal yard, for a room 15 ft. long and $13\frac{1}{2}$ ft. wide, if the strips run lengthwise. Find the cost, if the strips run across the room.

6. How many yards of carpet 27 in. wide will be required for a room 18 ft. long and 16 ft. wide, if the strips run lengthwise and there is a waste of $\frac{1}{5}$ of a yard in each strip in matching the pattern? What will be the cost of the carpet at $1.85 per lineal yard?

7. Find the cost of a carpet $\frac{3}{4}$ of a yard wide, at $1.62\frac{1}{2}$ per lineal yard, for a room $19\frac{1}{2}$ ft. long and $13\frac{1}{2}$ ft. wide, if the strips run lengthwise, and if there is a waste of $\frac{1}{8}$ of a yard on each strip in matching the pattern.

8. What will be the cost of a rug $2\frac{1}{2}$ yd. by 3 yd., at $ 1.25 per sq. yd., with a border $\frac{3}{4}$ of a yard wide, in addition, at $ .75 per lineal yard ?

263. To find the cost of papering.

Wall paper is sold by the roll, and in computations any part of a roll is considered a whole roll.

A roll is 8 yd. long and 18 in. wide, unless otherwise specified.

1. The width of a roll given above is that commonly used in America, but imported papers differ as to the width and the length of the roll.

2. Paper is often put up in *double* rolls, 16 yd. long, so as to economize the waste in cutting.   Double rolls are counted as 2 rolls each.

3. Borders or friezes are sold by the yard, and vary in width from 3 in. upward.

It is rarely possible to find the exact cost of papering a room, but the following process will approximate accuracy :

Rule. — *Measure the entire distance around the room in yards.   The number of strips will be double the number of yards.*

Find then how many strips can be cut from a roll, and divide the number of strips required to go around the room by the number that can be cut from a roll.   The quotient will be the number of rolls.

1. How many rolls of paper, 8 yd. long and 18 in. wide, will be required to paper the walls of a room 18 ft. long, 15 ft. wide, and having a height of 8 ft. from the baseboard, which is 9 in. high, to the ceiling, allowing for one door 3 ft. by 7 ft., and for two windows, each 3 ft. by 6 ft. ?

2. Find the number of double rolls of paper required to paper the walls of the reception-room described on page 212, making no deductions for doors or windows.

3. Find the number of double rolls of paper required for the walls of the sitting-room described on page 212.

4. Find the number of double rolls of paper required for the walls of the parlor represented in the same diagram.

5. How many double rolls of paper will be required for the walls of the hall shown in the diagram, making full deductions for the openings?

6. What will be the cost of papering the parlor represented on page 212, at $1.20 per roll for paper and putting it on, with a border or a frieze 18 in. wide, at $.50 per yard for the border and putting it on, allowing one half the area of the openings?

264. To compute the expense of paving.

Find the cost of paving:

1. A sidewalk 5 ft. wide, 40 ft. long, at 25¢ per sq. ft.

2. A sidewalk 36 ft. long, 5 ft. 6 in. wide, with brick, at $1.35 a sq. yd., the bricks to be laid on edge.

3. A courtyard 20 ft. by 24 ft. 9 in., with bricks laid flat in sand, at 80¢ a sq. yd.

4. How much less would it cost to make a brick sidewalk 4½ ft. wide and 260 ft. long, at $1.08 a sq. yd., than to lay a stone walk of the same dimensions, at 22¢ a sq. ft.

265. Brick and stone work.

Stone work is commonly estimated by the *perch*.

1. A perch of stone work is 16½ ft. long, 1½ ft. wide, and 1 ft. thick, or 24¾ cubic feet.

2. It is customary in many places to reckon masonry by the *cubic foot* instead of by the perch.

3. In estimating the work of laying stone and brick the corners are commonly doubled, but not in computing the quantity of material used.

4. Usually a deduction is made for one half of the openings.

5. A cubic foot of wall contains about 22 common bricks; hence, a wall contains 22 bricks for each square foot of face, if 12 in. thick, and 7 bricks more per square foot for each additional 4 in. in thickness; but as bricks vary, computation must be made for each size.

1. How many common bricks are there in a wall 20 ft. long, 6 ft. high, and 12 in. thick ?

2. What will it cost to build a wall 38 ft. long, 7 ft. high, and 16 in. wide, if built of common bricks at an expense of $ 11 per M, allowance being made for a gate 10 ft. wide ?

3. How many perches of stone will be required to build the walls of a cellar 36 ft. long and 24 ft. wide, the walls to be 8 ft. high and 18 in. thick, deducting 96 cu. ft. for openings ?

4. How much should a mason receive for building the walls of the above cellar, if he charges $ 1.60 a perch for his labor ?

5. At 27¢ per cubic foot, how much must be paid for building the walls of a cellar that is 44 ft. long and 38 ft. wide ; the walls to be 8 ft. high and 2 ft. thick, no allowance being made for openings ?

6. What will it cost to build of common bricks a house 32 ft. long, 30 ft. wide, and 25 ft. high, the walls being 16 in. thick, when brick costs $ 8.50 per M, and laying the brick is paid for at the rate of $ 2 per M, making full deductions for two doors, each 7 ft. by 3½ ft., and 12 windows, each 6 ft. by 3 ft. ?

266. **To find the quantity of wood.**

A cord of wood or stone is a quantity of material 8 ft. long, 4 ft. wide, and 4 ft. thick, or 128 cu. ft.

How many cords of wood are there in the following :

1. In a pile 18 ft. long, 4 ft. wide, and 6 ft. high ?

2. In a pile 23 ft. long, 4 ft. wide, and 4½ ft. high?

3. In a pile 28 ft. long, 3½ ft. wide, and 4 ft. high ?

4. In a pile 15 ft. long, 5 ft. wide, and 7 ft. high ?

5. A man bought a pile of wood 9 ft. long, 4 ft. wide, and $4\frac{1}{2}$ ft. high, at \$3.50 per cord. How much did it cost him?

6. What will be the cost of a pile of stones 25 ft. long, 4 ft. wide, and 5 ft. high, at \$3.80 per cord?

7. A man bought 5 loads of wood, each load 7 ft. long, $3\frac{1}{2}$ ft. wide, and 4 ft. high. What did it all cost at \$3.75 a cord?

8. How many cords of stone are there in a pile 75 ft. long, 4 ft. wide, and $5\frac{1}{2}$ ft. high?

9. How many cords of wood can be placed in a shed 24 ft. long, 20 ft. wide, and 16 ft. high?

267. To measure lumber.

In measuring lumber, boards 1 inch thick or less are estimated by the square foot of surface.

Thus, a board 1 foot wide and 15 feet long would contain 15 square feet, or 15 feet *board measure*, if the board were 1 inch or less in thickness.

When lumber is more than 1 inch in thickness, the number of feet board measure is obtained by multiplying the length in feet by the breadth in feet, and this product by the number of inches in thickness.

Thus, the number of feet *board measure* in a timber 18 feet long, 15 in. wide, and $2\frac{1}{4}$ in. thick is obtained as follows:

$$18 \text{ ft.} \times 1\frac{1}{4} \times 2\frac{1}{4} = 50\frac{5}{8} \text{ ft.}$$

The width of a board that tapers uniformly is measured at the middle, thus securing the average width.

The average width is one half the sum of the two ends.

How many feet are there in the following boards:

1. 12 ft. long, 15 in. wide.   **3.** 16 ft. long, 18 in. wide.

2. 15 ft. long, 14 in. wide.   **4.** 20 ft. long, 9 in. wide.

How many board feet are there in the following timbers?

5. 30 ft. by 15 in., and 4 in. thick.

6. 28 ft. by 14 in., and 6 in. thick.

7. 24 ft. long and 9 in. square.

8. What will be the cost of 25 joists 20 ft. long, 16 in. wide, and $3\frac{1}{2}$ in. thick, at $15 per M ?

9. What will be the cost of 20 planks 18 ft. long, 16 in. wide, and $2\frac{1}{2}$ in. thick, at $18 per M ?

10. What will be the cost of a board 20 feet long, 22 in. wide at one end and 16 in. at the other, and $1\frac{1}{2}$ in. thick, at $25 per M ?

268. To find the capacity of bins, etc.

2150.42 cubic inches = 1 bushel.

Find the contents in bushels of the following:

1. A box 3 ft. long, 2 ft. wide, and $2\frac{1}{2}$ ft. high.

2. A box 4 ft. long, $2\frac{1}{2}$ ft. wide, and 3 ft. high.

3. A box 5 ft. long, 3 ft. wide, and $4\frac{1}{3}$ ft. high.

4. How many bushels of grain will a bin hold that is 5 ft. long, $3\frac{1}{2}$ feet wide, and 6 ft. high ?

5. I wish to make a bin 5 ft. square that will contain 100 bushels of grain.   How high must the bin be made ?

6. A wagon-box is 11 ft. long, $3\frac{1}{2}$ ft. wide, and $2\frac{1}{2}$ ft. deep.   How many bushels of grain will fill it even full ?

269. To find the capacity of cisterns.

231 cubic inches = 1 gallon.

$31\frac{1}{2}$ gallons = 1 barrel.

Find the contents of the following:

1. A tank 3 ft. by 4 ft., and 5 ft. deep.

2. A tank $3\frac{1}{2}$ ft. by 4 ft., and 4 ft. deep.

3. A tank 4 ft. by $4\frac{1}{2}$ ft., and $5\frac{3}{4}$ ft. deep.

4. A tank $5\frac{1}{8}$ ft. by 6 ft., and $6\frac{1}{2}$ ft. deep.

5. How many gallons will a cistern contain that is 5 ft. square and 8 ft. deep?

6. How many barrels of water will a circular cistern 6 ft. in diameter and 8 ft. deep hold?

SUGGESTION. — The area of the bottom may be found by Art. 260. That multiplied by the depth will be the volume.

7. How many barrels would be required to fill a circular cistern 8 ft. in diameter and 16 ft. deep?

270. Approximate measurements.

1. A bushel is nearly $1\frac{1}{4}$ cu.ft. Hence $\frac{4}{5}$ of the number of cubic feet is very nearly the number of bushels.

2. A cubic foot of any liquid contains nearly $7\frac{1}{2}$ gallons; a barrel of $31\frac{1}{2}$ gallons about $4\frac{1}{5}$ cu. ft.

3. A ton of fine hay in a well-settled large stack, or mow, is about 450 cu. ft. A ton of clover hay is about 550 cu. ft.

A ton of Lehigh stove coal is about $34\frac{1}{2}$ cu. ft.

A ton of Schuylkill white ash stove coal is about 35 cu. ft.

A ton of red ash stove coal is about 36 cu. ft.

1. About how many bushels of grain will a box 4 ft. long, 3 ft. wide, and 5 ft. high hold?

2. A watering trough is 8 ft. long, 14 in. wide, and 12 in. deep. About how many gallons will it hold?

3. A tank 6 ft. square and 8 ft. deep will hold about how many barrels?

4. About how many tons of fine hay can be packed in a mow 20 ft. by 18 ft., and 8 ft. high?

5. How many tons, approximately, of clover hay are there in a stack 20 ft. long, 15 ft. wide, and 12 ft. high?

6. How many tons of Lehigh stove coal can be put in a bin 12 ft. long, 8 ft. wide, and 6 ft. deep? How many tons of Schuylkill white ash stove coal? How many tons of red ash stove coal?

GENERAL REVIEW EXERCISES.

271. 1. If 3 pears cost $5\frac{2}{5}$ cents, what will 5 pears cost at the same rate? What will 8 pears cost?

2. If 5 peaches cost $6\frac{2}{3}$ cents, what will 9 peaches cost at the same rate? What will 20 cost?

3. How much will 7 oranges cost at the rate of 6 oranges for $6\frac{6}{7}$ cents?

4. If 8 books are worth $\$11\frac{1}{5}$, what are 10 books worth at the same rate? What are 20 worth at the same rate?

5. If 9 ducks cost $\$6\frac{3}{7}$, what will 14 cost?

6. If 4 pigs cost $\$13\frac{1}{4}$, how much will 12 pigs cost at the same rate? How much will 16 cost?

7. How many sheep can be bought for $\$56$ when 4 sheep cost $\$14$?

8. A man gave $\$72$ for potatoes, at the rate of $\$8$ for $9\frac{1}{3}$ bushels. How many bushels did he buy?

9. How much must be paid for 22 yards of ribbon at the rate of 5 yards for $7\frac{8}{11}$ dimes?

10. What must be paid for 8 shovels when 5 shovels are sold for $\$3\frac{1}{4}$?

11. If $\frac{4}{5}$ of a barrel of flour costs $\$5$, what will 7 barrels cost? What will 10 barrels cost?

12. Mr. A gave $\frac{1}{5}$ of his month's salary for a coat and $\frac{1}{4}$ for board, and had $\$33$ left. What was his salary?

13. One third of the trees in an orchard bear apples, $\frac{1}{4}$ peaches, and all the other trees, which are 30, bear plums. How many trees are there in the orchard?

14. If $\frac{3}{8}$ of a ship is worth $15000, how much is $\frac{5}{8}$ of it worth?

15. Harry spent 80 cents for a book, which was $\frac{10}{12}$ of his money; with the remainder he bought oranges at 2 cents apiece. How many oranges did he buy?

16. A farmer bought a quantity of goods and paid $30 cash, which was $\frac{3}{5}$ of the value of the goods. How many cords of wood, at $3\frac{1}{3}$ per cord, will it take to pay for the remainder?

17. If 7 men can do a piece of work in $10\frac{2}{7}$ days, how long will it take 9 men to do the same work?

18. It required 6 days for 20 men to load a vessel. How many men would be required to load it in $2\frac{1}{2}$ days?

19. If it costs $40 to support a family of 8 persons for $2\frac{1}{2}$ weeks, what will it cost to support 11 persons 4 weeks?

20. Mr. B paid $\frac{1}{2}$ of his money for a horse, $\frac{1}{4}$ of the remainder for a suit of clothes, $\frac{1}{3}$ of the remainder for provisions, and had $60 left. How much money had he at first?

21. Three men engage to husk a field of corn. The first can do it in 10 days, the second in 12, and the third in 15 days. In what time can they do it together?

22. One half of Charles's money equals $\frac{4}{7}$ of Henry's, and Charles has $12 more than Henry. How much has each?

23. If a pole 12 ft. long casts a shadow 17 ft. long, what is the length of a pole which casts a shadow 85 ft. long at the same time?

24. A man bought a horse and carriage for $400, and the horse cost $\frac{3}{5}$ as much as the carriage. What was the cost of each?

25. At a certain election the successful candidate had a majority of 100, which was $\frac{1}{19}$ of all the votes cast. How many votes did the defeated candidate receive?

26. A, B, and C together have $2700. How much has each, if A has $3\frac{1}{2}$ times as much as B, and C as much as A and B together?

27. How many square feet are there in the surface of a cube whose dimensions are 3 inches?

28. Three men can do a piece of work in 5 days. The first can do it in 15 days, and the second can do it in 20 days. How long will it take the third to do it?

29. Three men bought a thrashing machine for $560. The first paid for $\frac{1}{4}$ of it, the second for $\frac{1}{3}$ of it, and the third paid for the rest. What should the third receive as his share of the profits, if they gained $300?

30. A lad spent on July 4th $\frac{1}{2}$ of his money and 6 cents more for firecrackers, and $\frac{1}{3}$ of it and 4 cents more for torpedoes. If that was all the money he had, how much had he?

SUGGESTION. — $\frac{1}{2}$ of his money and 6 cents, plus $\frac{1}{3}$ of it and 4 cents, is $\frac{5}{6}$ of it and 10 cents, which was equal to the whole of his money.

31. While A earns $3, B earns $4, and C earns $5. At the end of a certain time the earnings of all were $60. How much had each earned?

32. John bought a certain number of oranges at the rate of 4 for 5 cents, and sold them at the rate of 3 for 4 cents. He gained 25 cents. How many did he buy?

33. A fox is 90 rods before a hound, and runs 12 rods while the hound runs 13. How far will the fox run before he is overtaken?

34. One third of a certain number is 12 more than $\frac{1}{4}$ of it. What is the number?

35. If to a certain number you add $\frac{1}{4}$ of itself and $\frac{1}{5}$ of itself, the sum will be 87. What is the number?

36. An octavo book contains 480 pages. How many reams of paper will it require to print an edition of 1600 copies, making no allowance for waste?

37. Two men divided a lot of wood which they had purchased together for $45. One took 7 cords, and the other took 8 cords. What ought each to pay?

38. A and B hired a pasture for $30. A put in 4 horses for 5 weeks, and B 5 horses for 6 weeks. How much ought each to pay?

39. If to a certain number you add 17 more than $\frac{5}{8}$ of itself, the sum will be 82. What is the number?

40. R and W can do a piece of work in 15 days. If R does $\frac{2}{3}$ as much as W, in how many days can each do it alone?

41. A, B, and C own 720 acres of land. How much has each if A owns 3 times as much as C, and B 4 times as much as C?

42. S, T, and V have $580. How much has each if S has $\frac{2}{3}$ as much as V, and T has $\frac{3}{4}$ as much as V?

43. If 3 men or 5 boys can do a piece of work in 20 days, how long will it take 4 men and 10 boys to do it?

44. A certain piece of work can be done by 5 men or by 8 boys in 12 days. In how many days can 5 men and 8 boys do it?

45. A farmer put his grain into four bins. Into the first he put $\frac{3}{8}$ of it, into the second $\frac{1}{4}$, into the third $\frac{1}{5}$, and into the fourth 56 bushels. How many bushels of grain had he?

46. A man paid $36 for a cow, and $\frac{5}{6}$ of the price paid for the cow was $\frac{2}{9}$ of the cost of a horse. What did the horse cost?

47. A man in trade lost $\frac{2}{5}$ of the money he invested, after which he gained $700; he then had $3400. What was his total loss?

48. I paid $1.50 for flour at the rate of $6 a barrel. How many pounds did I get?

49. A pole whose length is 76 feet was broken into two parts, so that ⅘ of the first part was equal to ⅝ of the second part. What was the length of each part?

50. A man owning ¼ of a vessel sold ¾ of what he owned for $1200. What was the value of the vessel at that rate?

51. I have 8 lots, 5 of which are each 7 rods square, and the others contain each 10 square rods. How many square rods of land do I own?

52. How many square inches of surface has a cubical block whose dimensions are each 6 inches?

WRITTEN EXERCISES.

272. 1. If 36 sheep are worth $95, what are 60 sheep worth at the same rate?

2. If 14 men can build a house in 30 days, how long would it take 30 men to build it?

3. If 48 rods of ditching cost $72, what will 142 rods cost at the same rate?

4. At the rate of 840 miles in 24 hours, how far will a train of cars go in 19 hours?

5. If 120 acres of land produce 2520 bushels of wheat, how many bushels will 160 acres produce?

6. If 21 acres produce 35 tons of hay, how many acres will it require to produce 100 tons?

7. If 18¾ yards of cloth cost $38.50, what will 40½ yards of the same cloth cost?

8. If 36 men earn $234 in 5 days, how many men will earn $65 in the same time?

9. If the charges for transporting 19 cwt. of boxed goods from Harrisburg to Philadelphia are $7.03, what will it cost to transport 36 cwt. ?

10. If 26 acres of land cost $1200, how much will 140 acres cost?

11. If 26 acres of land are sold for $1200, how many acres can be bought for $5000 at the same rate ?

12. If it costs $120 to transport 1¼ tons of freight 590 miles, what will it cost to transport 2½ tons 400 miles ?

13. If 25 bushels of oats last 16 sheep 13 weeks, how long will twice as many bushels last half as many sheep ?

14. How many kegs of nails, @ $3⅓ a keg, can I get for 28 barrels of sweet potatoes @ $1.75 per barrel ?

15. What is ¾ of an acre of land worth, if ⅞ of an acre is worth $80 ?

16. If ⁵⁄₁₇ of a vessel is worth $17,000, how much is ⅞ of it worth ? How much is the whole vessel worth ?

17. A farmer paid $50.36 for building 38⅔ rods of stone wall. How much will it cost him to build 75 rods?

18. How many pounds of butter, at 24 cents a pound, must be given in exchange for 186 yards of muslin which is sold at the rate of 15 yards for a dollar ?

19. A farmer bought 65 sheep, at $3¼ apiece, and paid for them in hay, at $9½ per ton. How many tons of hay was he obliged to give in exchange for the sheep ?

20. How many acres of land, at $45 per acre, can I get for 96 oxen, at an average price of $42½ per head ?

21. E and F together own 26,750 acres of land. How many acres does each own, if 12 times E's portion equals 13 times F's ?

22. A, B, and C own 97,937 pounds of cotton. How much has each, if A owns 7 times as much as C, and B 9 times as much as C ?

23. The sum of two numbers is 9232, and their difference is 427. What are the numbers?

24. The sum of two fractions is $\frac{157}{164}$, and their difference is $\frac{16}{41}$. What are the two fractions?

25. A man has two farms worth $20,491. The first farm is worth $\frac{5}{6}$ as much as the second, plus $1560. What is the value of each farm?

26. Seven times John's property, plus $32,200, equals 21 times his property. How much is he worth?

27. If twice a number is increased by $\frac{5}{18}$ of the number, and 2691 more, the sum will be three times the number. What is the number?

28. If 5 times a number is diminished by $\frac{2}{7}$ of the number, and 1265 more, the result will be 4 times the number. What is the number?

29. What will 23 acres 8 square chains of land cost at $37.50 per acre?

30. A farm in the form of a trapezoid contained 100 acres, and its parallel sides were respectively 80 rd. and 120 rd. What was the distance between the parallel sides?

31. How many barrels of water will a cylindrical cistern hold, whose diameter on the bottom is 6 ft., and whose height is 6 ft.?

32. A pile of wood 63 ft. long, 4 ft. wide, and 8 ft. high was sold at $4.75 per cord. For how much was it sold?

33. How much will it cost to excavate a cellar 35 ft. long, 28 ft. wide, and 6 ft. deep at $.45 per cubic yard?

34. What is the cost of 2 beams of timber each 30 ft. long, 10 in. wide, and 10 in. thick at $30 per M?

35. A cubic foot of water weighs about 62 lb. 8 oz. At that rate how much does a barrel of water weigh?

36. A and B bought a horse for $ 100, of which A paid $ 30 and B $ 70. They sold it so as to gain $ 40. What was each one's share of the gain ?

37. M and N engaged in business. M furnished $ 900, and N $ 700. If they gained $ 320, what was each one's share of the gain ?

38. C can dig a well in 25 days, and C and D in 15 days. How long will it take D to dig what remains after C has dug ¼ of it ?

39. Two men enter into partnership. One furnishes $ 2500 capital, the other $ 2000. They gain $ 900. What is each one's share of the gain ?

40. H and K engage in trade. H furnishes $\frac{7}{17}$ of the capital, and K the remainder. Divide their loss of $ 493 fairly between them.

41. A man receives $ 3 a day for his labor, and pays $ .50 a day for his board. At the expiration of 30 days he receives $ 60. How many days was he idle ?

42. Mr. Samuel Grand purchased from Messrs. Cox & Davis 24 pr. kip boots @ $ 2.50 a pair, 18 pr. kid slippers @ $ 1.80, 36 pr. boys' shoes @ $ 1.20, and 24 pr. overshoes @ $ .45. Make out a receipted bill.

43. Two men hire a pasture for $ 75. One pastures 26 sheep for 9 weeks, the other 37 sheep for 11 weeks. What should each pay ?

44. Three men perform a piece of work. The first works 36 days; the second, 41 days; the third, 45 days. They receive $ 219.60. How much does each get, and what are the daily wages per man ?

45. Two men engaged in the clothing business with a joint capital of $ 5000. The first year's gain was $ 1760, of which one received $ 1056. How much capital did he furnish ?

46. What will it cost to build a wall 42 feet long, 15 ft. high, and 16 in. thick, of common bricks at $11.50 per M, laid in the wall, if an allowance is made for a gate 10 ft. by 10 ft., and the scaffold costs $9.45?

47. There is a wire fence inclosing a circular field 80 rods in diameter. What will be the area of a square field which the same fence will exactly inclose?

48. A, B, and C rent a farm for $300, of which A pays $80, B $100, and C $120. They raise 560 bushels of wheat. What is each man's share of the wheat?

49. A man has $3750, and owes $5275. How much can he pay on the dollar, and what will a man get to whom he owes $480?

50. Fifteen persons agree to purchase a tract of land, but 3 of the company withdrawing, the investment of each is increased $150. What does the land cost?

51. A, B, and C together invest $1200 in mining stocks. A puts in $280, B $365, and C the remainder. They gain $1800. What is the share of each?

52. The difference between two numbers is 17, and $\frac{6}{7}$ of the first equals $\frac{7}{8}$ of the second. What are the numbers?

53. I paid $650 for 3 horses, 6 cows, and 20 sheep. Each horse cost three times as much as each cow, and each cow three times as much as one sheep. How much did I pay for each?

54. A, B, and C gained $700, of which A received $\frac{1}{3}$, B $\frac{1}{4}$, and C the remainder. If the whole capital was 12 times C's gain, what was the capital of each?

55. A man lost $600 of his money, and then gained $\frac{3}{4}$ as much as he had left. He then had $\frac{1}{2}$ as much as he had at first. How much had he at first?

56. A, B, and C formed a partnership. A furnished

$1850, B $1950, and C $2050. They lost $2000. What was each man's share of the loss?

57. A grocer in selling molasses uses as a gallon measure one which lacks $\frac{1}{2}$ pint of being full measure. If he sells molasses by this measure to the value of $350, of how much money has he cheated his customers?

58. Divide the number $12\frac{3}{16}$ into two such parts that the first shall equal the second, plus $2\frac{1}{12}$.

59. A man bought a number of sheep for $225; 10 of them having died, he sold $\frac{4}{5}$ of the remainder for cost, and received $150 for them. How many did he buy?

60. A bankrupt owes one of his creditors $750, another $820, and a third $900. His property amounts to $1500. How much can he pay on the dollar, and how much will each of the creditors receive?

61. Two men together receive $600 for grading. The first furnishes 3 teams for 15 days, and the second 4 teams for 18 days. How much should each man receive?

62. I bought three farms for $15,000. The first cost $400 more than the second, and the third $500 less than the second. What was the cost of each?

63. What will be the cost of the lumber to cover a gable roof 28 ft. by 42 ft. at $18 per M, if the lumber is 1 inch thick? How many slates will be required to cover the roof if 3 slates cover a square foot?

64. A man died insolvent, owing $30,565, and his property was sold at auction for $25,000. How much did his estate pay on the dollar?

65. D, E, and F earned $3936. E earned three times as much as F, and D four times as much as E. How much did each earn?

66. How much cheaper will it be to pave a street $\frac{1}{4}$ of a mile long and 60 ft. wide with asphalt at $.22 per sq. ft., than to pave it with granite blocks at $3.10 per sq. yd.?

67. Three men contract to draw 4815 cords of wood for 50 cents a cord. If one furnished 3 teams, another 4, and another 5, what should each man receive? If it took them 36 days, how much did each team earn per day?

68. How many panels of fence 12 ft. long will it take to inclose a rectangular field 45 rd. long and 36 rd. wide?

69. Four persons rent a farm of 240 A. 96 sq. rd. at $6\frac{1}{2}$ an acre. The first puts in 275 sheep, the second 320, the third 400, and the fourth 495. What rent should each pay?

70. What is the distance around a water wheel if an arc of 18° of its circumference is 1 ft. 9 in. in length? What is its diameter?

71. If 9 men can plow 54 acres in 6 days, how many men can plow 60 acres in 5 days?

72. To find the height of a tree, I erected a stick 3 ft. high, which cast a shadow 1 ft. 9.5 in. The shadow of the tree at the same time was 48 ft. 10 in. What was its height?

73. How many square feet of boards are required for the two gables of a barn 32 ft. wide, the ridge being 8 ft. 6 in. higher than the plates?

74. How much will it cost to build two abutments for a bridge, each 18 ft. long, 12 ft. wide at the bottom, 8 ft. wide at the top, and 11 ft. high, at $2.50 a perch for stone and labor?

75. C and D have the same income. C spends $\frac{11}{12}$ of his, but D, by spending $65 more each year than C, at the end of a year, finds himself $10 in debt. How much does each spend yearly?

76. A man willed his estate worth $8000 as follows: to his wife $\frac{1}{3}$ of his money, to his daughter $\frac{1}{5}$, and to his son $\frac{7}{15}$. If the widow should die, what proportionate share would the son and daughter each receive?

PERCENTAGE.

273. **1.** A merchant lost $4 out of every $100 worth of goods sold on account of bad debts. What part of his sales did he lose?

2. A man spent $5 out of every $10 that he earned. How many hundredths of his earnings did he spend?

3. A company of soldiers engaged in battle lost 1 out of every 10 men. How many was that *per hundred* or *per cent?*

4. In a school 6 out of every 10 pupils are girls. How many hundredths of the number are girls? What per cent?

5. What is $\frac{5}{100}$, or 5 per cent, of $500? Of $1000? Of $2000? Of $3000? Of $5000?

6. What is $\frac{2}{100}$, or 2 per cent, of $400? Of $600? Of $1000? Of $1200? Of $1600?

7. What is 6 per cent of $600? Of $800? Of $1000?

274. The expression **Per Cent** means *by the hundred.*
It is a contraction of the Latin *per centum*, by the hundred.

275. The commercial **Sign of Per Cent** is %.
Thus, 8% is read 8 per cent.

276. That part of arithmetic which treats of processes involving per cent is termed **Percentage.**

277. Since per cent is a number of hundredths, it is usually expressed as a decimal.

It may also be expressed as a common fraction.   Thus,

5 per cent is written   5%,   .05, $\frac{5}{100}$.

10 per cent is written   10%,   .10, $\frac{10}{100}$.

12½ per cent is written 12½%, .12½, .125, $\frac{12\frac{1}{2}}{100}$.

⅗ per cent is written $\frac{3}{5}$%, .00⅗, .006, $\frac{\frac{3}{5}}{100}$ or $\frac{3}{500}$.

215 per cent is written 215%, 2.15.

278. Express decimally :

1. 10%.	7. 6¼%.	13. 125%.	19. $\frac{3}{4}$%.
2. 15%.	8. 8½%.	14. 132%.	20. $\frac{3}{5}$%.
3. 20%.	9. 12¾%.	15. 148%.	21. $\frac{7}{10}$%.
4. 25%.	10. 18⅛%.	16. 210%.	22. $\frac{9}{20}$%.
5. 50%.	11. 17⅝%.	17. 275%.	23. $\frac{5}{8}$%.
6. 75%.	12. 25⅞%.	18. 287½%.	24. $\frac{21}{25}$%.

279. Express by common fractions in their lowest terms :

1. 20%	7. 16⅔%.	13. 150%.	19. $\frac{5}{8}$%.
2. 35%.	8. 33⅓%.	14. 165%.	20. $\frac{3}{4}$%.
3. 42%.	9. 37½%.	15. 175%.	21. $\frac{7}{10}$%.
4. 56%.	10. 62½%.	16. 180%.	22. $\frac{11}{20}$%.
5. 75%.	11. 83⅓%.	17. 225%.	23. $\frac{17}{25}$%.
6. 85%.	12. 87½%.	18. 375%.	24. $\frac{49}{50}$%.

280. Express in per cent decimally:

1. $\frac{1}{2}$.	5. $\frac{1}{3}$.	9. $\frac{2}{5}$.	13. $\frac{7}{8}$.	17. $\frac{2}{3}$.
2. $\frac{1}{4}$.	6. $\frac{1}{6}$.	10. $\frac{3}{4}$.	14. $\frac{5}{12}$.	18. $\frac{5}{16}$.
3. $\frac{1}{5}$.	7. $\frac{1}{8}$.	11. $\frac{7}{10}$.	15. $\frac{1}{15}$.	19. $\frac{9}{25}$.
4. $\frac{1}{10}$.	8. $\frac{3}{8}$.	12. $\frac{3}{7}$.	16. $\frac{4}{9}$.	20. $\frac{13}{40}$.

Problems in percentage involve the following elements:

281. The number of which the per cent is to be found, or the **Base**.

282. The number of hundredths taken, or the **Rate**.

283. The number which is a certain number of hundredths of the base, or the **Percentage**.

284. The sum of the base and percentage, or the **Amount**.

285. The base less the percentage, or the **Difference**.

In the formulas, B represents the base; R, the rate; P, the percentage; A, the amount; and D, the difference.

286. To find the percentage when the base and rate are given.

Find:

$$1. \quad 10\% \text{ or } \tfrac{10}{100} \text{ or } \tfrac{1}{10} \text{ of } \$150.$$

$$2. \quad 25\% \text{ or } \tfrac{25}{100} \text{ or } \tfrac{1}{4} \text{ of } \$320.$$

$$3. \quad 50\% \text{ or } \tfrac{50}{100} \text{ or } \tfrac{1}{2} \text{ of } \$600.$$

$$4. \quad 12\tfrac{1}{2}\% \text{ or } \frac{12\frac{1}{2}}{100} \text{ or } \tfrac{1}{8} \text{ of } \$160.$$

Find:

5. 40% of 250 tons.	7. $33\frac{1}{3}\%$ of 660 lb.
6. 15% of 300 mi.	8. 60% of 200 rd.

9. 20% of 200 bu.

10. 30% of 400 gal.

11. 50% of 400 A.

12. 25% of 800 yd.

13. 65% of 500 bricks.

14. 75% of 600 sheep.

15. 80% of 120 horses.

16. 90% of 360 days.

WRITTEN EXERCISES.

1. What is $12\frac{1}{2}\%$ of $864.80?

EXPLANATION. — Since $12\frac{1}{2}\%$ of a number is $.12\frac{1}{2}$ of it, $12\frac{1}{2}\%$ of $864.80 is $.12\frac{1}{2}$ of $864.80, or $108.10.

$$\$864.80 \times .12\frac{1}{2} = \$108.10,$$
or
$$\frac{1}{8} \text{ of } \$864.80 = \$108.10.$$

Or,

Since $12\frac{1}{2}\%$ of a number is $\frac{12\frac{1}{2}}{100}$, or $\frac{1}{8}$ of it, $12\frac{1}{2}\%$ of $864.80 is $\frac{1}{8}$ of $864.80, which is $108.10.

FORMULA, $\qquad B \times R = P.$

Find:

2. 15% of $975.40.

3. 50% of $858.50.

4. $\frac{1}{2}\%$ of $576.40.

5. $37\frac{1}{2}\%$ of $1260.

6. 125% of $1864.

7. $1\frac{3}{4}\%$ of $2520.

8. A man bought 350 cows, and then sold 60% of them. How many cows had he left?

9. A farmer had 375 acres of land, and sold $33\frac{1}{3}\%$ of it. How much remained?

10. B bought 3480 barrels of flour, and then sold $16\frac{2}{3}\%$ of it. How many barrels remained?

11. C, having a flock of 575 sheep, sold 64% of them. How many had he left?

12. A man's income is $900 a year, and he spends $67\frac{1}{2}\%$ of it. How much does he spend?

13. D bought 1320 acres of land, and sold $37\frac{1}{2}\%$ of it. How much had he left?

14. In a school of 400 pupils, $62\frac{1}{2}\%$ are boys. How many boys are there in the school?

15. How much metal will be obtained from 375 tons of ore if the metal is $10\frac{1}{2}\%$ of the ore?

16. A farm cost $\$4750$, but since it was purchased the farm has decreased $16\frac{1}{2}\%$ in value. What is the present value of the farm?

17. If cloth will shrink $5\frac{1}{2}\%$ of its length in sponging, what will be the shrinkage of a piece of cloth containing 42 yards before sponging?

18. If a man's salary is $\$1350$ a year, and his expenses are $87\frac{1}{2}\%$ of that sum, how much can he save yearly?

19. A man having $\$27,000$, invested 18% in bank stock, $12\frac{1}{2}\%$ in bonds and mortgages, 34% in town property, and the rest in a farm. How much did the farm cost?

20. Mr. B receives a salary of $\$1800$ a year. He pays 15% of it for board, $8\frac{1}{3}\%$ for clothing, and 16% for other expenses. What are his yearly expenses, and how much does he save?

21. A man bequeathed 15% of his estate to a college, 10% to an asylum, 10% to a church, 5% to a public library, and the remainder he divided equally among his 7 children. What did each child receive, the estate being worth $\$150,000$?

287. To find the rate when the base and percentage are given.

1. What part of 25 is 5? How many hundredths of 25 is 5? What per cent?

2. What part of 40 is 4? How many hundredths? What per cent?

3. What part of 60 is 15 ? How many per cent ?

4. What per cent of 35 is 7 ? Of 50 is 10 ?

What per cent of

5. 24 is 12 ?	11. $50 are $30 ?	17. $\frac{4}{5}$ is $\frac{2}{5}$?
6. 36 is 12 ?	12. 60 qt. are 15 qt. ?	18. $\frac{5}{7}$ is $\frac{3}{7}$?
7. 40 is 8 ?	13. 75 gal. are 25 gal. ?	19. $\frac{8}{11}$ is $\frac{4}{11}$?
8. 50 is 20 ?	14. 64 bu. are 16 bu. ?	20. $\frac{5}{10}$ is $\frac{4}{10}$?
9. 80 is 40 ?	15. 72 lb. are 36 lb. ?	21. $\frac{15}{37}$ is $\frac{5}{37}$?
10. 90 is 30 ?	16. 96 ft. are 32 ft. ?	22. $\frac{1}{2}$ is $\frac{1}{4}$?

23. A farmer who had 40 sheep, sold 15. What per cent did he sell ? What per cent remained unsold ?

24. From a farm of 150 acres, 30 acres were sold. What per cent of it was sold ? What per cent remained unsold ?

WRITTEN EXERCISES.

1. A merchant who had 450 yd. of muslin sold 150 yd. What per cent of it did he sell ?

SOLUTION. — 150 yd. = $\frac{150}{450}$, or $\frac{1}{3}$, or $33\frac{1}{3}$ % of 450 yd.

Or,

1% of 450 yd. = 4.5 yd.

∴ 150 yd. is as many per cent of 450 yd. as 4.5 yd. is contained times in 150 yd., or $33\frac{1}{3}$ %.

FORMULA, $P \div B = R.$

What per cent of

2. 840 men are 420 men ?	8. 680 rd. are 510 rd. ?
3. 450 hr. are 150 hr. ?	9. 876 gal. are 584 gal. ?
4. 560 min. are 140 min. ?	10. $\frac{3}{7}$ is $\frac{2}{14}$?
5. 720 bu. are 120 bu. ?	11. $\frac{5}{8}$ is $\frac{3}{16}$?
6. 540 A. are 210 A. ?	12. $\frac{6}{27}$ is $\frac{1}{3}$?
7. 450 T. are 300 T. ?	13. $\frac{5}{10}$ is $\frac{1}{5}$?

14. A sheep grower sold 75 sheep from a flock of 300. What per cent of the flock did he sell ?

15. Out of 350 words a student spelled 329 correctly. What % of the words were spelled correctly?

16. A fruit grower transplanted 275 peach trees, and 40 of them died. What % of them died?

17. A farmer raised 250 bushels of oats, and sold all but 65 bushels. What % of his crop did he sell?

18. In a journey of 1560 miles, Mr. D traveled 195 miles by stage, and the rest of the distance by rail. What % of the distance did he travel by rail?

19. A grocer having on hand 1200 pounds of sugar, sold $\frac{1}{5}$ of it at one time, and $\frac{1}{3}$ of the remainder at another time. What % of the whole remained unsold?

20. A farmer raised 560 bushels of grain. He sold A 140 bushels; $\frac{1}{3}$ of the remainder he sold to B, and $\frac{3}{8}$ of what still remained to C. What % of the whole had he left?

21. A farmer raised 120 bushels of potatoes from 4 bushels of seed. What % of the crop was the seed?

22. A man paid \$15 for the use of land which cost \$275. What % does the land owner realize on his investment?

23. A gentleman, finding that he was constantly growing deeper in debt, to save his creditors, made an assignment. His property was worth \$5765.85, and his debts amounted to \$7125. What % was paid to the creditors?

24. A man's salary is \$4000. He spends 22% for fuel and rent, 12% for clothing, 3% for books, and \$1018 for other purposes. What % of his salary has he left?

288. To find the base when the percentage and rate are given.

1. Of what sum is \$10 25% or $\frac{25}{100}$ or $\frac{1}{4}$?

2. Of what sum is 40 20% or $\frac{20}{100}$ or $\frac{1}{5}$?

3. Of what number is 80 40% or $\frac{40}{100}$ or $\frac{2}{5}$?

4. Of what number is 30 12$\frac{1}{2}$% or $\frac{1}{8}$?

Find the number of which:

5. 20 is 20%.	**11.** 50 is 25%.	**17.** $\frac{2}{3}$ is 50%.
6. 45 is 5%.	**12.** 60 is 60%.	**18.** $\frac{3}{4}$ is 25%.
7. 60 is 1%.	**13.** 60 is 75%.	**19.** $\frac{5}{7}$ is 12$\frac{1}{2}$%.
8. 25 is $\frac{1}{2}$%.	**14.** 30 is 16$\frac{2}{3}$%.	**20.** $\frac{3}{10}$ is 33$\frac{1}{3}$%.
9. 40 is 10%.	**15.** 80 is 66$\frac{2}{3}$%.	**21.** .5 is 10%.
10. 40 is 40%.	**16.** 210 is 87$\frac{1}{2}$%.	**22.** .05 is $\frac{1}{2}$%.

23. My expenses were $400, which sum was 62$\frac{1}{2}$% of my income. How much was my income?

24. A fire destroyed 33$\frac{1}{3}$% of a stock of goods, and the value of the goods destroyed was $2000. What was the value of the entire stock?

25. The attendance at a school was 35 less than the whole number of pupils enrolled, and the absentees were 25% of the enrollment. How many pupils attended the school?

WRITTEN EXERCISES.

1. A magazine contained 36 pages of advertisements, which was 30% of the whole number of pages. How many pages were there in the magazine?

SOLUTION.

30% or $\frac{30}{100}$ or $\frac{3}{10}$ of the number of pages = 36.

∴ $\frac{1}{10}$ of the number of pages = 12.

And the whole number of pages = 120.

Or,

30% of the number of pages = 36.

∴ 1% of the number of pages = $\frac{1}{30}$ of 36, or 1.2.

And the whole number of pages = 100 times 1.2, or 120.

FORMULA, $P \div R = B.$

Find the number of which:

2. 102 is 24%.	9. 7.5 is $\frac{3}{4}$%.	16. 86.5 is $16\frac{2}{3}$%.
3. 228 is $9\frac{1}{2}$%.	10. 11.8 is $\frac{5}{6}$%.	17. 45 is 1.5%.
4. 8.25 is $2\frac{1}{2}$%.	11. 817 is 19%.	18. $\frac{3}{8}$ is $1\frac{1}{3}$%.
5. 55.9 is 13%.	12. .96 is $\frac{1}{2}$%.	19. $\frac{5}{7}$ is 7.5%.
6. 798 is $33\frac{1}{3}$%.	13. 2.17 is $3\frac{1}{2}$%.	20. 36 is $\frac{3}{4}$%.
7. 896 is 112%.	14. 812 is 175%.	21. 44 is .4%.
8. 981 is 90%.	15. 1250 is 200%.	22. 7 is $2\frac{1}{3}$%.

23. A farmer sold 786 bushels of potatoes, which were 75% of his entire crop. How many bushels did he raise?

24. A merchant sold 25% of his goods for $6650. At this rate what were the goods worth?

25. If a man rents a house for $520 per annum, which is 13% of the value of the property, what is its value?

26. A farmer sold 315 bushels of wheat, which was 30% of his crop. What was his entire crop?

27. A man spends $1239 a year, which is 84% of his salary. What is his salary?

28. A teacher spends 65% of his income, and can thus save $420. What is his income?

29. Mr. Rook sold a horse for $225, which was 90% of what he paid for it. What did the horse cost him?

30. A merchant-vessel has 289 tons of leather on board, which is 17% of the whole cargo. How many tons of cargo does she carry?

31. The distance between two stations on a certain railroad is 14.5 miles, which is $12\frac{1}{2}$% of the whole length of the road. What is the length of the road?

32. An assignee paid off debts to the amount of $870, which was $33\frac{1}{3}\%$ of the total indebtedness. What was the total indebtedness?

33. Into a vessel containing pure vinegar there were thrown $12\frac{3}{4}$ gallons of water, which was $18\frac{3}{4}\%$ of the dilution. What was the quantity of pure vinegar?

34. On Monday a merchant's sales amounted to $185.70, and that sum was $12\frac{1}{2}\%$ of his sales for the week. How much were his sales for the week?

35. A farmer sold 1240 bushels of corn, which was $62\frac{1}{2}\%$ of the number of bushels raised. How much did he raise?

289. **To find the base when the amount and rate are given.**

1. If a merchant gains 20% of the cost in selling goods, how many per cent of the cost does he get for them?

2. If a sum of money is increased by 25%, or $\frac{1}{4}$ of itself, how many per cent of the original sum will it be? What part?

3. A boy who bought 20% as many marbles as he had, found that he then had 60. How many had he at first?

4. A clerk's wages were increased 10%, and he then received $66 per month. What were his wages before the increase?

What number increased by:

5. 10% of itself $= 55$?

6. 30% of itself $= 26$?

7. 50% of itself $= 48$?

8. 20% of itself $= 60$?

9. 25% of itself $= 50$?

10. $33\frac{1}{3}\%$ of itself $= 60$?

11. $12\frac{1}{2}\%$ of itself $= 90$?

12. $37\frac{1}{2}\%$ of itself $= 77$?

13. $16\frac{2}{3}\%$ of itself $= 56$?

14. 25% of itself $= 2\frac{1}{2}$?

15. 40% of itself $= 2\frac{1}{3}$?

16. 60% of itself $= \frac{8}{9}$?

17. A bookseller sold a book for $1.25, gaining 25% of the cost. What did it cost him?

18. The retail price of molasses is 50 cents per gallon, and the merchant makes a profit upon it of 25% of the cost. What is the cost?

WRITTEN EXERCISES.

1. What number increased by 27% of itself equals 508?

SOLUTION. — Since the number is increased by 27% of itself,

$$127\% \text{ of the number} = 508.$$
$$\therefore 1\% \text{ of the number} = 4.$$
$$\text{And the number} = 400.$$

Or,

$$\tfrac{127}{100} \text{ of the number} = 508.$$
$$\therefore \tfrac{1}{100} \text{ of the number} = 4.$$
$$\text{And the number} = 400.$$

FORMULA, $$B = A \div (1 + R).$$

What number increased by:

2.	12% of itself = 560 ?	7.	16⅔% of itself = 700 ?
3.	17% of itself = 702 ?	8.	2½% of itself = 820 ?
4.	31% of itself = 786 ?	9.	20% of itself = 1620 ?
5.	38% of itself = 966 ?	10.	37½% of itself = 682 ?
6.	62% of itself = 648 ?	11.	100% of itself = 1796 ?

12. A has 372 sheep, which are 20% more than B has. How many sheep has B?

13. A clerk's salary was increased 15%, and now it is $1050. What was his former salary?

14. A farmer raised 750 bushels of corn, which was 50% more than the number of bushels of wheat raised. How many bushels of wheat did he raise?

15. A grocer expended $ 36.48 for vegetables, which was $33\frac{1}{3}\%$ more than he expended for butter and eggs. How much did he expend for butter and eggs ?

16. A drover sold cows and sheep for $ 6105. If he received 65% more for the cows than for the sheep, how much did he get for the cows ?

17. A house cost $ 2072, which is 40% more than a barn cost. What was the cost of the barn ?

18. B bought a farm for a certain sum. He expended for stock 11% of the price of the farm, and found that the cost of both was $ 8214. What did he pay for the farm ?

19. C raised 496 bushels of wheat, which was $33\frac{1}{3}\%$ more than $\frac{2}{3}$ of what D raised. How many bushels did D raise ?

20. The population of a certain town is 8118, which is $12\frac{1}{2}\%$ more than it was three years ago. What was the population then ?

21. A drover sold 275 sheep for $ 1375, which was $37\frac{1}{2}\%$ more than they cost. What did the sheep cost per head ?

22. E bought a farm for $ 7402.50, which was $17\frac{1}{2}\%$ more than F paid for his farm. How much did F pay for his farm ?

290. **To find the base when the difference and rate are given.**

1. If a merchant loses 20% of the cost in selling goods, what per cent of the cost does he get for them ?

2. If a sum of money is decreased by 25%, or $\frac{1}{4}$ of itself, how many per cent of the original sum is it ? What part ?

3. A lad lost 20%, or $\frac{1}{5}$ of his marbles, and found that he had 40 marbles left. How many had he at first ?

4. A clerk whose wages had been reduced 10% was receiving $ 63 per month. What were his wages before the reduction?

What number decreased by

5. 10% of itself = 90 ?	**11.** 30% of itself = 56 ?
6. 20% of itself = 48 ?	**12.** 25% of itself = 60 ?
7. 33⅓% of itself = 80 ?	**13.** 50% of itself = 72 ?
8. 12½% of itself = 70 ?	**14.** 50% of itself = 7½ ?
9. 37½% of itself = 65 ?	**15.** 40% of itself = 4½ ?
10. 16⅔% of itself = 75 ?	**16.** 25% of itself = 2¼₁ ?

17. A merchant who sold his goods at 20% below cost, received 80 cents per yard for silk. What did it cost him?

18. The retail price of bananas was 16 cents per dozen, but the price was 20% below cost. What did they cost?

WRITTEN EXERCISES.

1. What number diminished by 40% of itself equals 432?

SOLUTION. — Since the number is diminished by 40% of itself,

$$\therefore 60\% \text{ of the number} = 432.$$
$$1\% \text{ of the number} = 7.2.$$
$$\text{And the number} = 720.$$

Or,

$$\tfrac{60}{100} \text{ or } \tfrac{3}{5} \text{ of the number} = 432.$$
$$\tfrac{1}{5} \text{ of the number} = 144.$$
$$\text{And the number} = 720.$$

FORMULA, $B = D \div (1 - R).$

What number diminished by

2. 25% of itself = 270 ?	**5.** 15% of itself = 544 ?
3. 50% of itself = 325 ?	**6.** 90% of itself = 12.6 ?
4. 30% of itself = 427 ?	**7.** 4½% of itself = 382 ?

8. A boy spent 25% of his money, and then had $12.36 left. How much had he at first?

9. A clerk after spending 65% of his salary had $385 left. What was his salary?

10. Mr. Kirk sold 340 bushels of wheat, and had 15% of it left. How many bushels had he at first?

11. A clothier sold a suit for $31.20, which was 20% less than the price he asked for it. What was his asking price?

12. A man spent $45.75, and then had 40% of his money left. How much had he at first?

13. The expenses of a firm during the month of November were $185.68. The expenses in November were 12% less than during the month of December. What were the expenses in December?

14. Mr. Hallam deposited 85% of his money in a bank, and afterward drew out 20% of the sum deposited, and then had $3859 in the bank. What was the amount of his money?

15. 35% of a regiment being sick, only 637 men were able to enter battle. How many men were there in the regiment?

16. At a forced sale a bankrupt sold his farm for $7500, which was $33\frac{1}{3}$% less than its real value. What was the value of the farm?

17. A man bought 1785 locust posts, which was $62\frac{1}{2}$% less than the number of chestnut rails purchased. How many chestnut rails did he buy?

18. A merchant's sales on Monday amounted to $385.84. His sales on Monday were $16\frac{2}{3}$% of 54% less than the amount of goods sold on Tuesday. What was the amount of Tuesday's sales?

PROFIT AND LOSS.

291. 1. When 25% is gained, what part is gained?

2. For what must sugar that cost 5 cents per lb. be sold so as to gain 20% of the cost? What is the gain per lb.?

3. A merchant sold goods that cost him 25 cents per yd. at a loss of 10% of the cost. What was the loss?

4. If boots that cost $4 a pair are sold for $5, what part of the cost is gained? What per cent?

5. When I sell butter for 25 cents per lb. that cost 20 cents, what part of the cost do I gain? What per cent?

6. Grain that cost 60 cents per bu. was damaged so that it was sold for 40 cents per bu. What per cent of the cost was lost?

7. Dictionaries that cost $6 were sold for $4. What per cent of the cost was lost?

8. By selling goods at a gain of 5 cents per yd., 25% or ¼ of the cost was gained. What was the cost?

9. Goods were sold at a loss of 20% of the cost. If the loss per yd. was 4 cents, what was the cost per yd.?

10. A grain dealer sold wheat at a gain of 8 cents per bu., which was an advance of 10% of the cost. What was the cost?

11. The loss upon a quantity of damaged books was 25 cents per copy, and that sum was 12½% of the cost. What did they cost apiece?

12. A horse was sold for $75 less than it cost. If the loss was 25% of the cost, what was the cost?

13. Flour was sold at a profit of 12½% of the cost, and the gain per barrel was 80 cents. What did it cost per bbl.?

14. A grocer made a profit of 6 cents per lb. by selling tea at an advance of 20% of the cost. What did it cost?

15. By selling flour at $7 per barrel, $16\frac{2}{3}\%$ of the cost was gained. What did the flour cost?

SOLUTION. — Since $16\frac{2}{3}\%$, or $\frac{1}{6}$ of the cost was gained, the selling price must have been $\frac{7}{6}$ of the cost. Since $\frac{7}{6}$ of the cost was $7, $\frac{1}{6}$ was $\frac{1}{7}$ of $7, or $1. And since $\frac{1}{6}$ of the cost was $1, the entire cost was $6.

16. By selling silk at 90 cents per yd., 10% of the cost was lost. What did the silk cost per yd.?

17. A man's profits upon bicycles was 40% of the cost when he sold them at $140 each. What did they cost?

18. I sold goods at $1.25 per yd., and gained 25% of the cost. What did the goods cost?

19. A tennis outfit cost me $24. If the dealer who sold it made a profit of $33\frac{1}{3}\%$, how much did it cost him?

20. A pair of skates cost a boy $2.50, but the merchant sold them at a gain of 25%. What did they cost him?

21. A coat was sold, at a loss of $16\frac{2}{3}\%$ of the cost, for $15. How much did it cost?

22. A carriage was sold for $25 more than it cost. If that sum was 25% of the cost, what was the cost?

23. A clothier sold a coat for $25 that cost him $20. What per cent of the cost did he gain?

24. A drover averaged a profit of $10 per head upon a drove of cattle. If that was 25% of the cost, what did they cost him per head?

25. A merchant wishes to sell lumber that cost $15 per M at a gain of $33\frac{1}{3}\%$ of the cost. What must he get for it?

26. Furniture that cost $80 was sold at a loss of $12\frac{1}{2}\%$. For how much was it sold?

292. PRINCIPLE. — *Gain or loss is reckoned at a certain per cent of the cost, or sum invested.*

WRITTEN EXERCISES.

1. A grocer bought a hogshead of sugar for $48.93, and sold it at a gain of 15%. What was his gain?

2. A man bought a team for $350, and sold it at a gain of 20%. What did he receive for it?

3. A dealer invested $2460 in shoes, and sold them at a gain of 25%. How much did he gain?

4. A farm was bought for $4675, and sold at a gain of 8%. What was the gain?

5. A piano that cost $215 was sold at a gain of 40%. For how much was it sold?

6. A drover paid $1890 for cattle that he was obliged to sell at a loss of $16\frac{2}{3}\%$. What was the loss?

7. A house that cost $3600 was sold at a gain of 18%. How much was received for it?

8. A merchant sold goods that cost $2180, at a gain of $33\frac{1}{3}\%$. How much did he receive for them?

9. A ship that cost $115,000 was sold at a loss of $12\frac{1}{2}\%$. How much was received for it?

10. I bought 1260 lb. of sugar at $4\frac{1}{4}$¢ a pound, and sold it at a gain of 10%. How much did I sell it for?

11. E bought 2360 bu. of wheat at $.85 per bushel, and sold it at a gain of $18\frac{3}{4}\%$. How much did he get for it?

12. What per cent is gained by selling tea at 70 cents per lb. that cost 60 cents?

SOLUTION. $.70 − $.60 = $.10, gain.

$.10 ÷ $.60 = $16\frac{2}{3}\%$.

Or,

The part of the cost gained is $\frac{10}{60}$, or $\frac{1}{6}$, which is equal to $16\frac{2}{3}\%$.

13. Flour that cost $4.50 per barrel was sold for $4.95 per barrel. What was the gain per cent?

14. A house that cost $3200 was sold for $3680. What was the gain per cent?

15. A man whose salary was $2400 had it increased to $3000. What was the per cent of increase?

16. A dealer paid $650 for 200 tons of coal, and sold it for $780. What was the gain per cent?

17. A merchant bought 350 yards of silk at $1.12½ a yard, and sold it at a profit of $131.25. What per cent did he gain?

18. A merchant bought goods at 20% less than their market value, and sold them at 20% above market value. What was his gain per cent?

19. A horse that cost $145.50 was sold for $194. What was the gain per cent?

20. What is the gain per cent if goods which cost $7500 are sold for $9375?

21. A man paid $6450 for a farm, and spent on improvements a sum equal to 60 per cent of the purchase price. He then sold the farm for $11,868. What was the gain per cent on the whole cost?

22. A horse was sold at an advance of $75, which was a gain of 25%. What was the cost of the horse?

SOLUTION. — 25% or .25 or ¼ of the cost of the horse = $75.

∴ The cost of the horse = $300.

23. A jeweler made $20 on a watch by selling it at a profit of 40%. What did the watch cost?

24. A painting was sold for $3.60 less than cost, which was a loss of 20%. What was the cost?

25. By selling cloth at an advance of 28¢ per yard, I make a profit of 25%. What did it cost?

26. A dealer sold a quantity of wheat at a profit of 12½%, and gained $250. What was the cost of the wheat?

27. A grocer lost 8% by selling 56 pounds of butter for $1.12 less than cost. What did it cost him per pound?

28. A farmer gained 15% by selling land at an advance of $11.25 per acre. What was the cost per acre?

29. A man lost 16⅔% by selling a house for $538 less than cost. What did it cost?

30. The gain on a quantity of lumber was $918.75, which was a profit of 21%. What was the cost of the lumber?

31. A speculator gained $1650 by selling land at a profit of 37½%. What was the cost of the land?

32. A merchant gained in one year $3650 on goods sold at a profit of 20%. What was the cost of the goods?

33. A man bought a farm for $97.75 per acre, which price was 15% more than was previously paid for it. What was the previous price per acre?

SOLUTION. The purchase price = 115% of previous price.

∴ 115% of previous price = $97.75.

1% of previous price = $.85.

∴ The previous price = $85.00.

34. A stationer lost 22% by selling paper at $2.925 per ream. What did it cost him?

SOLUTION. The selling price = 78% of the cost.

∴ 78% of the cost = $2.925.

1% of the cost = $.0375.

∴ The cost = $3.75.

35. A farmer sold a cow for $44.50 and gained 25%. What was the cost of the cow?

36. A city lot was sold for $1260, which was an advance of 12% on its cost. What did it cost?

37. A horse and a wagon were sold for $235, at a gain of $10\frac{1}{2}$%. What did they cost?

38. A merchant sold a bill of goods for $136.44, thereby gaining 20%. What did the goods cost him?

39. A carriage was sold for $361, which was a loss of 5%. What was the cost?

40. A dealer sold some cattle for $980.28, thereby losing 10%. What did they cost him?

41. At a forced sale a house was sold for $4527, which was a loss of $33\frac{1}{3}$%. What was its cost?

42. A stock of goods was sold for $4575, which was a loss of $3\frac{1}{2}$%. What did the goods cost?

43. A bookseller bought books at $12\frac{1}{2}$% discount from the retail price, which was $2 per volume, and sold them at the retail price. What was his gain per cent?

44. A farmer bought 80 acres of land at $50 per acre, and spent $1800 for improvements. How must he sell it per acre so as to gain 15%?

45. A merchant marked cloth at 25% advance on the cost. The goods being damaged, he was obliged to take off 20% of the marked price, selling it at $1 per yard. What was the cost?

46. Mr. H sold two houses for $3600 each. On one he gained 25%, and on the other he lost 25%. How much was gained or lost by the transaction?

47. What per cent is gained in buying coal by the long ton, at $4.50 a ton, and selling it by the short ton, at the same price?

COMMISSION.

293. 1. An agent sells $1000 worth of goods. How much will he receive for his services if he gets 2% of the sales?

2. If an agent purchases $3000 worth of silks, how much will he receive for his services if he gets 3% of the cost of the goods?

3. A planter paid his agent 5% of the sum received for his cotton. If the cotton was sold for $5000, how much did the agent receive for his services, or how much was his *commission*?

4. At 2% commission, what will a man receive for selling property to the value of $800? How much will be left after paying the commission, or how much will be the *net proceeds*?

5. If 2% commission is paid for buying goods, what is the cost of every dollar's worth of goods bought? Since every dollar's worth of goods bought costs the purchaser $1.02, how many dollars' worth can be bought for $102? For $204?

6. How many dollars' worth of goods can be bought for $618, after making allowance for the agent's commission of 3%?

294. A person who buys or sells goods, or transacts business for another, is called a **Commission Merchant,** or **Agent,** or **Broker.**

295. The compensation allowed a commission merchant is called his **Commission** or **Brokerage.**

296. The merchandise sent to a commission merchant to be sold is called a **Consignment.**

297. The person who sends the merchandise is called the **Consignor.**

298. The person to whom the merchandise is sent is called the **Consignee.**

299. The sum left after the commission and expenses have been paid is called the **Net Proceeds.**

300. PRINCIPLE. — *The commission is reckoned at a certain rate per cent upon the value of the sales and purchases.*

WRITTEN EXERCISES.

301. 1. What will be an agent's commission for selling $696 worth of goods at $2\frac{3}{4}\%$?

SOLUTION. — $2\frac{3}{4}\%$ or $.02\frac{3}{4}$ of $696 = $19.14, the commission.

2. If I send my agent $4590 to invest in goods, after deducting his commission of 2%, how much will he invest in goods for me?

SOLUTION. — Since the agent receives a commission of 2% for his services, it requires $1.02 to purchase $1 worth of goods. Therefore, he can purchase as many dollars' worth of goods for me as $1.02 is contained times in $4590, or $4500 worth.

3. An agent sold goods to the amount of $1260. What was his commission at $3\frac{1}{2}\%$?

4. What is the commission at $2\frac{1}{2}\%$ for selling 680 bu. of wheat at $1.10 per bushel?

5. An agent collects $3450. How much is remitted to the employer after deducting 5% commission.

6. A real estate agent was paid $375 for collecting rents. How much did he collect, his commission being 5% ?

7. If $7415 which I send my agent includes what he is to invest in wheat for me and his commission of 2% on the purchase, how many bushels will I get, when wheat is worth $.85 per bu.?

8. My agent has bought 585 bbl. of flour at $4.50 per barrel. His commission is $2\frac{1}{2}\%$. How much money must I remit to pay the cost of the flour and the commission?

9. A commission merchant sold goods to the amount of $4800, charging $3\frac{1}{4}\%$ commission. After paying $25 charges, he invested the balance in raw material, and charged $2\frac{1}{2}\%$ for the investment. How much was invested?

10. A speculator sent $14,616 to his agent in Chicago, which he directed him to invest in wheat. After deducting $1\frac{1}{2}\%$ commission, how many bushels of wheat did he buy at $.90 a bushel?

11. A lawyer collected 80% of a debt of $2360, and charged 5% commission on the sum collected. How much did the creditor receive?

12. A merchant sent his agent in New Orleans $3536.25 to be expended in cotton after deducting his commission of $2\frac{1}{2}\%$. How much was invested in cotton?

13. A commission merchant having sold a consignment of cotton for $2560, retained $100 to pay freight charges amounting to $10.40 and his own commission. What rate per cent commission did he charge?

COMMERCIAL DISCOUNT.

302. A deduction from the price or value of anything is called a **Commercial Discount**.

303. Manufacturers and wholesale dealers issue *price lists*, from which prices various discounts are allowed.

Sometimes several discounts are allowed the purchaser. In such cases, the first discount is to be deducted, then the second is to be computed upon the remainder and deducted, and so on for each successive discount.

Thus, when the discounts allowed are 50%, 10%, and 5%, the 50% is first deducted; from the remainder 10% is deducted; and from that remainder 5% is deducted.

304. The amount of a bill less the discounts is called the **Net Amount**.

WRITTEN EXERCISES.

305. Find the net amounts of the following bills:

1. $450, discounts, 20% and 10%.

2. $760, discounts, 20% and 15%.

3. $840, discounts, 25% and 5%.

4. $976, discounts, 35% and 10%.

5. $8.75, discounts, 10% and 10%.

6. $6.80, discounts, 40% and 5%.

7. $350, discounts, 30% and 15%.

8. $375.20, discounts, 10%, 10%, and 10%.

9. $280.50, discounts, 15%, 10%, and 5%.

10. Find the net amount of a bill of $520, the discounts being 15% and 10%.

11. What is the difference on a bill of $320, between a direct discount of 35% and successive discounts of 20% and 15%?

12. What is the net amount of a bill of $60.80, the discounts being 30% and 10%?

13. What is the net amount of a bill of goods, the list price of which is $345, trade discount 8%, and 5% off for cash?

14. A bill of goods at list prices amounted to $420.65. The discounts were 25% and 10%. What was due on the bill?

15. On a bill of goods amounting to $230, what is the difference between a discount of 45% and successive discounts of 25%, 15%, and 5%?

16. What is the net amount of a bill of $450, discounts being 30%, 10%, and 5%?

17. What is the net amount of a bill of $360, discounts being $12\frac{1}{2}$% and 8%? Find a single discount equivalent to these two successive discounts.

TAXES.

306. 1. If a man pays annually for public purposes 1% of the value of his property, estimated at $ 10,000, what is the amount of his *tax ?*

2. If I am taxed $1\frac{1}{2}$% on land, houses, etc., or *real estate* estimated at $ 8000, what is the amount of my tax?

3. If a man is taxed $1\frac{1}{2}$% on his money, mortgages, cattle, or *personal property*, estimated at $ 5000, what is the amount of his tax ?

307. Fixed property, as land, etc., is called **Real Estate.**

308. Movable property, as money, mortgages, cattle, lumber, etc., is called **Personal Property.**

309. A sum of money assessed upon the persons, property, or business of individuals is called a **Tax.**

1. A tax upon property is reckoned at a certain rate per cent upon the estimated or assessed value of the property.

2. A tax upon the person is a fixed sum assessed upon each person. It is called a *Poll* or *Capitation Tax.*

Non-resident tax-payers are not subject to a poll tax.

310. The officers appointed to estimate the taxable value of property are called **Assessors.** They receive a salary.

The officer appointed to collect the taxes is called a **Collector.** He receives either a salary or a per cent of the tax collected.

311. A list of the names of the taxable inhabitants, with the assessed valuation of each person's property and the amount of his tax, is termed an **Assessment Roll.**

312. Before taxes are assessed, a complete inventory of all the taxable property must be made.

If the assessment includes a *poll tax,* a complete list of all the taxable polls must also be made out.

WRITTEN EXERCISES.

313. 1. A village must raise $8795 on property assessed at $989,387, and there are 670 persons subject to a poll tax of $1 each. A's property is assessed at $10,000, and he is a resident of the village. What will be his tax?

SOLUTION.

$8795 − $670 = $8125, amount to be levied upon property.

$8125 ÷ $989,387 = .00821, or $8\frac{21}{100}$ mills on $1.

$10,000 × .00821 = $82.10, A's property tax.

$ 1.00, A's poll tax.

$83.10, A's entire tax.

314. To facilitate the computation of taxes, assessors usually prepare a table like the following. The rate at which this table is computed is .00821.

PROP.	TAX.	PROP.	TAX.	PROP.	TAX.	PROP.	TAX.
$1	$.00821	$10	$.0821	$100	$ .821	$1000	$ 8.21
2	.01642	20	.1642	200	1.642	2000	16.42
3	.02463	30	.2463	300	2.463	3000	24.63
4	.03284	40	.3284	400	3.284	4000	32.84
5	.04105	50	.4105	500	4.105	5000	41.05
6	.04926	60	.4926	600	4.926	6000	49.26
7	.05747	70	.5747	700	5.747	7000	57.47
8	.06568	80	.6568	800	6.568	8000	65.68
9	.07389	90	.7389	900	7.389	9000	73.89

2. Find B's tax upon property assessed at $8550.

SOLUTION.

Tax, by table on $8000 = $65.68

"   "   "   "   500 =   4.105

"   "   "   "   50 =   .4105

"   "   "   " $8550 = $70.1955, B's property tax.

3. Find C's tax upon property assessed at $5780.

4. What is D's tax, whose property is assessed at $12,650, and who pays for 2 polls?

5. What is E's tax, whose property is assessed at $6759, and who pays for 3 polls?

6. What is the tax on property valued at $13,417.40?

7. In a town containing 390 polls, assessed at $1 each, the assessment roll shows the valuation of the property to be $987,680. The amount of tax to be raised is $5822.24. What is the rate of taxation?

8. At the rate of $9.50 on $1000, find the tax paid by a man who pays a poll tax of $1.25, and whose property is valued at $19,430.

9. The taxable property in a certain town is valued at $1,360,000, and a tax of $8840 is voted for school purposes. What is the rate of taxation?

10. In the same town A's property is assessed at $3150, B's at $4200, and C's at $5595. How much tax is each required to pay?

11. If the rate of taxation is $7\frac{1}{2}$ mills on a dollar, and the tax on a farm is $48.15, what is its assessed value?

DUTIES OR CUSTOMS.

315. Taxes levied by the government upon goods imported from other countries are termed **Duties.**

316. When the duty is a certain per cent of the cost of the goods it is called an **Ad Valorem Duty.**

317. When the duty is a fixed tax upon an article without regard to its value, it is called a **Specific Duty.**

318. An inventory or list of the goods, and the prices at which they were purchased, is termed an **Invoice** or **Manifest.**

319. Before computing the duties on certain classes of merchandise, allowances are made for *tare,* or the weight of the box, bag, etc., for *leakage, breakage,* etc.

WRITTEN EXERCISES.

320. **1.** What is the duty on 420 yards of broadcloth, invoiced at $1.75 per yard, at 25% ad valorem?

2. What is the duty, at $2\frac{1}{4}$¢ per pound, on 2800 lb. of rice, allowing 5% for tare?

3. A merchant imported goods invoiced at £530 5s. What was the duty at 45% ad valorem?

4. What was the cost per dozen of 6 gross of penknives invoiced at $638.24 if the duty was 40% ad valorem?

5. A merchant imported 1560 yards of Irish linen, invoiced at 38¢ per yard. What was the duty at 35% ad valorem?

6. What is the duty, at 25% ad valorem, on 280 chests of tea, each containing 60 pounds, invoiced at 45¢ a pound?

7. What is the duty, at $2\frac{1}{2}$¢ a pound, on 36 boxes of raisins, each weighing 24 lb., tare $5\frac{1}{2}$ lb. a box?

8. What is the duty, at $33\frac{1}{3}$% ad valorem, on 45 tons of steel, of 2240 lb. each, invoiced at $5\frac{1}{2}$¢ per pound?

9. What is the duty, at 25% ad valorem, on 80 dozen watch crystals, invoiced at $1.50 a dozen, an allowance of 5% being made for breakage?

10. What is the duty on 18 pieces of Brussels carpeting, of 60 yd. each, invoiced at 45¢ per yd., the specific duty being 38¢ per yd., and the ad valorem duty 35%?

11. Find the duty paid on the following importation: 320 lb. of knit-goods, valued at $1225, at 35¢ per lb. specific duty and 40% ad valorem; 120 yd. of silk invoiced at $1.25 per yard, at 50% ad valorem; and 500 yd. of lace, invoiced at $87\frac{1}{2}$¢ per yard, at 40% ad valorem.

INSURANCE.

321. 1. How much will it cost to secure myself against loss by fire, or to *insure* my property for $ 6000, if an annual sum or *premium* of 1% is charged by those who assume the risk ?

2. What will be the cost of insuring a building worth $ 10,000, at $\frac{3}{4}$%, for $\frac{1}{2}$ of its value ?

3. A merchant insured a stock of goods worth $12,000 for $\frac{3}{4}$ of its value, at 1%. What was his annual premium ?

4. I paid an annual premium of $ 75 for insuring my property at $\frac{3}{4}$%. For how much was it insured ?

322. Indemnity against loss or damage is termed **Insurance.** Insurance is of two kinds, **Property Insurance** and **Personal Insurance.**

323. The contract between the insurance company and the person insured is called the **Policy.**

324. The sum paid for insurance is called the **Premium.**

1. A company in which the person insured participates in the profits and shares the losses, is called a *Mutual Insurance Company.*

2. Many mutual companies charge fixed rates of premium, and return to each policy holder annually his share of the surplus.

3. Another kind of mutual company assesses upon each person insured his share of the loss, whenever a loss occurs. Such companies are sometimes called *Assessment Companies.*

4. A company, in which the capital to meet the losses is contributed by stockholders who alone share in the profits and losses of the business, is called a *Stock Company.*

PROPERTY INSURANCE.

325. Property Insurance includes indemnity against loss or damage by fire, or *Fire Insurance;* against loss or damage by casualties at sea, or *Marine Insurance;* against loss or damage to cattle, horses, etc., or *Live Stock Insurance*, etc.

WRITTEN EXERCISES.

326. 1. How much is the annual premium on a policy of insurance on a factory for $8500, if the rate is $2\frac{3}{4}\%$?

2. A house was insured for $3600, at $1\frac{1}{2}\%$. What was the premium ?

3. A factory worth $45,000 is insured for $\frac{2}{3}$ of its value, at $1\frac{3}{4}\%$. How much is the premium ?

4. A man insured a row of 7 houses at $5800 each, paying an annual rate of $1\frac{3}{4}\%$. How much does it cost him ?

5. If a premium of $75 is paid for an insurance of $6400 on a house, what is the rate of insurance ?

6. A cargo worth $9670 was insured for $\frac{9}{10}$ of its value, at $3\frac{1}{2}\%$. In case of shipwreck, what would be the actual loss to the owner ?

7. What will it cost to insure a building worth $9840 for $\frac{2}{3}$ of its value, at $\frac{7}{8}\%$?

8. A dealer paid $375 for the insurance of a cargo of grain, at $1\frac{1}{4}\%$. What was the amount of insurance ?

9. A merchant sent his agent in St. Paul $3493.50 to invest in flour at $4.25 per barrel after deducting a commission of $2\frac{3}{4}\%$. The flour was insured at $1\frac{1}{8}\%$, and $268.25 was paid for transportation. If the flour was then sold at a gain of 10% on the whole cost, what was the selling price per barrel ?

PERSONAL INSURANCE.

327. Indemnity against loss of life, or *Life Insurance;* against loss occasioned by accidents, or *Accident Insurance;* against loss occasioned by sickness, or *Health Insurance*, are varieties of **Personal Insurance**.

Of these the most important kind is Life Insurance.

328. The policies issued by life insurance companies are of various kinds, the chief of which are the **Life Policy** and the **Endowment Policy.**

1. A policy which secures the payment of a sum of money at the death of the person insured is called a *Life Policy.*

2. A policy which secures the payment of a sum of money at a specified time or at death, if it occurs before the specified time, is termed an *Endowment Policy.*

WRITTEN EXERCISES.

329. 1. How much will be the annual premium on a life insurance policy for $ 4000, at $ 25.70 per $ 1000 ?

2. What is the annual premium on a life policy of $ 6500, at $ 29.50 per $ 1000 ?

3. A man paid a Mutual Insurance Company for 30 years an annual premium on a life policy for $ 3000, of $ 26.30 per $ 1000. Of this premium 15% was returned as dividends. How much did he pay in all ?

4. My life is insured for $ 9000, at an annual cost of $ 315. What is the annual premium per $ 1000 ?

5. If a person who is insured for $ 6000, at an annual premium of $ 31.40 per $ 1000, dies after 12 payments, how much more will his heirs get than has been paid in premiums ?

6. A man insured his life for $ 8000, paying $ 26.30 per $ 1000. If he should live 20 years after he was insured, what would be the amount of the premiums paid ?

7. A man at the age of 35 secured a policy upon his life for $ 5000, paying the first year $ 172.50, which included $ 1 for examination. What was the premium paid upon $ 1000 ?

INTEREST.

330. **1.** When a sum equal to 6% of the money loaned is paid for the use of it for 1 yr., how much must be paid for the use of $100 for 1 yr.? For 2 yr.? For 3 yr.?

2. When the sum paid for the use of money is 10% annually, what must be paid for the use of $240 for 1 yr.? For 6 mo.? For 3 mo.? For 1 mo.? For $\frac{1}{2}$ mo.? For 10 da., or $\frac{1}{3}$ of a month? For 20 da.?

3. If $500 is loaned for 2 yr., at 6% per year, what will be the amount due at the end of that time?

331. The sum paid for the use of money is called **Interest.**

332. The sum for the use of which interest is paid is termed the **Principal.**

333. The sum of the principal and interest is called the **Amount.**

334. In computing interest it is usual to regard a year as 12 months, and a month as 30 days.

335 To compute interest.

1. What is the interest of $100 for 1 yr. at 5%? For 2 yr.? For 3 yr.? For 4 yr.? For 10 yr.?

2. What is the interest of $200 for 2 yr. at 6%? For 3 yr.? For $1\frac{1}{2}$ yr.? For $2\frac{1}{2}$ yr.? For 1 yr. 6 mo.?

3. What is the interest of $400 for 1 yr. at 4%? For $1\frac{1}{2}$ yr.? For $1\frac{1}{4}$ yr.? For 1 yr. 3 mo.? For 1 yr. 6 mo.? For 1 yr. 8 mo.?

WRITTEN EXERCISES.

336. **1.** What is the interest of $ 375.15 for 4 yr. at 5% ?

SOLUTION.

$375.15, Principal.
.05, Rate.

$18.7575, Interest for 1 yr.
4

$75.0300, Interest for 4 yr.

Find the interest of :

2. $ 496.84 for 5 yr. at 8%.
3. $ 389.50 for 4 yr. at 7%.
4. $ 541.76 for 6 yr. at 5%.
5. $ 756.38 for 7 yr. at 8%.

6. $ 250.50 for 4 yr. at 6%.
7. $ 375.65 for 7 yr. at 8%.
8. $ 460.70 for 5 yr. at 7%.
9. $ 695.49 for 10 yr. at 6%.

10. Find the interest of $ 453.20 for 2 yr. 8 mo. at 5%.

SOLUTION.

$453.20
.05

$22.6600, Int. for 1 yr.
2

$45.3200, Int. for 2 yr.
½ of the int. for 1 yr. = 11.3300, Int. for 6 mo.
⅓ of the int. for 6 mo. = 3.7766, Int. for 2 mo.

$60.4266, Int. for 2 yr. 8 mo.

Find the interest of :

11. $ 687.35 for 3 yr. 6 mo. at 6%.
12. $ 476.38 for 4 yr. 8 mo. at 6%.
13. $ 380.40 for 4 yr. 5 mo. at 7%.
14. $ 425.60 for 5 yr. 7 mo. at 5%.
15. $ 368.52 for 6 yr. 4 mo. at 9%.
16. $ 410.30 for 7 yr. 3 mo. at 7%.

17. $ 564.80 for 8 yr. 5 mo. at 8%.

18. $ 672.50 for 5 yr. 7 mo. at 4%.

19. $ 150.18 for 2 yr. 6 mo. at 6%.

20. $ 175.40 for 3 yr. 7 mo. at 5%.

21. $ 233.50 for 2 yr. 5 mo. at 8%.

22. $ 317.42 for 4 yr. 3 mo. at 7%.

23. $ 510.12 for 4 yr. 8 mo. at 5%.

24. $ 468.72 for 5 yr. 6 mo. at 6%.

25. $ 496.88 for 6 yr. 9 mo. at 8%.

26. $ 784.75 for 7 yr. 8 mo. at 9%.

27. Find the amount of $ 240.15 for 2 yr. 5 mo. 13 da. at 6%.

SOLUTION.

$ 240.15
.06

$ 14.4090, Int. for 1 yr.
2

$ 28.8180, Int. for 2 yr.

$\frac{1}{6}$ of the int. for 1 yr. = 4.8030, Int. for   4 mo.

$\frac{1}{4}$ of the int. for 4 mo.= 1.2007, Int. for   1 mo.

$\frac{1}{3}$ of the int. for 1 mo.= .4002, Int. for   10 da.

$\frac{1}{5}$ of the int. for 10 da.= .0800, Int. for   2 da.

$\frac{1}{2}$ of the int. for 2 da. = .0400, Int. for   1 da.

$ 35.3419, Int. for 2 yr. 5 mo. 13 da.

$ 240.15 , Principal.

$ 275.49 , Amount.

It is customary to disregard the mills if they are less than 5, and to call them 1 cent if they are more than 5.

The method of computing interest illustrated above is called the method by *Aliquot Parts* or the *Business Method*.

Find the interest and amount of:

28. $ 313.50 for 2 yr. 3 mo. at 6%.

29. $ 935.75 for 3 yr. 5 mo. at 7%.

30. $ 269.50 for 2 yr. 7 mo. 10 da. at 5%.
31. $ 468.75 for 1 yr. 5 mo. 15 da. at 7%.
32. $ 274.08 for 2 yr. 7 mo. 5 da. at 6%.
33. $ 364.50 for 2 yr. 8 mo. 20 da. at 5%.
34. $ 286.09 for 3 yr. 5 mo. 10 da. at 8%.
35. $ 368.75 for 3 yr. 8 mo. 15 da. at 7%.
36. $ 368.18 for 4 yr. 6 mo. 12 da. at 6%.
37. $ 580.90 for 5 yr. 8 mo. 18 da. at 8%.
38. $ 275.60 for 1 yr. 9 mo. 15 da. at 5%.
39. $ 468.25 for 2 yr. 7 mo. 11 da. at 6%.
40. $ 815.27 for 3 yr. 8 mo. 21 da. at 10%.
41. $ 125.00 for 2 yr. 4 mo. 10 da. at 5%.
42. $ 184.50 for 1 yr. 2 mo. 18 da. at 8%.
43. $ 560.25 for 3 yr. 5 mo. 10 da. at 7%.
44. $ 376.47 for 2 yr. 9 mo. 13 da. at 6%.
45. $ 1000 for 3 yr. 7 mo. 21 da. at 7%.
46. $ 4120 for 5 yr. 3 mo. 18 da. at 5%.
47. $ 3180 for 2 yr. 10 mo. 16 da. at 4%.
48. $ 2875 for 4 yr. 11 mo. 17 da. at 6%.

Find the amount of :

49. $ 685.20 from June 12, 1892, to Aug. 10, 1893, at 6%.

yr.	mo.	da.
1893	8	10
1892	6	12
1	1	28

SOLUTION. — The time is 1 yr. 1 mo. 28 da., and the amount of $ 685.20 for the time and rate is $ 732.94.

Find the amount of :

50. $ 423.36 from June 7, 1890, to Dec. 15, 1891, at 6%.
51. $ 346.85 from Sept. 10, 1891, to Apr. 8, 1892, at 5%.
52. $ 427.93 from Apr. 23, 1892, to Nov. 13, 1892, at 6%.
53. $ 684.14 from Oct. 15, 1891, to Mar. 8, 1892, at 7%.
54. $ 713.62 from Nov. 18, 1892, to Apr. 13, 1893, at 8%.

337. The six per cent method.

This method is very convenient because of the ease with which the interest of $1 can be computed. Thus,

The interest of $1 for 1 yr. = $.06.
The interest of $1 for 1 mo. = $.005.
The interest of $1 for 6 da. = $.001.
The interest of $1 for 1 da. = $.000⅙.

1. What is the interest of $480.60 for 3 yr. 4 mo. 12 da. at 6% ?

SOLUTION.

The interest of $1 for 3 yr.   = $.18
The interest of $1 for 4 mo.   =   .02
The interest of $1 for 12 da.   =   .002

The interest of $1 for 3 yr. 4 mo. 12 da. = $.202

The interest of $480.60 = $.202 × 480.60, or $97.08.

What is the interest of:

    2. $575.40 for 2 yr. 2 mo. 6 da. at 6% ?

    3. $434.70 for 3 yr. 4 mo. 18 da. at 6% ?

    4. $387.62 for 2 yr. 6 mo. 12 da. at 6% ?

    5. $292.47 for 3 yr. 8 mo. 24 da. at 6% ?

    6. $436.45 for 4 yr. 7 mo. 15 da. at 6% ?

    7. $672.36 for 1 yr. 9 mo. 21 da. at 6% ?

    8. $945.50 for 3 yr. 4 mo. 18 da. at 6% ?

    9. $392.00 for 5 yr. 7 mo. 24 da. at 6% ?

338. When the interest of any sum of money at 6% has been found, the interest of the same sum at 7% may be found by adding ⅙ of the interest to the result; at 8% by adding 2/6 of the interest, etc. Consequently, the 6% method may be used to compute interest at any rate.

What is the interest of:

      10. $280.75 for 3 yr. 2 mo. 12 da. at 7% ?

      11. $315.40 for 5 yr. 7 mo. 18 da. at 8% ?

      12. $416.26 for 8 yr. 9 mo. 15 da. at 5% ?

      13. $620.35 for 7 yr. 5 mo. 19 da. at 9% ?

      14. $575.38 for 9 yr. 7 mo. 13 da. at 4% ?

339. Method by days.

When the time is short, interest is computed for the actual number of days, considering a year as 360 days.

   1. What is the interest of $108.12 from March 15 to June 10 at 6% ?

SOLUTION. — From March 15 to June 10 is 87 days. The interest of $1 for 87 da. at 6% is $.014½. Therefore the interest of $108.12 is $.014½ × 108.22, or $1.57 ; or,

$$\$108.12 = \text{the principal.}$$

1% of principal	= $1.0812,	Int. for 60 da.
⅓ of int. for 60 da. =	.3604,	Int. for 20 da.
¼ of int. for 20 da. =	.0901,	Int. for 5 da.
1⁄10 of int. for 20 da. =	.0364,	Int. for 2 da.

$$\$1.5681, \text{ Int. for 87 da.}$$

In computing the number of days, reckon *from* the day upon which the sum was loaned, and *include* the day upon which it was paid.

Find the interest of :

   2. $840 from Mar. 1, 1891, to May 5, 1891, at 6%.

   3. $950 from Feb. 3, 1891, to Apr. 15, 1891, at 6%.

   4. $879 from Jan. 18, 1891, to June 1, 1891, at 6%.

   5. $895 from Mar. 20, 1891, to Aug. 18, 1891, at 6%.

   6. $965 from May 25, 1891, to Oct. 10, 1891, at 6%.

   7. $1050 from Apr. 1, 1891, to July 22, 1891, at 6%.

   8. $1120 from Jan. 1, 1892, to Mar. 8, 1892, at 6%.

   9. $3000 from Feb. 2, 1892, to Sept. 8, 1892, at 6%.

340. The method by months.

1. What is the interest of $290.75 for 2 yr. 3 mo. 21 da. at 7%?

SOLUTION.

21 da.=$\frac{21}{30}$ or $\frac{7}{10}$ of a month. Therefore 2 yr. 3 mo. 21 da.=27.7 mo.

$$\begin{array}{r} \$290.75 \\ .07 \\ \hline 12)\overline{\$20.3525}, \text{ Int. for 1 yr.} \\ \$1.6960, \text{ Int. for 1 mo.} \\ 27.7, \\ \hline \$46.9792, \text{ Int. for 27.7 mo., or 2 yr. 3 mo. 21 da.} \end{array}$$

What is the interest of:

2. $270.60 for 1 yr. 2 mo. 15 da. at 7%?

3. $285.45 for 3 yr. 4 mo. 20 da. at 5%?

4. $315.65 for 2 yr. 3 mo. 10 da. at 6%?

5. $573.95 for 6 yr. 5 mo. 24 da. at 8%?

6. $397.85 for 2 yr. 3 mo. 5 da. at 6%?

7. $463.28 for 1 yr. 2 mo. 7 da. at 7%?

8. $395.18 for 3 yr. 4 mo. 8 da. at 5%?

9. $793.64 for 5 yr. 6 mo. 9 da. at 4%?

341. To compute accurate interest.

As has been said, a year is usually considered as 12 months of 30 days each, or 360 days, when the time is less than a year and expressed in months and days. Sometimes, however, the interest is computed for the *exact* number of days, 365 days constituting a year.

Accurate interest for a given number of days will, therefore, be that number of 365ths of the interest for 1 yr., or the ordinary interest diminished by $\frac{5}{365}$, or $\frac{1}{73}$ of itself.

Find the accurate interest at 6% of:

1. $650.25 for 61 da.

2. $785.75 for 58 da.

3. $872.90 for 73 da.

4. $920.40 for 82 da.

5. $3296.80 for 110 da.

6. $5375.80 for 295 da.

ANNUAL INTEREST.

342. Simple interest upon the principal, and upon any interest overdue, is called **Annual Interest.**

1. The contract should contain the words "interest payable annually" or "annual interest."

2. In some States annual interest is illegal.

WRITTEN EXERCISES.

343. 1. Find the amount of $3500 for 4 yr. 6 mo., with interest payable annually at 6%.

SOLUTION.

Int. of $3500 for 4½ yr. =	$945.00

The annual interest is $210.

The interest for the first yr. remains unpaid for 3½ yr.; the interest for the second yr. 2½ yr., etc. Therefore the unpaid interest drew interest for 3½, 2½, 1½, and ½ yr., or 8 yr., and the interest upon $210 for that time is — $100.80

∴ The entire interest due is — $1045.80

$3500 + $1045.80 = $4545.80, Amt.

Find the amount of the following with annual interest:

2. $1200 for 3 yr. 4 mo. at 6%.

3. $1420 for 4 yr. 6 mo. at 6%.

4. $1825 for 5 yr. 8 mo. at 7%.

5. $1976 for 3 yr. 6 mo. 12 da. at 6%.

6. $2300 for 3 yr. 5 mo. 18 da. at 8%.

7. $2760 for 5 yr. 3 mo. 6 da. at 5%.

8. $3500 for 4 yr. 7 mo. 24 da. at 9%.

9. $4100 for 3 yr. 5 mo. 15 da. at 6%.

10. $5450 for 4 yr. 8 mo. 24 da. at 6%.

11. $10,000 for 5 yr. 6 mo. 15 da. at 5%.

12. $7090 for 6 yr. 3 mo. 12 da. at 6%.

COMPOUND INTEREST.

344. Interest upon the principal and its unpaid interest combined at regular intervals is **Compound Interest.**

1. Interest is usually compounded annually, semi-annually, or quarterly, according to agreement.

2. Compound interest cannot usually be enforced by law, even if it is specified in the contract.

3. Most savings banks allow compound interest upon balances remaining on deposit for a full interest term.

WRITTEN EXERCISES.

345. 1. Find the compound interest of $ 250 for 2 yr. 3 mo. at 6%.

SOLUTION.

$250	Principal.
15	Interest for 1st yr. at 6 %.
$265	Principal for 2d yr.
15.90	Interest for 2d yr. at 6 %.
$280.90	Principal for 3d yr.
4.21	Interest for 3 mo. at 6 %.
$285.11	Amount for 2 yr. 3 mo. at 6%.
250	Original principal.
$35.11	Compound interest for 2 yr. 3 mo. at 6 %.

1. Unless it is specified otherwise in the agreement, interest is understood to be compounded annually.

2. If interest is compounded semi-annually, the rate must be considered one half the annual rate, if quarterly, one fourth, etc.

3. When the time consists of years, months, and days, the amount is to be found for the greatest number of entire periods, as years, half-years, quarter-years, etc., and the simple interest upon this for the rest of the time.

Find the compound interest of the following :

2. $ 275 for 2 yr. 2 mo. at 6%.

3. $ 310 for 3 yr. 6 mo. at 7%.

4. $ 425 for 2 yr. 5 mo. at 5%.

5. $ 650 for 2 yr. 9 mo. at 6%.

6. $ 535 for 3 yr. 5 mo. at 7%.

7. $ 580 for 3 yr. 8 mo. 20 da. at 6%.

8. $ 260 for 2 yr. 6 mo. at 6%, payable semi-annually.

9. $ 450 for 2 yr. 2 mo. at 8%, payable quarterly.

10. What is the compound interest of $ 325.10 for 3 yr. 2 mo. at 6% ?

SOLUTION.

By referring to the table upon the next page, it will be seen that the amount of $ 1 for 3 yr. at 6% is $ 1.191016. Computing the interest upon this sum for 2 mo., the amount of $ 1 for 3 yr. 2 mo. is $ 1.202926.

Therefore the amount of $ 325.10 is 325.10 times that sum.

This product minus the principal is the compound interest.

Find the compound interest of the following, making use of the table :

11. $ 420.80 for 4 yr. 6 mo. at 6%.

12. $ 430.75 for 3 yr. 4 mo. at 5%.

13. $ 510.60 for 5 yr. 6 mo. at 7%.

14. $ 750.80 for 6 yr. 7 mo. at 6%.

15. $ 672.28 for 2 yr. 3 mo. 18 da. at 6%.

16. $ 856.57 for 4 yr. 8 mo. 10 da. at 8%.

17. $ 889.37 for 6 yr. 9 mo. 21 da. at 7%.

18. $ 985.50 for 8 yr. 7 mo. 19 da. at 6%.

19. $ 357.50 for 9 yr. 3 mo. 10 da. at 5%.

20. $ 613.25 for 3 yr. 2 mo. 5 da. at 6%.

21. $ 5240.75 for 5 yr. 21 da. at 5%.

22. $ 3745 for 4 yr. 2 mo. at 8%.

23. $ 43.75 for 8 yr. 3 mo. 5 da. at 5%.

24. $ 745.27 for 6 yr. 9 mo. 18 da. at 6%.

25. $ 319.50 for 8 yr. 2 mo. 5 da. at 7%.

26. $ 3246.98 for 1 yr. 6 mo. 15 da. at 5%.

27. $ 4921.50 for 4 yr. 9 mo. 24 da. at 7%.

Compound Interest Table.

Showing the amount of $ 1, at various rates, compound int. from 1 to 20 yr.

Yrs.	2½ per cent.	3 per cent.	3½ per cent.	4 per cent.	5 per cent.	6 per cent.
1	1.025000	1.030000	1.035000	1.040000	1.050000	1.060000
2	1.050625	1.060900	1.071225	1.081600	1.102500	1.123600
3	1.076891	1.092727	1.108718	1.124864	1.157625	1.191016
4	1.103813	1.125509	1.147523	1.169859	1.215506	1.262477
5	1.131408	1.159274	1.187686	1.216653	1.276282	1.338226
6	1.159693	1.194052	1.229255	1.265319	1.340096	1.418519
7	1.188686	1.229874	1.272279	1.315932	1.407100	1.503630
8	1.218403	1.266770	1.316809	1.368569	1.477455	1.593848
9	1.248863	1.304773	1.362897	1.423312	1.551328	1.689479
10	1.280085	1.343916	1.410599	1.480244	1.628895	1.790848
11	1.312087	1.384234	1.459970	1.539454	1.710339	1.898299
12	1.344889	1.425761	1.511069	1.601032	1.795856	2.012197
13	1.378511	1.468534	1.563956	1.665074	1.885649	2.132928
14	1.412974	1.512590	1.618695	1.731676	1.979932	2.260904
15	1.448298	1.557967	1.675349	1.800944	2.078928	2.396558
16	1.484506	1.604706	1.733986	1.872981	2.182875	2.540352
17	1.521618	1.652848	1.794676	1.947901	2.292018	2.692773
18	1.559659	1.702433	1.857489	2.025817	2.406619	2.854339
19	1.598650	1.753506	1.922501	2.106849	2.526950	3.025600
20	1.638616	1.806111	1.989789	2.191123	2.653298	3.207136

Yrs.	7 per cent.	8 per cent.	9 per cent.	10 per cent.	11 per cent.	12 per cent.
1	1.070000	1.080000	1.090000	1.100000	1.110000	1.120000
2	1.144900	1.166400	1.188100	1.210000	1.232100	1.254400
3	1.225043	1.259712	1.295029	1.331000	1.367631	1.404908
4	1.310796	1.360489	1.411582	1.464100	1.518070	1.573519
5	1.402552	1.469328	1.538624	1.610510	1.685058	1.762342
6	1.500730	1.586874	1.677100	1.771561	1.870414	1.973822
7	1.605781	1.713824	1.828039	1.948717	2.076160	2.210681
8	1.718186	1.850930	1.992563	2.143589	2.304537	2.475963
9	1.838459	1.999005	2.171893	2.357948	2.558036	2.773078
10	1.967151	2.158925	2.367364	2.593742	2.839420	3.105848
11	2.104852	2.331639	2.580426	2.853117	3.151757	3.478549
12	2.252192	2.518170	2.812665	3.138428	3.498450	3.895975
13	2.409845	2.719624	3.065805	3.452271	3.883279	4.363492
14	2.578534	2.937194	3.341727	3.797498	4.310440	4.887111
15	2.759031	3.172169	3.642482	4.177248	4.784588	5.473565
16	2.952164	3.425943	3.970306	4.594973	5.310893	6.130392
17	3.158815	3.700018	4.327633	5.054470	5.895091	6.866040
18	3.379932	3.996019	4.717120	5.559917	6.543551	7.689964
19	3.616527	4.315701	5.141661	6.115909	7.263342	8.612760
20	3.869684	4.660957	5.604411	6.727500	8.062309	9.646291

PROMISSORY NOTES.

346. A written promise to pay a sum of money at a specified time is called a **Promissory Note** or a **Note**.

347. The person who signs the note is the **Maker** or **Drawer**. The person to whom it is payable is the **Payee**. The person who owns the note is the **Holder**.

348. The sum promised to be paid is the **Face** of the note.

349. A higher rate of interest than that authorized by law is called **Usury**.

The penalty for making usurious contracts varies in the different States, from the loss of the whole debt and interest to nothing.

350. When no rate of interest is specified, the *legal rate* in the place where the note is made is always understood.

SOME FORMS OF NOTES.

$ 827.36.   BUFFALO, N.Y., June 1, 1892.

Four months after date, I promise to pay Henry B. Sampson, or order, Eight Hundred Twenty-Seven $\frac{36}{100}$ Dollars, for value received.

DAVID S. GRAHAM.

$ 3000.   CHICAGO, ILL., July 10, 1892.

For value received, two months after date, I promise to pay George D. Holmes, or bearer, Three Thousand Dollars, with interest.

SAMUEL R. GOODRICH.

351. A note should contain the place where it was made, the date, the time when payable, the amount or face of the note written in words, the words " for value received " and " with interest," if such is the contract, and the place where it is to be paid.

1. Notes are often made payable at a certain time after date. They may be also made payable *on demand*, or at a specified date, as " *On August 5, 1892, I promise to pay,*" etc.

2. The amount of the note should be written in words to avoid error and fraud.

3. If the words "for value received" are omitted, the owner of the note may have to prove that the maker received the value specified in the note. If the words "with interest" are omitted, the note will not draw interest until it is due. After it is due it will draw interest at the legal rate prevailing at the place where it was made.

4. If no place of payment is named in the note, it is payable at the maker's place of business.

352. A person who writes his name across the back of a note to transfer it to another person or to guarantee its payment, is called an **Indorser.**

The payee may indorse a note by writing his name and nothing else on the back of the note. It is then payable to the person owning it, or to the bearer. This is called indorsement in *blank.*

He may write "Pay to A—— B——." It is then payable to A—— B—— only.

He may write "Pay to A—— B—— or order," and it is then payable to any person to whom A—— B—— may order it paid. This is called *special* indorsement.

He may write "Pay A—— B—— or bearer," and it is then payable to the one who presents it, or the bearer.

There are also other forms of indorsement.

353. A note that is payable to the order of the *payee* or to the *bearer* is a **Negotiable Note.**

Thus, both the foregoing notes are negotiable.

354. A note that is payable to the *payee only* is a **Non-Negotiable Note.**

Thus, if the words "or order" and "or bearer" were omitted from the above notes, the notes would be non-negotiable.

355. A note is *payable,* or is said to *mature,* at the time specified in it, except in some states where three days extra, called *days of grace,* are allowed before payment can be *legally* enforced. In these states a note matures on the last day of grace.

1. Days of grace are not allowed in Ariz., Cal., Colo., Conn., D. C., Del., Fla., Ida., Ill., Me., Md., Mass., Mont., N. H., N. J., N. Y., N. D., Ore., O., Pa., R. I., Tenn., Ut., Va., Vt., Wash., W. Va., Wis.

2. If, when a note is unpaid at its maturity, the holder fails to *protest it*, that is, to notify the indorsers in a manner prescribed by law that it is unpaid, they are released from responsibility regarding its payment.

3. The protest must be served upon the indorsers at the latest, upon the day following that upon which the note matures.

356. A note signed by two or more persons, who become jointly and individually responsible for its payment, is called a **Joint** and **Several** Note.

WRITTEN EXERCISES.

357. **1.** Write a negotiable note for $500.25, making yourself the payee, and James J. Rogers the maker. Interest at the legal rate.

2. Write a non-negotiable note for $315.17, making W. R. Howard the payee, payable on demand without interest.

3. Write two forms of negotiable notes for $3184.25, due in three months to James P. Hermann, with interest.

4. Indorse them properly for transferring one to bearer, and the other to H. H. Hurd, or order.

5. Write a note from the following data: face, $5000; negotiable; maker, P. G. Sloane; payee, J. S. Orton; payable on demand; rate of interest, the legal rate.

6. Write a negotiable note for $1200, making David R. Swan the payee, Stephen Baird the maker, and payable on demand with interest at 5%.

7. Write a negotiable note for $350.75, payable to D. C. Morrison, due in 60 days from date with interest, and signed by H. G. Goodspeed & Co.

Find the interest of:

8. $175 from Jan. 2, 1877, to Oct. 14, 1878, at 6%.

9. $380 from Mar. 14, 1879, to Aug. 20, 1880, at 5%.

10. $575 from Sept. 6, 1880, to Oct. 4, 1881, at 7%.

11. $860 from Mar. 15, 1882, to May 31, 1883, at 5%.

PARTIAL PAYMENTS.

358. A payment in part of a note or other obligation is a **Partial Payment**.

The payments, with the date at which they were paid, are usually indorsed upon the back of the note or other obligation.

Business men often settle notes and accounts running for a year or less, upon which partial payments have been made, by the MERCANTILE RULE.

RULE. — *Find the amount of the principal at the time of settlement.*

Find the amount of each payment, from the time it was made until the time of settlement, and from the amount of the principal subtract the amount of the payments.

WRITTEN EXERCISES.

359. 1. A note of $760, dated Jan. 10, 1890, was indorsed as follows: Mar. 13, 1890, $175; July 28, 1890, $360. What remained due Dec. 22, 1890, at 6%?

2. On a note for $1245, dated Jan. 12, 1890, were the following indorsements: May 15, 1890, $236; June 20, 1890, $350; Aug. 10, 1890, $180; Sept. 3, 1890, $220. How much was due Oct. 30, 1890, at 6%?

3. On a note dated Aug. 15, 1885, for $3500, were the following indorsements: Oct. 10, 1885, $320; Feb. 5, 1886, $476; Apr. 20, 1886, $525; June 24, 1886, $700. What amount was due Aug. 3, 1886, at 7%?

4. What is the balance due Apr. 1, 1892, on a note for $1500, dated Apr. 1, 1891, with interest at 8%, on which the following payments have been made: June 10, 1891, $270; Aug. 23, 1891, $328; Sept. 10, 1891, $145; Nov. 1, 1891, $195; Feb. 13, 1892, $200?

360. Most of the States have adopted the **United States Rule** for computing the amount due, when partial payments have been made.

361. Some additional rules that have been adopted for computing the indebtedness upon a promissory note or other obligation will be found under Art. 614.

1. A note was given, Jan. 1, 1890, for $700. The following payments were indorsed upon it: May 6, 1890, $85; July 1, 1891, $40; Aug. 20, 1891, $100; Jan. 10, 1893, $350. How much was due Sept. 30, 1894, with interest at 6%?

PROCESS.

Principal		$700.00
Int. to May 6, 1890, — 4 mo. 5 da.		14.58
Amount		714.58
First payment		85.00
New principal		629.58
Int. from May 6, 1890, to July 1, 1891, — 1 yr. 1 mo. 25 da.		43.55
Second payment, less than interest due	$40.00	
Int. on $629.58 from July 1, 1891, to Aug. 20, 1891, — 1 mo. 19 da.		5.14
Amount		678.27
Third payment to be added to second	$100.00	140.00
New principal		538.27
Int. from Aug. 20, 1891, to Jan. 10, 1893, — 1 yr. 4 mo. 20 da.		44.85
Amount		583.12
Fourth payment		350.00
New principal		233.12
Int. from Jan. 10, 1893, to Sept. 30, 1894, — 1 yr. 8 mo. 20 da.		24.08
Amount due, Sept. 30, 1894		$257.20

UNITED STATES RULE. — *Find the amount of the principal to a time when a payment, or the sum of the payments, equals or exceeds the interest due, and from this amount subtract such payment or payments. With the remainder as a new principal, proceed as before.*

2. A note for $850, dated June 24, 1887, was indorsed as follows: Apr. 1, 1888, $250; Nov. 18, 1888, $300. How much was due on the note Jan. 1, 1889, the rate of interest being 6%?

3. A note of $1000, dated Apr. 2, 1881, was indorsed as follows: June 1, 1881, $200; Sept. 10, 1881, $350. How much was due Apr. 2, 1882, interest being at 7%?

4. A note of $1115, dated July 6, 1883, was indorsed as follows: Sept. 15, 1883, $180; Jan. 2, 1884, $225; Mar. 20, 1884, $300. What was due May 1, 1884, the rate of interest being 6%?

5. A note was given Jan. 1, 1885, for $750. The following payments were indorsed upon it: Mar. 1, 1885, $125; July 6, 1885, $325; Dec. 10, 1885, $75. How much was due June 1, 1886, with interest at 6%?

6. A note of $900, dated Apr. 2, 1886, was indorsed as follows: Sept. 8, 1886, $115; June 20, 1887, $175; Dec. 14, 1887, $200. What amount was due May 26, 1888, with interest at 7%?

7. A note of $1200, dated Jan. 1, 1887, had the following indorsements: Aug. 1, 1887, $175; Dec. 1, 1887, $225; July 1, 1888, $250; Nov. 1, 1888, $100. What amount was due Jan. 1, 1889, with interest at 7%?

8. A note of $1450, dated Sept. 20, 1886, was indorsed as follows: Jan. 8, 1887, $20; June 8, 1887, $180; Oct. 20, 1887, $210; Apr. 15, 1888, $15. What was due June 24, 1888, with interest at 8%?

9. A note of $1800 dated Aug. 2, 1887, was indorsed as follows: Jan. 4, 1888, $200; Jan. 4, 1889, $100; June 5, 1889, $500. What amount was due Jan. 3, 1890, with interest at 8%?

PROBLEMS IN SIMPLE INTEREST.

362. The principal, time, and interest given, to find the rate.

1. What is the interest of $100 for 1 yr. at 1%? At 4%? At 6%?

What was the rate:

2. When the interest of $100 for 1 yr. was $7?
3. When the interest of $100 for 2 yr. was $16?
4. When the interest of $200 for 3 yr. was $36?
5. When the interest of $50 for 3 yr. was $15?

WRITTEN EXERCISES.

363. What is the rate per cent, when the interest:

1. Of $450 for 2 yr. 4 mo. is $52.50?

SOLUTION.--The interest of $450 for 2 yr. 4 mo. at 1% is $10.50.

$52.50 ÷ $10.50 = 5. ∴ The rate is 5%.

2. Of $325 for 1 yr. 6 mo. is $19.50?
3. Of $480 for 2 yr. 3 mo. is $64.80?
4. Of $240 for 1 yr. 9 mo. is $29.40?
5. Of $375 for 1 yr. 5 mo. is $31.87½?
6. Of $500 for 2 yr. 2 mo. is $26.25?
7. Of $475 for 3 yr. 4 mo. is $95?

8. A house that cost $6000 was rented for $490. If $100 was paid for taxes and repairs, what rate of interest did the purchase money yield?

9. Mr. Donat borrowed $1575 on the 1st of April. On the 1st of November following he paid the amount, which was $1630.125. What rate of interest did he pay?

10. The annual income of a farm that cost $10,500 was $785. The expenses were $260. What rate per cent did the farmer realize on his investment?

364. The principal, rate, and interest given, to find the time.

1. How much is the interest of $100 for 1 yr. at 6%?

2. How much is the interest of $300 for 1 yr. at 5%? For 5 yr.?

3. $100 loaned at 6%, brings an income of $24. For how long was it loaned? How long, when the interest was $18? $24? $3? $4? $2? $1.50?

WRITTEN EXERCISES.

365. In what time will:

1. $280 produce $25.20, with interest at 6%?

SOLUTION. — The interest of $280 for 1 yr. at 6% is $16.80.

$25.20 ÷ $16.80 = 1½.   ∴ The time is 1½ yr.

2. $300 produce $37.50 interest at 5%?

3. $480 produce $74.28 interest at 3%?

4. $400 produce $62.06⅔ interest at 7%?

5. $940 produce $432.40 interest at 6%?

6. $860 produce $247.25 interest at 5%?

7. $984 produce $288.64 interest at 8%?

8. $998 produce $185.145 interest at 5%?

9. $1200 produce $1200 interest at 7%?

10. $1500 produce $1500 interest at 8%?

11. How long must $530 be at interest at 6% to amount to $641.30?

12. A man borrowed $1200 at 5½%, and retained it until it was doubled. How long did he have it?

13. When will $475, put at interest at 6% April 1, 1891, amount to $489.25.

14. A certain sum of money was put at interest at 8% June 24, 1850. When was the interest double the principal?

366. The rate, time, and interest given, to find the principal.

1. At 6% what sum will yield an income annually of $6? Of $12? Of $18? Of $3? Of $4? Of $2?

2. At 6% what sum will yield an income of $12 in 2 yr.? Of $18 in 3 yr.? Of $15 in 1 yr.? Of $25 in 5 yr.? Of $4 in 1 yr.?

WRITTEN EXERCISES.

367. 1. What sum of money at $4\frac{1}{2}$% will produce $75.40 interest in 3 yr. 4 mo.?

> Int. of $1 for 3 yr. 4 mo. at $4\frac{1}{2}$% = $.15.
>
> $75.40 ÷ $.15 = 502.66$\frac{2}{3}$, ∴ 502.66\frac{2}{3}$ is the principal.

EXPLANATION. — Since the interest of $1 for 3 yr. 4 mo., at $4\frac{1}{2}$%, is $.15, it will require a sum equal to as many times $1 to produce $75.40 interest, as $.15 is contained times in that number, or 502.66\frac{2}{3}$.

What sum of money will produce :

2. $25.50 interest in 2 yr. at 5%?

3. $33.75 interest in 2 yr. 3 mo. at 6%?

4. $43.86 interest in 3 yr. 4 mo. at 6%?

5. $49.75 interest in 6 mo. 18 da. at 7%?

6. $50.32 interest in 5 mo. 27 da. at 8%?

7. $38.40 interest in 9 mo. 15 da. at 9%?

8. $45.80 interest in 2 mo. 21 da. at 6%?

9. $68.50 interest in 7 mo. 25 da. at 5%?

10. $95.35 interest in 4 yr. 7 mo. at 7%?

11. What principal at 6%, loaned from June 24, 1891, to Sept. 10, 1893, will amount to $2575?

12. What principal will produce $17.78 interest from Jan. 10, 1892, to March 13, 1892, at 6%?

13. What may I offer for a residence which pays $895 rent per year, so that I may receive $6\frac{1}{2}$% interest on the investment?

TRUE DISCOUNT.

368. **1.** What will be the amount of $100 in 1 yr. at 6% ? In 2 yr. ?

2. What is the value *now* of $106 to be paid in 1 yr., when money is loaned at 6% ? Of $112 to be paid in 2 yr. ? Of $118 to be paid in 3 yr. ?

3. What is the present value of $212 to be paid in 1 yr., when money is loaned at 6% ? Of $224 to be paid in 2 yr. ?

4. What is the present worth of a debt of $672 due in $1\frac{1}{2}$ yr., when money is loaned at 8% ? Of $348 due in 2 yr. ?

369. A deduction made from a debt is termed a **Discount.**

370. A sum of money which, when put at interest at a specified rate, will amount to a debt when it becomes due, is the **Present Worth** of the debt due at some future time.

371. The difference between a debt and its present worth is the **True Discount.**

WRITTEN EXERCISES.

372. **1.** What is the present worth of a debt of $975.50 payable in 1 yr. 6 mo., when money is loaned at 6% ? What the discount ?

$1.09 = Amount of $1 for $1\frac{1}{2}$ yr.

$975.50 ÷ $1.09 = 894.95, ∴ $894.95 is the present worth.

$975.50 − $894.95 = $80.55, True discount.

EXPLANATION. — Since every dollar put at interest now at 6% will amount to $1.09 in 1 yr. 6 mo., it will require as many dollars now to amount to $975.50 as $1.09 is contained times in $975.50, or $894.95.

The debt $975.50 − $894.95 = $80.55, the true discount.

RULE. — *Divide the amount due, by the amount of $1, for the given time and rate, and the quotient will be the present worth.*

Subtract the present worth from the amount due, and the remainder will be the true discount.

What are the present worth and discount of the following:

2. $ 576.75 payable in 9 mo., when money is worth 6% ?

3. $ 760.85 payable in 10 mo., when money is worth 5% ?

4. $ 437.50 payable in 1½ yr., when money is worth 7% ?

5. $ 648.60 payable in 2 yr., when money is worth 5½% ?

6. $ 1200 payable in 1 yr. 4 mo. 18 da., when money is worth 6% ? When money is worth 5% ?

7. $ 1608 payable in 1 yr. 3 mo. 20 da., when money is worth 8% ? When money is worth 6% ?

8. $ 2575 payable in 5 mo. 17 da., when money is worth 7½% ? When money is worth 6½% ?

9. $ 1357.85 payable in 90 da., when money is worth 8% ? When money is worth 7½ % ?

10. $ 3180.50 payable in 2 yr. 3 mo. 21 da., when money is worth 5½ % ?

11. A owes $ 175.90, due in 3 yr. 8 mo., which he wishes to pay immediately. How much should he pay, money being worth 5% ?

12. A merchant was offered a credit of 3 months on a bill of goods amounting to $ 3468, or a discount of 2% for cash. How much better was the latter offer, money being worth 7% ?

13. Mr. Hyatt owes me $460.75, due in 8 mo. 15 da. If he desires to pay me now, what sum should I accept, money being worth 6½% ?

14. What is the difference between the true discount of $ 248.76, due in 2 yr. 3 mo. 15 da., and the interest of $ 248.76 for 2 yr. 3 mo. 15 da., money being worth 6% ?

BANK DISCOUNT.

373. An institution chartered under the law to receive money for safe keeping, to loan money, or to issue notes or bills to circulate as money, is called a **Bank**.

374. A considerable part of the business of most banks is the paying of notes before they are due.

375. If a bank becomes satisfied that a note is valid or properly secured by indorsement, it may advance the sum due at maturity (Art. 355) less the simple interest on that sum for the time the note has still to run. The note, which is retained at the bank, is then said to be *discounted*.

Banks usually discount for short periods, not exceeding 3 or 4 mo.

376. The number of days from the time a note is discounted to the time when it legally matures is called the **Term of Discount**.

1. In a majority of the states and territories when a note falls due on Sunday or on a legal holiday, it matures on the next *succeeding* business day, and the term of discount includes that day ; consequently, in such of these states as allow days of grace, 4, 5, or even 6 days of grace may be allowed before a note *legally matures*.

However, in a few states, a note matures on the business day next *preceding*, but the term of discount is considered to be the full time.

2. A list of the states and territories which do not allow days of grace is given in Art. 355, Note 1.

Throughout this book, in examples involving the term of discount of notes, when no place is mentioned, days of grace are to be reckoned.

377. Simple interest collected in advance for the term of discount upon the sum due on a note at its maturity is called **Bank Discount**.

A bank usually demands that the notes which it discounts be made payable at that bank.

378. The sum due on a note at its maturity, less the bank discount, is called the **Proceeds** or **Avails** of a note.

379. To find the time when notes mature, the term of discount, the discount, and the proceeds:

1. $ 350.86. BUFFALO, N.Y., July 5, 1899.

Three months after date, for value received, I promise to pay David B. Graham, or order, Three Hundred Fifty $\frac{86}{100}$ Dollars, at the First National Bank.

DANIEL R. SLAUSON.

Discounted August 1, 1899, at 6%.

SOLUTION.

Since days of grace are not allowed in the State of New York, the note *matures* on Oct. 5.

The *term of discount* is from Aug. 1 to Oct. 5, 65 da.

The *bank discount* is the interest of $ 350.86 at 6% for 65 da., which is $ 3.80.

The *proceeds* = $ 350.86 − $ 3.80 = $ 347.06.

NOTE. — Although the time in the note is expressed by *months*, the term of discount is reckoned by counting the actual number of days from the date of discount to the date of maturity.

2. $ 685.30. MINNEAPOLIS, MINN., Jan. 7, 1892.

Sixty days after date, I promise to pay to the order of William S. Watson, Six Hundred Eighty-five $\frac{80}{100}$ Dollars, for value received, at The Commercial National Bank.

HENRY G. DANFORTH.

Discounted Feb. 3, 1892, at 8%.

SOLUTION.

The note *matures* nominally 60 days after Jan. 7, or on Mar. 7; but since 3 days of grace are allowed in Minnesota, the note *legally matures* on Mar. 10. The date of maturity is commonly indicated thus: Mar. $^7/_{10}$.

The *term of discount* is from Feb. 3 to Mar. 10, 36 da.

The *bank discount* is the interest of $ 685.30, at 8%, for 36 da., counting 360 da. a year.

The discount is, therefore, $ 5.48.

The proceeds = $ 685.30 − $ 5.48 = $ 679.82.

NOTE. — In computing interest by days, 360 days are usually considered a year.

3. $764.75. PORTLAND, ME., Feb. 4, 1896.

Three months after date, for value received, I promise to pay Francis Damon, or order, Seven Hundred Sixty-four $\frac{75}{100}$ Dollars, at the Girard Bank.

D. B. BARTON.

Discounted Mar. 10, 1896, at 6 %.

4. $537.45. PROVIDENCE, R.I., May 14, 1896.

Three months after date, for value received, I promise to pay Henry R. Grover, or order, Five Hundred Thirty-seven $\frac{45}{100}$ Dollars, at the First National Bank.

DONALD MCNAUGHTON.

Discounted May 25, 1896, at 6 %.

5. $850.50. RICHMOND, VA., Oct. 6, 1899.

Sixty days after date, for value received, I promise to pay William Sanford, or order, Eight Hundred Fifty $\frac{50}{100}$ Dollars, at the Union Bank.

SAMUEL J. DUNDSON.

Discounted Nov. 1, 1899, at 6 %.

6. $235.68. RICHMOND, VA., JAN. 8, 1896.

Four months after date, for value received, I promise to pay C. F. Cramer, or order, Two Hundred Thirty-five $\frac{68}{100}$ Dollars, at the Merchants' Bank.

HENRY C. PEAKE.

Discounted April 12, 1896, at 6 %.

7. $472.48. SAN FRANCISCO, CAL., April 2, 1898.

Five months after date, for value received, I promise to pay R. B. Goodrich, or order, Four Hundred Seventy-two $\frac{48}{100}$ Dollars, at the Citizens' Bank.

H. BOYLE THOMPSON.

Discounted May 29, 1898, at 7 %.

8. $1000. New Orleans, La., June 24, 1891.

Four months after date, for value received, I promise to pay Mary C. Platt, or order, One Thousand Dollars, at the First National Bank.

Draper S. Andrews.

Discounted Sept. 10, 1891, at 5%.

9. $1100. Atlanta, Ga., July 5, 1891.

Three months after date, I promise to pay G. E. Fillmore, or order, Eleven Hundred Dollars, at the Mechanics' Bank, with interest at 6%. Value received.

J. T. Hosmer.

Discounted Aug. 5, 1891, at 6%.

If a note bears interest, find the discount on the *amount* of the note at its maturity.

10. 135\frac{50}{100}$. Des Moines, Ia., May 3, 1891.

Sixty days after date, I promise to pay F. H. Stowell, or order, One Hundred Thirty-five $\frac{50}{100}$ Dollars, with interest at 6%, for value received.

A. L. Munson.

Discounted May 20, 1891, at 6%.

11. $637.85. Detroit, Mich., Feb. 16, 1891.

Four months after date, for value received, I promise to pay to the order of C. G. Lamson, Six Hundred Thirty-seven $\frac{85}{100}$ Dollars, with interest at 7%.

Spencer C. Granger.

Discounted Apr. 4, 1891, at 7%.

12. $1200. Galveston, Tex., Aug. 3, 1891.

Ninety days after date, I promise to pay Peter R. Goodwin, or order, Twelve Hundred Dollars, for value received, at the First National Bank.

Robert C. Cropsey.

Discounted Sept. 2, 1891, at 8%.

380. To find the face of a note when the proceeds, time, and rate are given.

1. What is the bank discount of a note for $1, due in 1 mo. 27 da. at 6%? What are the proceeds?

2. Since $.99 is the proceeds of $1 when discounted at a bank for 1 mo. 27 da. at 6%, of what sum is $1.98 the proceeds for the same time and rate? $2.97? $3.96? $4.95?

3. Of what sum is $1.97 the proceeds when a note is discounted at a bank for 2 mo. 27 da.? $2.955?

WRITTEN EXERCISES.

381. 1. The proceeds of a note for 2 mo. 12 da. discounted at a bank at 7% were $1182.50. What was the face of the note?

SOLUTION.

$$\$1 - \$.0145\tfrac{5}{6} = \$.9854\tfrac{1}{6}, \text{ Proceeds of } \$1.$$
$$\$1182.50 \div \$.9854\tfrac{1}{6} = 1200, \therefore \$1200 \text{ is the face of note.}$$

RULE. — *Divide the proceeds by the proceeds of $1 at the given rate for 3 days more than the specified time.*

2. The proceeds of a note for 3 mo. when discounted at a bank at 6% were $590.70. What was its face?

3. What must be the face of a note at 60 da., the proceeds of which when discounted at a bank at 6%, are $336.43?

4. The proceeds of a note for 1 mo. 18 da. when discounted at a bank at 5% were $1869.35. What was its face?

5. A gentleman wishes to raise $1000 by having his note for 2 mo. discounted at a bank at 6%. What must be the face of the note?

6. For what sum must a note for 2 mo. 17 da. be made so that the proceeds after it has been discounted at a bank at 7% may be $895?

STOCKS AND BONDS.

382. **1.** Into how many shares of $100 each can the capital stock of a company amounting to $100,000 be divided.

Shares will be regarded as $100 each unless otherwise specified.

2. How much of the capital does a man own who has 50 shares? 75 shares? 100 shares?

3. How much stock is represented by a certificate entitling the holder to 50 shares? To 100 shares?

4. What is the market value of 20 shares of stock when it is sold at the original or *par value?*

5. What is the market value of 20 shares of stock when it is sold at 5% *above* the original or *par value?*

6. What is the market value of 20 shares of stock when it is sold at 5% *below* the original or par value?

7. What will be the cost of a share of stock at 5% above par value, if I pay a *stockbroker* $\frac{1}{8}$% of the par value of the stock for purchasing it?

8. What will be the cost of a share of stock at 5% below par value, if I pay $\frac{1}{8}$% for purchasing it?

9. What is the value of 10 shares of bank stock at 90% of its par value?

10. What will 4 shares of stock cost at 5% above the par value, if $\frac{1}{8}$% of the par value is paid to the broker for purchasing it?

11. A company with a capital stock of $100,000 gained $10,000 above its expenses. What % of the capital stock was the gain, and if the gain was divided among the stockholders, what % of dividend did each receive?

12. If the gain or *dividend* upon the capital stock is 10%, when money is loaned at 5%, would the stock sell above or below par?

13. If the dividend was only 1% of the capital stock, how would the stock sell?

14. If a company whose capital stock is $100,000 loses $10,000, what % of the capital stock is the deficiency or loss?

15. If the loss must be made good by the stockholders, how much must a man pay who owns 10 shares of the stock, or what will be his *assessment?*

16. What will be the annual income of a written obligation called a *bond* for $10,000, if it pays 10% interest annually?

383. When a large sum of money is to be raised for the purpose of carrying on some enterprise, usually a number of people contribute a portion of the sum or capital stock, and thus form a **Company.**

384. As soon as the money is subscribed or raised, a **Charter,** or legal document, which defines the powers and limitations of the company, is obtained.

One of the special advantages of a charter is that it commonly limits each stockholder's liability to the amount he has contributed, whereas as a member of an *unincorporated* company or a firm, each person is liable for all the debts of the company.

385. Each person receives a **Certificate** which shows what amount he has contributed. This certificate usually specifies the *number of shares* of stock to which the person is entitled, and the *original value* of each share.

386. The value of the shares of stock named in the certificate is called the **Par Value.**

When the business is very profitable, the market value of the shares of stock is *high* or *above par*, or *at a premium;* when the business is unprofitable the shares are *low* or *below par*, or *at a discount.*

387. When the stock subscribed by a stockholder is not all paid in at one time, the several portions paid in are called **Installments.**

388. When the business of the company has been prosperous, the gain is divided among the stockholders, and each one's share is termed a **Dividend.**

389. When the business has not been prosperous, the stockholders are required to make up the deficiency by an **Assessment.**

390. The prices of stocks vary according to the prosperity of the business, so that some stocks sell above par, and others below. The sum for which stocks sell is called the **Market Value.**

391. A written obligation under seal, securing the payment of a sum of money before a specified time, is called a **Bond.**

When the United States, any state, city, county, town, village, or incorporated company wishes to raise funds for some purpose, bonds are prepared and sold. The bonds are thus secured by the property of those who issue them, and bear a fixed rate of interest payable annually, semiannually, or quarterly.

392. When the bonds are recorded by their numbers and the names of the persons owning them, they are called **Registered Bonds.**

Registered Bonds cannot be transferred without a change being made in the record kept by the company.

393. Bonds to which interest certificates, called **Coupons,** are attached are called **Coupon Bonds.**

The coupons are cut off and presented for payment, at banks or elsewhere, when interest is due.

394. Government bonds and state bonds are of various kinds, and they are briefly described by abbreviations for rate of interest, date of payment, etc.

Thus, U.S. 4's, 1907, reg., means United States registered bonds, bearing 4% interest, payable in 1907.

Bonds are discussed with Stocks because they are bought and sold at the Stock Exchange, though there is little intrinsically common to Stocks and Bonds. Bonds pay regular interest at fixed rates; the income from Stocks is variable.

395. A person whose business it is to buy and sell stocks is called a **Stock Broker,** and the compensation he receives for his services is called **Brokerage.**

396. PRINCIPLE. — *Brokerage is computed upon the par value of the stock.*

WRITTEN EXERCISES.

397. 1. What is the cost of 500 shares Hanover and King's Point Canal Co. stock at $50\frac{1}{2}$, brokerage $\frac{1}{8}\%$?

$$50\frac{1}{2}\% + \frac{1}{8}\% = 50\frac{5}{8}\%.$$
$$50\frac{5}{8}\% \text{ of } \$100 = \$50.62\frac{1}{2}, \text{ cost of 1 share.}$$
$$\$50.62\frac{1}{2} \times 500 = \$25312.50, \text{ the entire cost.}$$

EXPLANATION. — Since $50\frac{1}{2}\%$ of the par value of the stock is the price paid for it, the entire cost of the stock, including the rate for brokerage, is $50\frac{5}{8}\%$ of the par value of the stock. And since the par value of a share of the stock is $100, the cost of a share will be $50\frac{5}{8}\%$ of $100, or $50.62\frac{1}{2}$, and the cost of 500 shares of the stock will therefore be 500 times $50.62\frac{1}{2}$, or $25312.50.

2. Find the cost of 150 shares Canadian Pacific R.R. stock at 89, brokerage $\frac{1}{8}\%$.

3. How much will 76 shares C., B., & Q. R.R. stock cost at 102, brokerage $\frac{1}{8}\%$?

4. What will be the cost of 45 shares U.S. Express Co. stock at 55, brokerage $\frac{1}{8}\%$?

5. How much must be paid for 120 shares Columbia Coal Co. stock at $33\frac{3}{4}$, brokerage $\frac{1}{8}\%$?

6. What must be paid for $6000 in U.S. currency, 5's, '96 at $8\frac{1}{4}\%$ premium, brokerage $\frac{1}{8}\%$?

7. How much will 125 shares N.Y. C. & H. R. R.R. stock cost at $113\frac{1}{2}$, brokerage $\frac{1}{8}\%$?

8. I bought 180 shares Long Island R.R. stock at 94, and afterwards sold them at $101\frac{1}{2}$. How much did I gain, the brokerage in each case being $\frac{1}{8}\%$?

9. What will be the cost of 85 shares of railroad stock at $8\frac{3}{4}\%$ discount, brokerage $\frac{1}{8}\%$?

10. What must be paid for 375 shares Telegraph stock at $12\frac{3}{4}\%$ premium, brokerage $\frac{1}{8}\%$?

11. What will be the cost of $12,500 in U.S. 4's, '97 reg, at $16\frac{3}{8}\%$ premium, brokerage $\frac{1}{8}\%$?

12. I bought 130 shares Rock Island R.R. stock at $106\frac{1}{4}$, and afterwards sold them at $109\frac{3}{4}$. What was the gain, brokerage in each case $\frac{1}{8}\%$?

13. How many shares of bank stock, at 5% discount, can be purchased for $3805, if $\frac{1}{8}\%$ is paid for brokerage ?

$100\% - 5\% = 95\%,$
$95\% + \frac{1}{8}\% = 95\frac{1}{8}\%,$
$3805 \div 95\frac{1}{8} = 40.$

EXPLANATION. — Since the stock was bought at 5% discount, it was bought at 95% of its par value, but the brokerage increased the cost $\frac{1}{8}\%$, so that each dollar's worth of stock cost $95\frac{1}{8}\%$ of its par value, or $95\frac{1}{8}$ per share. Therefore, as many shares of stock can be bought for $3805 as $95\frac{1}{8}$ is contained times in $3805, which is 40 times. Therefore 40 shares can be bought.

14. How many shares Oregon Navigation Co.'s stock, at 78, can be bought for $9375, brokerage $\frac{1}{8}\%$?

15. How many shares Reading R.R. stock, at $61\frac{1}{4}$, can be bought for $6874, brokerage $\frac{1}{8}\%$?

16. Find the number of pipe line certificates, at $115\frac{3}{4}$, that can be bought for $18,520, each certificate being $100.

17. What income will be realized from investing $4190.63 in 5% stock, purchased at 93, allowing $\frac{1}{8}$% for brokerage?

$$\$4190.63 \div \$93\tfrac{1}{8} = 45.$$

Par value 45 shares = $4500.

$$\$4500 \times .05 = \$225, \text{ annual income.}$$

EXPLANATION. — Since the stock cost $93\frac{1}{8}$% of its par value, every share cost $93\frac{1}{8}$; and as many shares can be bought for $4190.63 as $93\frac{1}{8}$ is contained times in that sum, which is 45 times, or 45 shares. Since the stock paid 5% income, the entire income from 45 shares or $4500 is 5% of $4500, which is $225.

18. What will be the annual income from investing $3457.50 in 5% stock, purchased at $57\frac{1}{2}$, allowing $\frac{1}{8}$% for brokerage?

19. What income will be derived from $4565 invested in Mich. 7's at 114, brokerage $\frac{1}{8}$%?

20. What income will a man derive from $10,777.375 invested in railroad bonds paying an annual dividend of 10%, if he buys them at $98\frac{3}{4}$, brokerage $\frac{1}{8}$%?

21. Which is the more profitable, and how much, to invest $6000 in 6% stock at 75, or in 5% stock, purchased at 60%?

22. How much will be realized from investing $15,180 in $4\frac{1}{2}$% bonds, purchased at $94\frac{3}{4}$, brokerage $\frac{1}{8}$%?

23. How much must be invested in 6% stock, purchased at 90, to secure to the purchaser an income of $900 annually?

$$\$900 \div \$6 = 150.$$

Par value 150 shares = $15,000.

$$\$15,000 \times .90 = \$13,500, \text{ cost of stock.}$$

EXPLANATION. — Since the income from 1 share is $6, it will require as many shares to secure an income of $900 as $6 is contained times in $900, which is 150 times, or 150 shares; and since the stock is selling at 90% of its par value, 90% of $15,000, which is $13,500, is the cost.

24. How much must be invested in 7% city bonds, bought at $101\frac{1}{2}$, brokerage $\frac{1}{8}$%, to yield an annual income of $840?

25. How much must I invest in D. and H. Canal Co. R.R. stock at 142, brokerage $\frac{1}{8}$%, to secure an income of $1600, if the stock pays a dividend of 10%?

26. What sum must be invested in U. S. 4's at $121\frac{1}{4}$, brokerage at $\frac{1}{8}$%, to secure an annual income of $900?

27. When Wisconsin Central 5's are selling at $95\frac{1}{2}$, how much must be invested to produce an income of $1000, brokerage $\frac{1}{8}$%?

28. What per cent income on my investment will I receive, if I buy 6% stock at 20% premium?

$6 \div $120 = .05$, or 5%.

EXPLANATION. — Since 1 share of the stock costs $120, and the income from it is $6, the income is $\frac{6}{120}$, or 5% of the investment.

29. A man received 6% dividend on stock bought at 25% below par. What rate of interest did he receive on his investment?

30. What is the rate per cent of income realized from 6% bonds bought at 90?

31. How much must I pay for New York 6's so that I may realize an income of 9% on the investment?

$6 \div .09 = $66\frac{2}{3}$.
$66\frac{2}{3} = 66\frac{2}{3}$% of par value.

EXPLANATION. — Since I wish to realize 9% on my investment and the stock yields an income of $6 per share, $6 must be 9% of the price I should pay for the stock. Therefore, I must pay $66\frac{2}{3}$ per share or $66\frac{2}{3}$% of its par value.

32. What must be paid for stock which pays a dividend of 10%, so as to realize 7% on the investment?

33. How much must I pay for stock which pays a dividend of 12% so that I may realize 8% on the investment?

REVIEW EXERCISES.

ORAL EXERCISES.

398. 1. A man who had $360 spent 25% of his money. How much had he left?

2. B's salary was $1500 per year, and he saved $33\frac{1}{3}\%$ of it. How much did he spend?

3. In selling a suit of clothes a merchant took 10% less than the price asked and received $36. What was the asking price?

4. If a man who earns $60 a month spends $45 for necessary expenses, what per cent of his earnings does he save?

5. What per cent of $36 is $24?

6. What per cent of the cost does a jeweler make by selling a watch for $20 that cost him $14?

7. Of what sum is 60 dollars $62\frac{1}{2}\%$?

8. A cow cost $45, which was 15% of the cost of a horse. What did the horse cost?

9. A dealer sold coal at $4.80 a ton, which was 20% more than it cost him. What did he pay for it?

10. A merchant sold a pair of shoes for $1.50, thereby losing 25% of the cost. What was the cost?

11. I bought a horse for $200, and sold it at an advance of 20%. What did I get for it?

12. What per cent is gained by selling goods that cost 10 cents a yard at $12\frac{1}{2}$ cents a yard?

13. An agent gets a discount of 20% from the retail price of articles, and sells them at the retail price. What is his gain per cent?

14. By selling butter at 6 cents a pound more than cost, a grocer made 20%. What did he pay for it?

15. I sold two cows for $45 each. On one I gained 25%, and on the other I lost 25%. Did I gain or lose by the transaction, and how much?

16. A boy bought apples at the rate of 3 for 5 cents, which he sold at the rate of 4 for 10 cents. What per cent did he gain?

17. A boy lost 80 cents, which was just 20% of his money. How much money had he?

18. B gained $18, which was 30% of what he then had. How much had he at first?

19. A merchant bought 125 barrels of flour, and after losing 20% of it, he sold 25% of the remainder. What per cent of the whole had he left?

20. A cistern containing 60 bbl. of water receives by one pipe 5% of its contents in an hour, and by another loses 15%. How much remains in it at the end of an hour?

21. When a man sells goods at a price from which he received a discount of 40%, what is his gain per cent?

22. What per cent does a merchant gain who buys flour at $4.50 a barrel, and sells it at $6 a barrel?

23. A book was sold for 90 cents, which was at a gain of 20%. What would have been the gain per cent if it had been sold for $1?

24. An agent sold $870 worth of goods at a commission of $3\frac{1}{3}$%. How much did he receive?

25. A book agent received $60 for selling $150 worth of books. What was his rate of commission?

26. A real estate agent received $120 for selling a house and lot, at 2% commission. For how much was the property sold?

27. A company declares a dividend of $12\frac{1}{2}$%. How much will a stockholder owning 20 shares receive?

28. An agent received $324 with which to buy peaches, after deducting his commission of 8%. How much did he expend for peaches ?

29. A house worth $6000 was insured for ⅔ of its value, at 1¼%. What was the premium ?

30. What is the interest of $300 for 3 years 4 months, at 6% ?

WRITTEN EXERCISES.

399. 1. The number of youth of school age in a certain city is 16,767, which is 34½% of the number of inhabitants. What is the population of the city ?

2. A man invested $8160 in land, which was 62½% of all his money. How much money had he left ?

3. A farm was sold for $6300, which was 12½% more than it cost. What was the cost of the farm ?

4. By selling wheat at a gain of 15%, a speculator received $20,125. What did the wheat cost him ?

5. If a teacher who receives a yearly salary of $900 pays $250 a year for board, and $100 for other expenses, what per cent of his salary does he save ?

6. A speculator had 6000 barrels of flour that cost him $4.50 a barrel. He sold 30% of the lot at an advance of 10% of the cost, and 50% of the remainder at an advance of 12½% of the cost. He then closed out the lot at $5 a barrel. How much did he gain on the flour ?

7. A man left $4500 to his wife, which was 62½% of the sum bequeathed to his children, and the sum bequeathed to his wife and children was 75% of his estate. What per cent of the estate did the wife receive ?

8. A drover bought horses at $145 a head, paid $11 for taking each of them to market, and then sold them at $175.50 a head. What was the gain per cent ?

9. A man paid $ 4860 for a farm, and sold it for $ 5346. What was the gain per cent ?

10. An agent in Savannah received $ 12,180 with which to purchase cotton, after deducting his commission of $1\frac{1}{2}\%$. How much did he expend for cotton, and what was his commission ?

11. What will be the total cost of 800 yards of carpeting, at $ 1.60 a yard, if a merchant pays $1\frac{3}{4}\%$ commission for purchasing it ?

12. A company with a capital of $ 76,500 declares a dividend of 7%, and still has a surplus of $ 2500. What were the net earnings of the company ?

13. The owners of a ship paid $ 306 for an insurance policy of $ 13,600. What was the rate of premium ?

14. A grain dealer paid $ 225 for insuring a cargo of wheat at $1\frac{1}{2}\%$. For how much was it insured ?

15. For what sum must a cargo of goods valued at $12,360 be insured, at $1\frac{3}{4}\%$, to cover both property and premium, in case of loss ?

16. If the assessed valuation of a town is $ 2,360,000, and the town has 640 polls, paying $ 1.50 each, what must be the rate of taxation in order to raise $ 10,400 ?

17. A manufacturer imported from Spain 30 bales of wool, 300 lb. each, invoiced at 32 cts. per pound, and 25 bales, 250 lb. each, invoiced at 30 cts. per pound. What was the duty, at 20% ad valorem ?

18. A speculator bought 65 shares W. U. Telegraph stock at 90, and sold them at $94\frac{3}{4}$. How much did he gain, brokerage in each case being $\frac{1}{8}\%$?

19. A man borrowed $ 160 Apr. 1, 1889, and paid it Dec. 8, 1891, with interest at 6%. What amount did he pay ?

20. My taxes were $ 315.25. What was the assessed valuation of my property, if the rate of taxation was .015 ?

21. A note of $300, dated May 12, 1887, is due in 4 years, with interest at 6%, payable annually. If both interest and principal remain unpaid, what will be the amount due on the note May 12, 1891?

22. What is the compound interest of $750 for 3 yr. 8 mo. 12 da., at 6%?

23. What principal will yield $13.50 interest in 9 mo. 18 da., at 6%?

24. What is the difference between the present worth and proceeds of $560 due in 2 yr. 6 mo., at 6%? (No grace.)

25. A grain speculator bought 6000 bushels of wheat, at 95 cents per bushel, cash. He sold it the same day at an advance of $3\frac{1}{2}$%, receiving in payment a note due in 1 mo., without interest, which he had discounted at a bank at 6%. What was his gain in cash?

26. A piano, the list price of which was $420, was sold at a discount of 30% and 10%. If the freight was $6.50, and the drayage $2.75, what was the net cost of the piano?

27. What was the list price of an article whose net cost was $4.50, after deducting discounts of 40% and 10%?

28. What are the net proceeds of a sale of 300 bbl. pork at $20 per barrel, less the following charges: freight, 40¢ per barrel; insurance, $\frac{1}{4}$%; commission, $2\frac{1}{2}$%?

29. After getting a note, without interest, discounted at a bank for 3 mo. at 6%, I had $354.42. What was the face of the note? (Allow days of grace.)

30. I sold $\frac{2}{5}$ of my property for cash, at a gain of $33\frac{1}{3}$%, and the rest for $\frac{2}{3}$ of the cost of the whole, receiving in payment a note due in 3 months, without interest, which I got discounted at a bank, at 6%. What was my gain per cent, if my property cost $24,000?

31. A man sold 144 shares of Mass. 5's at par, and invested the proceeds in Mich. 7's at 120. What was the change in his annual income?

EXCHANGE.

400. 1. When A owes B $500, and B owes A $500, how may the accounts be settled without any transfer of money taking place?

2. When A in Chicago owes B in New York $500, and C in New York owes A $1000, how can A pay his indebtedness to B without remitting the money?

3. What will be the indebtedness of A, B, and C to each other after the transaction has taken place?

4. A and C live in the same city, and B in a distant city. A owes B $2000, and B owes C $1000. How may B pay his indebtedness to C without remitting the money?

5. What will be their indebtedness to each other after A has paid B's order, or *draft?*

6. What will a draft for $500 cost, payable when it is presented, or *at sight*, if ½% premium is charged for it?

7. How much should be deducted from the price of the above draft if it is not to be paid until two months, money being worth 6%?

8. What will be the cost of a draft for $50, payable at sight, if it is purchased at 1% discount?

9. What will be the cost of a sight draft for $300, purchased at ½% premium?

10. If A in Nashville owes B in New Orleans $1000, and C in New Orleans owes D in Nashville $1500, how may A pay his indebtness without remitting the money?

11. If the premium is $\frac{1}{8}\%$, how much will it cost me to remit a draft for $ 800 from Cincinnati to Cleveland?

12. If a man sells a draft for $ 500, at a premium of $\frac{3}{4}\%$, how much does he receive for it?

13. A wishes to send to his agent in New Orleans a draft for $ 5000. If the premium on exchange is $\frac{3}{4}\%$, how much will the draft cost him?

14. When I pay $ 2025 for a sight draft on New York for $ 2000, what is the premium, or *rate* of exchange?

15. When I can buy a sight draft on Chicago for $ 2000, paying for it $ 1980, what is the rate of exchange?

16. If Mr. Burt pays $ 4975 for a sight draft on Cincinnati for $ 5000, at what rate is exchange?

401. The method of making payments in distant places without transmitting money is termed **Exchange**.

1. Thus, when A in San Francisco owes B in New York $ 500, and C in New York owes D in San Francisco $ 500, C may go to B and pay him $ 500 for an order upon A in San Francisco for $ 500, and then send it to D. A then pays D, and the indebtedness is paid without the transmission of money.

2. Exchange is therefore a very convenient and safe way of cancelling debts.

3. The business is carried on largely by banks, which charge a small sum for transacting the same.

402. The written order of one party to another, to pay a specified sum of money to the party named in his order, is termed a **Draft** or **Bill of Exchange**.

An order upon a *bank*, by a person who has money deposited in it, is called a **Check**.

403. The person who makes the order is the **Drawer**. The person to whom the order is addressed is the **Drawee**. The person to whom the money is to be paid is the **Payee**.

404. When a drawee accepts a draft, he writes the word "accepted" upon the face of the draft with the date of acceptance.

405. A draft made payable on presentation is termed a **Sight Draft.** A draft payable at a specified time after presentation or after sight is a **Time Draft.**

The laws in the various states as to grace on drafts are not strictly in accord with those concerning grace on notes. In the examples given grace is allowed on time drafts, but not on sight drafts.

FORM OF A DRAFT.

$ 290 18/100.   Cincinnati, O., July 20, 1892.

At sight, pay to the order of David Henderson & Co., Two hundred Ninety 18/100 Dollars, value received, and charge to the account of

American Book Company.

To Cone & Carson, Bankers,
    Denver, Colorado.

DOMESTIC EXCHANGE.

406. **Domestic Exchange** treats of drafts payable in the country in which they are made.

1. When the bankers of Denver have not sufficient money on deposit in New York to meet the drafts they are making upon New York, they must send money to meet them. This naturally raises the **price** of drafts in Denver, or exchange on New York is *at a premium.*

2. When the bankers of Denver have large sums of money deposited in the banks of New York upon which they receive no interest, they are often anxious to sell drafts on New York *at a discount*, so that they may get money to use at home without the expense of having it forwarded by express.

WRITTEN EXERCISES.

407. **1.** What will be the cost of a sight draft upon New York for $10,000, at $\frac{1}{4}\%$ premium?

$$\$1 + \$.00\tfrac{1}{4} = \$1.00\tfrac{1}{4}.$$
$$\$1.00\tfrac{1}{4} \times 10,000 = \$10,025.$$

EXPLANATION. — Since exchange on New York is at $\frac{1}{4}\%$ premium, every dollar of the draft will cost 1.00\frac{1}{4}$, and a draft for $10,000 will cost 10,000 times 1.00$\frac{1}{4}$, or $10,025.

2. What will be the cost in Boston of a draft for $5000 on St. Paul, payable 2 mo. after date, the rate of exchange being at $\frac{1}{2}\%$ premium?

$$\$1 + \$.00\tfrac{1}{2} = \$1.005.$$
$$\$1.005 - \$.0105 = \$.9945.$$
$$\$.9945 \times 5000 = \$4972.50.$$

EXPLANATION. — Since the exchange on St. Paul is at $\frac{1}{2}\%$ premium, every dollar of the draft would cost $1.005 if paid at sight. But since the draft is not to be paid in St. Paul for 2 mo. and 3 da., the banker in Boston, who has the use of the money for that time, inasmuch as he is not obliged to pay the draft for 2 mo. 3 da., allows the bank discount on the face of the draft for that time. The bank discount in Minnesota for that time at the legal rate is $.0105, and this subtracted from $1.005 gives the cost of $1 of the draft. Since the cost of $1 of the draft is $.9945, the cost of $5000 is 5000 times that sum, or $4972.50.

3. What will be the cost in St. Louis, Mo., of a sight draft on Philadelphia for $1200, the rate of exchange being at $\frac{3}{4}\%$ premium?

4. What will be the cost in Denver of a sight draft on Boston for $1500, exchange being at $\frac{3}{8}\%$ discount?

5. What must be paid in New York for a sight draft on Cleveland for $800, when exchange is at $\frac{5}{8}\%$ premium?

6. What will be the cost in Cincinnati of a draft for $1600 on Topeka, payable 2 mo. after date, exchange being at $\frac{1}{4}\%$ premium, and interest at 8%?

7. What must be paid for a draft for $475, payable 30 days after date, at $\frac{1}{8}\%$ premium, and interest at 6%?

8. What must be paid for a draft drawn at Philadelphia on Indianapolis for $600, payable 90 days after date, at $\frac{3}{8}\%$ discount, interest at 6%?

9. Find the cost of a draft for $900, payable in 60 days, when exchange is at $\frac{1}{8}\%$ premium, and interest at 7%.

10. What will be the cost of a draft on Galveston for $1200, payable in 60 days, exchange being at $1\frac{1}{2}\%$ discount, and interest at 8%?

11. What must be paid for a draft of $550, at 30 days, exchange being at $\frac{5}{8}\%$ premium, and interest at 4%?

12. Find the cost of a draft on Des Moines for $1750, payable 90 days after date, exchange being at $1\frac{1}{4}\%$ discount, and interest at 7%.

13. How large a sight draft on New Orleans can be purchased for $5000, when the exchange is at $1\frac{1}{2}\%$ premium?

$1 + $.015 = $1.015.
$5000 ÷ $1.015 = 4926.11 —

EXPLANATION. — Since exchange is at $1\frac{1}{2}\%$ premium, it will cost $1.015 to buy a draft for $1, and $5000 will buy a draft for as many dollars as $1.015 is contained times in $5000, or $4926.11.

14. How large a draft in Buffalo, N.Y., can be purchased for $3000, payable 2 mo. after sight in Raleigh, N.C., exchange being at 1% discount?

$1.00 − $.01 = $.99.
$.99 − $.0105 = $.9795.
$3000 ÷ $.9795 = 3062.78 +

EXPLANATION. — Since exchange is at 1% discount, it would cost $.99 to buy a draft of $1, if it were payable at sight. But since the draft is not to be paid until 2 mo. 3 da.,

the banker in Buffalo, who has the use of the money for that time, allows bank discount upon the face of the draft for that time, or $.0105 for every dollar. Therefore, since it costs $.9795 to purchase a draft of $1, $3000 will purchase a draft for as many dollars as $.9795 is contained times in $3000, or $3062.78.

15. How large a sight draft can be purchased on Cincinnati for $2800, when the rate of exchange is at $\frac{3}{4}\%$ premium?

16. How large a sight draft can be bought on Boston, Mass., for $1260, when the exchange is at $1\frac{1}{4}\%$ premium?

17. How large a sight draft on New York can be purchased in St. Joseph, Mo., for $1800, when the exchange is at $\frac{5}{8}\%$ discount?

18. How large a draft, payable 30 days after sight, can be bought for $2000, exchange being at 1% premium, and money being worth 6%?

19. Find the face of a draft on Detroit, at 60 days sight, bought for $650, exchange being at $1\frac{1}{4}\%$ premium, and money being worth 6%.

20. What is the face of a draft on New Orleans, at 90 days sight, which may be bought for $1000, exchange being at $\frac{7}{8}\%$ discount, and money being worth 7%?

FOREIGN EXCHANGE.

408. Foreign Exchange treats of drafts drawn in one country and payable in another.

1. Drafts drawn in one State and payable in another are sometimes considered as foreign drafts or bills of exchange.

2. Foreign bills of exchange are drawn upon Antwerp, Amsterdam, Hamburg, Bremen, Berlin, and other commercial centers, but drafts upon London and Paris are much more common since they are paid in any part of Europe.

409. Three drafts or bills of the same date and tenor, named respectively the *first*, *second*, and *third* of exchange are sent by different mails, so that if one is lost the other may be presented. Such a set is called a **Set of Exchange.**

When one bill of the set is paid the others are void.

410. The value of a *pound sterling* or *sovereign* in American gold is $4.8665.

The value of a franc is about $.193, or 5.18 francs per dollar.

The values of the pound sterling and the franc given above, are the values when exchange is at par, but they are continually fluctuating on account of the demand for bills of exchange, the rate being above or below par according as the demand is large or small.

WRITTEN EXERCISES.

411. **1.** What is the cost in New York of a sight draft on London for £312 15 s. 5 d., when exchange is $4.87 for a pound sterling?

SOLUTION.

£312 15 s. 5 d. = £312.7708, value in pounds and decimals of a pound.
$4.87 × 312.7708 = $1523.193 +, the cost of the draft.

2. How large a bill of exchange at sight on London can be bought in New York for $2984.38, exchange being at $4.86 for a pound sterling?

SOLUTION.

$2984.38 ÷ $4.86 = 614.0699.   ∴ $2984.38 = £614.0699.
£614.0699 = £614 1 s. 4¾ d., the face of the draft.

3. What must be paid in New York for a bill of exchange at sight on London for £425 8 s., when sterling exchange is quoted at $4.87½?

4. What will a sterling bill at sight for £317 9 s. cost in Philadelphia when exchange is quoted at $4.90½?

5. How large a draft at sight on London can be bought in Chicago for $1950, when exchange is $4.86⅔?

6. How large a bill of exchange at sight on London can be bought in New York for $2875.80, when exchange is quoted at $4.87½?

7. How large a bill of exchange at sight on London can be bought in New York for $4000, when exchange is $4.865?

8. How much must be paid for a bill of exchange on Paris, at sight, for 5000 francs, exchange being 5.16 francs to the dollar?

9. What must be paid for a sight bill of exchange on Paris for 7865 francs, exchange being 5.18 francs to the dollar?

10. Find the cost of a bill of exchange at sight on Bremen for 5344 marks, exchange being at $.95 (per 4 marks).

PARTNERSHIP.

412. **1.** If two men, who have equal sums invested in the same business, gain $100, what is each man's share of the gain?

2. If one man furnishes $\frac{2}{3}$ of the capital, and another $\frac{1}{3}$ of it, and the gain is $1200, what should be the gain of each?

3. Mr. A furnishes $3000 of the capital, and Mr. B. furnishes the rest, which is $5000. What part of the profits should each receive?

4. Four partners furnish money in the proportion of $2000, $3000, $4000, and $5000 respectively. What part of the gain should each one receive?

5. Three men engage in business and furnish the following sums respectively: A, $5000; B, $4000; C, $3000. How much of the gain should each receive, if $1200 was gained during the year?

6. The profits of a company were $800 for a certain time. What share of the profits did each partner receive, if the capital contributed by them was $900, $700, and $800 respectively?

7. A and B formed a partnership after A had been doing business alone for 6 months. A had $5000 invested during the year, and B had $10,000 invested for 6 months. The gain was $5000. What was each one's share of the gain?

8. The cost of a pasture was $27. A had in it 5 cows for 3 weeks, and B 3 cows for 4 weeks. What should each one pay?

308

413. An association of two or more persons for the purpose of conducting business is a **Partnership.**

414. The persons associated in business are **Partners.** They are termed collectively a *company,* a *firm,* or a *house.*

415. PRINCIPLE. — *The gains and losses of a firm are shared in proportion to the amount of capital each partner invests, and the length of time it is used in the business.*

WRITTEN EXERCISES.

416. 1. A, B, and C engaged in business, A furnishing $9000 of the capital, B $5000, and C $6000. If they gained $6000, what was each partner's share of the gain?

SOLUTION.

$9000 + $5000 + $6000 = $ 20,000, the entire capital.

$\frac{9000}{20000}$ or $\frac{9}{20}$ = A's share of the capital.

∴ $\frac{9}{20}$ of $6000 = $2700, A's share of the gain.

$\frac{5000}{20000}$ or $\frac{1}{4}$ = B's share of the capital.

∴ $\frac{1}{4}$ of $6000 = $1500, B's share of the gain.

$\frac{6000}{20000}$ or $\frac{3}{10}$ = C's share of the capital.

∴ $\frac{3}{10}$ of $6000 = $1800, C's share of the gain.

2. A, B, and C formed a partnership in business, A furnishing $8000 of the capital, B $4500, and C $3500. They gained $3200 the first year. What was each partner's share of the gain?

3. A, B, and C formed a partnership, A putting in $4500, B $5400, and C $4200. On closing the business they found they had lost $2400. What was the loss of each?

4. Three men engaged in business. A furnished $6000 of the capital, B $9600, and C $6400. They made a net

gain of $4800, and then sold out for $30,000. What was each partner's share of the gain?

5. A, B, C, and D formed a partnership. A put in $5625, B $5250, C $7125, and D $6000. What was each partner's share of a profit amounting to $6960?

6. A, B, and C formed a partnership, A contributing $5500, B $6500, and C $4500. When the business was closed up C received $1500 for his share of the gain. How much should each of the others receive?

7. A and B were engaged in business two years, making an annual profit of $8190. During the first year A owned $\frac{2}{3}$ of the stock, and during the second year B owned $\frac{3}{4}$ of it. What was each partner's share of the total profits?

8. E, F, G, and H formed a partnership with a capital of $30,000. E furnished $6000, F $7000, G $8000, and H the remainder. They gained 18% of the joint stock. What was each partner's share of the profit?

9. Three partners had a gain of $6250 to divide according to each member's investment. A invested $10,000, B invested $15,000, and C invested $25,000. What was the net gain of each?

10. A, B, and C engage in business together. A puts in $20,000, and after 3 mo. he takes in B as a partner with $20,000. At the end of 3 mo. more they take in C as a partner, with a capital of $10,000. If they gained during the year $7800, what was each partner's share of the gain?

SOLUTION.

$20,000 employed for 12 mo. = $240,000 for 1 mo., A's capital.
$20,000 employed for 9 mo. = $180,000 for 1 mo., B's capital.
$10,000 employed for 6 mo. = $\underline{\$ \ 60,000}$ for 1 mo., C's capital.

The entire capital for 1 mo. = $480,000

$\therefore$ A's share of the gain is $\frac{240000}{480000}$ or $\frac{1}{2}$ of $7800, which is $3900.
B's share of the gain is $\frac{180000}{480000}$ or $\frac{3}{8}$ of $7800, which is $2925.
C's share of the gain is $\frac{60000}{480000}$ or $\frac{1}{8}$ of $7800, which is $975.

11. A, B, and C entered into partnership. A put in $2800 for 10 months, B $3200 for 1 year, and C $4000 for 8 months. They gained $2952. What was each one's share of the gain?

12. A and B entered into partnership for one year. A had $1200 in the business during the first four months, and $800 more during the remainder of the year. B had $1000 during the first six months, and then took out $200. At the end of the year they found they had lost $1580. What was each partner's loss?

13. A, B, and C hired a pasture for $128. A pastured 6 horses for 8 weeks, B 12 oxen for 10 weeks, and C 40 cows for 12 weeks. If 2 horses eat as much as 3 oxen, and 3 oxen as much as 5 cows, how much did each man pay?

14. A, B, and C engaged in business. A's capital was in trade 4 months, B's 5 months, and C's 12 months. A's gain was $800, B's $1000, and C's $1200, and the whole capital was $25,675. How much capital did each furnish?

15. D and E rented a pasture for $480. D put in 400 sheep, and E 320. At the end of 4 months they disposed of half their stock, and allowed F to put in 210 sheep. What rent should each pay at the end of the 8 months?

16. A, B, and C formed a partnership. A put in $3000 for 5 months, and then increased it $1500 for 4 months more. B put in $9000 for 4 months, and then withdrawing half his capital, continued the remainder 3 months longer. C put in $5500 for 7 months. They gained $3630. What was each partner's share of the gain?

17. A and B entered into partnership Jan. 1, each furnishing $3000 capital. Apr. 1, A added $500, and Sept. 1, he added $500 more. June 1, B added $1000. What share of the profits should each receive at the end of the year, if they gained $2500?

RATIO.

---

417. **1.** How does $3 compare with $6? $5 with $15? $8 with $24?

2. How does 2 compare with 12? 3 with 18? 5 with 25?

3. What relation is 2 to 10? 5 to 25? 6 to 30?

4. What relation is 4 to 12? 10 to 40? 6 to 36?

5. How does 12 compare with 2? 18 with 3? 25 with 5?

6. How does 18 compare with 6? 15 with 5? 40 with 10?

7. What is the relation of 4 to 8? *Between* 4 and 8?

8. What is the relation of 12 to 4? Between 12 and 4?

418. The relation of one number to another of the same kind is **Ratio.**

1. This relation may be expressed in two ways: thus, when it is asked, "what is the relation of 4 to 8?" the answer may be 4 is $\frac{1}{2}$ of 8, called the *geometrical* ratio, or 4 is 4 less than 8, called the *arithmetical* ratio.

2. When the relation of one number to another is sought, the *first* number is the dividend and the *second* the divisor.

3. When the relation *between* two numbers is sought, either may be regarded as dividend or divisor.

419. The numbers compared are the **Terms of the Ratio.**

420. The *first* term is the **Antecedent** and the *second* the **Consequent.**

Thus in the ratio of 5 to 10, 5 is the antecedent and 10 the consequent.

421. The colon (:) is the **Sign** of ratio.

Thus, the ratio of 6 to 15 is expressed 6 : 15.

Since the ratio of one number to another is expressed by the quotient arising from dividing the antecedent by the consequent, the colon may be regarded as the sign of division without the dividing line.

422. The antecedent and consequent together form a **Couplet.**

EXERCISES.

423. What is the ratio of :

1. 3 to 6 ? 15 to 30 ? 9 to 18 ? 54 to 6 ?
2. 5 to 10 ? 20 to 10 ? 7 to 21 ? 28 to 4 ?
3. 8 to 16 ? 16 to 4 ? 6 to 42 ? 33 to 3 ?
4. 12 to 36 ? 36 to 6 ? 8 to 24 ? 56 to 7 ?
5. 18 to 36 ? 40 to 8 ? 18 to 54 ? 72 to 12 ?
6. 15 to 45 ? 35 to 7 ? 14 to 56 ? 85 to 17 ?

What is the ratio of :

7. $\frac{2}{5}$ to $\frac{4}{5}$?

SUGGESTION. — The ratio of $\frac{2}{5}$ to $\frac{4}{5}$ is the same as the ratio of 2 to 4.

8. $\frac{3}{10}$ to $\frac{6}{10}$? $\frac{3}{11}$ to $\frac{1}{11}$? $\frac{4}{13}$ to $\frac{12}{13}$? $\frac{15}{14}$ to $\frac{5}{14}$?
9. $\frac{5}{12}$ to $\frac{10}{12}$? $\frac{14}{19}$ to $\frac{2}{19}$? $\frac{3}{20}$ to $\frac{21}{20}$? $\frac{25}{20}$ to $\frac{5}{20}$?
10. $\frac{6}{27}$ to $\frac{12}{27}$? $\frac{18}{41}$ to $\frac{9}{41}$? $\frac{7}{37}$ to $\frac{42}{37}$? $\frac{56}{61}$ to $\frac{8}{61}$?

What is the ratio of :

11. $\frac{2}{3}$ to $\frac{3}{4}$?

SUGGESTION. — $\frac{2}{3} = \frac{8}{12}$, and $\frac{3}{4} = \frac{9}{12}$; therefore, the ratio of $\frac{2}{3}$ to $\frac{3}{4}$ is the ratio of $\frac{8}{12}$ to $\frac{9}{12}$, or the ratio of 8 to 9 or $\frac{8}{9}$.

12. $\frac{1}{2}$ to $\frac{2}{3}$? $\frac{3}{4}$ to $\frac{4}{5}$? $\frac{2}{7}$ to $\frac{2}{3}$? $\frac{3}{8}$ to $\frac{5}{6}$?
13. $\frac{2}{7}$ to $\frac{5}{8}$? $\frac{5}{9}$ to $\frac{9}{11}$? $\frac{4}{7}$ to $\frac{9}{5}$? $\frac{5}{9}$ to $\frac{3}{7}$?
14. $\frac{3}{13}$ to $\frac{5}{26}$? $\frac{8}{15}$ to $\frac{12}{45}$? $\frac{7}{11}$ to $\frac{8}{12}$? $\frac{9}{10}$ to $\frac{10}{11}$?

PROPORTION.

424. 1. Name two numbers having the relation to each other that 5 has to 10.

2. Name two numbers having the relation that 4 has to 12. 3 to 15.

3. Name two numbers having the relation that 6 has to 30. 10 to 40.

Name two numbers having the relation of:

4. 5 to 20. 4 to 24. 7 to 21. $\frac{2}{3}$ to $\frac{5}{3}$.

5. 6 to 24. 6 to 36. 5 to 40. $\frac{2}{3}$ to $\frac{3}{4}$.

6. 7 to 35. 8 to 32. 9 to 27. $\frac{3}{5}$ to $\frac{5}{7}$.

7. 8 to 48. 7 to 56. 6 to 54. $\frac{4}{9}$ to $\frac{3}{4}$.

8. 9 to 72. 8 to 72. 9 to 108. $\frac{7}{8}$ to $\frac{1}{2}$.

9. What number has the relation to 8 that 5 has to 20?

What number has the relation

10. To 24 that 6 has to 12? To 15 that $\frac{1}{3}$ has to $\frac{1}{2}$?

11. To 30 that 7 has to 21? To 25 that $\frac{2}{3}$ has to $\frac{5}{6}$?

12. To 48 that 9 has to 36? To 32 that $\frac{3}{4}$ has to $\frac{4}{3}$?

13. To 72 that 5 has to 60? To 48 that $\frac{2}{3}$ has to $\frac{2}{5}$?

14. To 88 that 8 has to 64? To 70 that $\frac{3}{5}$ has to $\frac{7}{10}$?

15. If the earnings of 6 men are $30 in a given time, how will the earnings of 10 men compare with the earnings of 6 men in the same time?

16. Since a ratio is the quotient of the antecedent divided by the consequent, or a fraction, what changes may be made upon it without changing its value ?

17. Write two equal ratios. Multiply the first term by the last term, and compare their product with the product of the intermediate terms.

425. An equality of ratios is a **Proportion.**

Thus, 8 : 16 as 4 : 8 is a proportion.

426. A double colon (::) is the **Sign** of proportion.

It is written between the ratios.

It has sometimes been regarded as the extremities of the sign of equality (=).

The sign of equality is often used in proportion instead of the double colon.

427. A proportion must have four terms, viz. two antecedents and two consequents. When any three are given, the other may be found.

428. The *first* and *third* terms of a proportion are the **Antecedents** of the proportion, and the *second* and *fourth* terms are the **Consequents.**

Thus in the proportions 5 : 8 : : 10 : 16, 5 and 10 are the *antecedents*, and 8 and 16 the *consequents*.

429. The *first* and *last* terms are the **Extremes,** and the *second* and *third* terms are the **Means** of a proportion.

Thus in the proportion 10 : 12 : : 5 : 6, 10 and 6 are the *extremes*, and 12 and 5 are the *means*.

430. PRINCIPLES. — 1. *The product of the extremes is equal to the product of the means.*

2. *The product of the extremes divided by either mean gives the other mean.*

3. *The product of the means divided by either extreme gives the other extreme.*

EXERCISES.

431. Find the term that is wanting in the following:

1. $36 : 18 :: 12 : ?$
2. $27 : 54 :: ? : 8.$
3. $24 : 72 :: 21 : ?$
4. $? : 16 :: 18 : 9.$
5. $9 : ? :: 6 : 24.$
6. $20 : 5 :: ? : 4.$
7. $30 : 20 :: 18 : ?$
8. $45 : 60 :: ? : 24.$
9. $48 : 24 :: 8 : ?$
10. $50 : 75 :: 100 : ?$
11. $2.5 : 22.5 :: ? : 5.4.$
12. $? : 5 :: 27 : 12.5.$
13. $\frac{2}{3} : ? :: 12 : 18.$
14. $? : 10 :: 3\frac{1}{3} : 6\frac{2}{3}.$
15. $\frac{2}{3} : \frac{3}{4} :: \frac{7}{8} : ?$
16. $\frac{4}{5} : \frac{5}{6} :: ? : \frac{3}{4}.$
17. $\frac{3}{7} : \frac{2}{3} :: \frac{4}{9} : ?$
18. $\frac{1}{8} : ? :: \frac{7}{10} : \frac{4}{5}.$
19. £$? :$ £$24 :: 30 : 6.$
20. $\$4 : \$10 :: 6$ bu. $: ?$
21. $\$5 : \$40 :: 9$ lb $: ?$
22. $\$.16 : \$.32 :: ? : 4$ qt.
23. $\$6 : \$15 :: ? : 75$ yd.
24. 10 men $: 14$ men $:: \$20 : ?$
25. $? : 35$ lb. $:: \$4 : \$7.$
26. 15 pwt. $: ? :: 21 : 10.$
27. 3.5 A. $: 10.5$ A. $:: ? : 18.$
28. 12 men $: 42$ men $:: 16$ days $: ?$
29. 18 mi. $: 4$ mi. $:: 20 : ?$
30. 16 horses $: 28$ horses $:: \frac{4}{7} : ?$
31. 21 da. $: 35$ da. $:: ? : \frac{3}{5}.$
32. $\frac{5}{8} : \frac{3}{5} :: 10$ bu. $: ?$
33. $\frac{3}{7} : 5 :: ? : 40.$
34. $4 : \frac{2}{9} :: ? : 10.$

SIMPLE PROPORTION.

432. A ratio between any two numbers is a **Simple Ratio**.

433. An equality of two simple ratios is a **Simple Proportion**.

Thus, $8 : 12 : : 16 : 24$ is a simple proportion.

WRITTEN EXERCISES.

434. 1. If 9 yd. of silk cost $\$27$, what will 18 yd. cost?

EXPLANATION. — It is evident that the cost of 18 yd. is greater than the cost of 9 yd., consequently the answer sought is greater than $\$27$.

$$\begin{array}{llll} \text{yd.} & \text{yd.} & \$ & \$ \\ (1) \quad 9 & : 18 & : : 27 : & ? \end{array}$$

$$\begin{array}{llll} \text{yd.} & \text{yd.} & \$ & \$ \\ (2) \quad 18 & : 9 & : : ? : & 27. \end{array}$$

(1) By Art. 445 $? = \dfrac{18 \times 27}{9} = 54.$

(2) By Art. 445 $? = \dfrac{\overset{2}{\cancel{18}} \times 27}{9} = 54.$

Arranging $\$27$, and the answer sought as a couplet of the proportion, the other couplet of the proportion must be expressed to correspond with the couplet first arranged. That is, in proportion (1) the consequent of the second couplet is greater than the antecedent, therefore the consequent of the first couplet must be greater than the antecedent, and the couplet is written 9 yd. : 18 yd.

Solving according to Art. 430, the value of 18 yd. is $\$54$.

In proportion (2), the proportion may be interpreted thus :

Greater : less : : Greater : less.

2. If 6 men can dig a ditch in 48 da., in what time can 8 men dig it?

SUGGESTION. — 8 men can do the work in less than 48 da., consequently the answer is less than 48 da., and the proportions may be expressed as follows :

(1) 8 men : 6 men : : 48 da. : ?

That is,   Greater : less : : Greater : less.

(2) 6 men : 8 men : : ? : 48 da.

That is,   Less : greater : : Less : greater.

Rule. — *Select the number which is the same kind as the answer, and from the conditions of the problem discover whether the answer is to be greater or less than that number.*

Arrange these two terms as a couplet, and then arrange the terms of the other couplet to conform to the conditions of the first couplet.

Divide the product of the extremes or means by the single extreme or mean. The result will be the term sought.

Use cancellation whenever it is possible to do so.

3. If 15 tons of hay cost $120, how much must be paid for 25 tons ?

4. If the interest upon a sum of money for 9 months is $318.69, what will be the interest for $11\frac{1}{2}$ months ?

5. A can do a certain piece of work in 18 days, working 10 hours per day. In how many days can he do the same work, by laboring 14 hours per day ?

6. If sound travels 6160 ft. in $5\frac{1}{2}$ seconds, how far does it travel in a minute ?

7. How high is a church spire whose shadow is 162 ft. long, when a flag-staff 60 ft. high casts a shadow 72 ft. long ?

8. B did a piece of work in 18 days, thereby earning $2.80 a day. What would he have earned per day, had he done the work in 16 days ?

9. If $600 yields $140 interest in a certain time, what interest will $750 yield in the same time ?

10. A farmer sowed 6 bu. of grain on $4\frac{4}{5}$ acres. How many bushels, at this rate, would he need for a field containing $13\frac{1}{2}$ acres ?

11. If a garrison of 150 men consumes 26 barrels of flour in 9 weeks, how many barrels will it consume in $22\frac{1}{2}$ weeks ?

12. If 165 bushels of potatoes are raised on $1\frac{1}{32}$ acres, how many bushels can be raised on $3\frac{1}{4}$ acres ?

13. If $2\frac{3}{4}$ barrels of beef cost $20.75, how much will $7\frac{1}{2}$ barrels cost?

14. If it requires 42 yards of carpet which is $\frac{3}{4}$ of a yard wide to cover a floor, how many yards of carpet one yard wide will be needed to cover the same floor?

15. Thirty men can dig a ditch in 20 days. After they have been digging 12 days, how many more men must be employed to finish it in 6 days more?

16. At the time when a man 5 ft. 8 in. in height casts a shadow 4 ft. 6 in. long, what is the height of a tree that casts a shadow 46 ft. 6 in. long?

17. Two cog-wheels, one having 26 cogs, and the other 20 cogs, run together. In how many revolutions of the larger wheel will the smaller gain 12 revolutions?

18. If 15 men can do a piece of work in 36 days, in how many days can they perform the same work with the assistance of 9 men more?

19. A piece of work can be done in 40 days by 25 men. After 18 days, 13 men quit work. In how many days can the rest finish the work?

20. If a garrison of 200 men has provisions for 8 months, how many men must leave at the end of 5 months that the provisions remaining may last the rest 8 months longer?

21. If it requires 15 compositors 15 days to set up a book of 675 pages, how many days will they need to set up a book of 900 pages?

22. If a railway train runs 444 miles in 8 hr. 40 min., in what time can it run 1060 miles, at the same rate of speed?

23. A farmer raised 405 bushels of beets upon 1 A. 20 sq. rd. of land. How many bushels can he raise upon a field containing 7 A. 85 sq. rd.?

24. A train which runs $35\frac{1}{4}$ miles per hour leaves Chicago at 8:25 A.M. How far will it have traveled at 2:30 P.M.

COMPOUND PROPORTION.

435. The product of two or more simple ratios is a Compound Ratio.

436. A proportion in which either or both ratios are compound is a **Compound Proportion.**

WRITTEN EXERCISES.

437. 1. If 6 men can mow 24 acres of grass in 2 days by working 10 hours per day, how many days will it take 7 men to mow 56 acres of grass by working 12 hours per day?

EXPLANATION. — A compound proportion is one involving several conditions. The first condition in this problem is: If 6 men can mow the grass in 2 days, how long will it take 7 men to do the work? The solution of this is expressed by proportion (1). The second condition is: If the men can mow 24 acres of grass in x days, how long a time will it take them to mow 56 acres? This is solved by simple proportion in proportion (2), giving y days.

(1) $7 : 6 :: 2 : x.$

(2) $24 : 56 :: x : y.$

(3) $12 : 10 :: y : z.$

Or,

(4) $\left.\begin{cases} 7 : 6 \\ 24 : 56 \\ 12 : 10 \end{cases}\right\} :: 2 : z.$

$z = \dfrac{\text{Means}}{\text{Extremes}}\quad \dfrac{6 \times 56 \times 10 \times 2}{7 \times 24 \times 12} = 3\tfrac{1}{3}.$

The third condition is: If the work can be done by the men in y days by working 10 hours per day, how many days will be required to do the work if they work 12 hours per day? This solved by simple proportion, by proportion (3), gives z days.

Since every proportion is an equality of ratios, the products of these proportions term by term will be an equality of ratios, or a proportion. Since x and y appear in both antecedent and consequent, they may be omitted from the product, since antecedent is the same as numerator, and consequent the same as denominator, and the simple proportions will assume the form of (4). Solving, the answer is found to be $3\tfrac{1}{3}$ da.

The problem may be stated at the outset as in proportion (4) by writing for the third term the one that is of the same kind as the answer, and then arranging couplets by considering their relation to the answer sought.

RULE. — *Use for the third term the number which is of the same kind as the answer required.*

Arrange the other couplets according to the relation of the third term to the answer sought.

The product of the means divided by the product of the extremes will be the answer.

Problems in compound proportion are readily solved by what is termed the *cause* and *effect* method.

Example 1, stated by cause and effect, is as follows :

1st cause.	2d cause.	1st effect.	2d effect.
6 men	7 men		
2 days	? days	24 acres :	56 acres.
10 hours	12 hours		

$$\left. \begin{array}{c} 6 \text{ men} \\ 2 \text{ days} \\ 10 \text{ hours} \end{array} \right\} : \left. \begin{array}{c} 7 \text{ men} \\ ? \text{ days} \\ 12 \text{ hours} \end{array} \right\} : : \left\{ 24 \text{ acres} : \left\{ 56 \text{ acres}. \right. \right.$$

2. If 11 men build 45 rods of wall in 6 days of 10 hours each, how many men will be required to build 81 rods of wall in 12 days of 11 hours each ?

3. Three workmen dig a ditch 20 rd. long and 3 ft. wide in 10 days. How long will it take 5 workmen to dig a ditch 45 rd. long and 4 ft. wide ?

4. If 18 men can perform a piece of work in 12 days, how many men could perform another piece of work 4 times as great in $\frac{1}{8}$ of the time ?

5. If the freight charges on 125 cattle, averaging 900 pounds, is $200 for 150 miles, what should be the charges on 275 cattle, averaging 1200 pounds, for 225 miles ?

6. If a block of marble 7 ft. long, 3 ft. wide, and 2 ft. thick weighs 6930 lb., what will be the weight of a block of the same kind 10 ft. long, 4 ft. wide, and 3 ft. thick ?

7. If the capacity of a bin 24 ft. long, $4\frac{1}{2}$ ft. wide, and $4\frac{2}{3}$ ft. deep is 405 bushels, what is the capacity of a bin 16 ft. long, 5 ft. wide, and $4\frac{1}{2}$ ft. deep ?

8. If it costs $180 to build a wall 60 ft. long, 14 ft. high, and 1 ft. 6 in. thick, what will it cost to build a wall 200 ft. long, 18 ft. high, and 1 ft. 4 in. thick ?

9. If 15 men, working 12 hr. a day, can hoe 60 acres in 20 days, how long will it take 35 boys, working 10 hr. a day, to hoe 90 acres, the work of 5 men being equal to that of 7 boys?

10. If 16 men can excavate a cellar 40 ft. long, 36 ft. wide, and 8 ft. deep in 12 days of 8 hours each, in how many days of 10 hours each can 8 men excavate a cellar 30 ft. long, 27 ft. wide, and 6 ft. deep?

11. If 5 iron bars, 4 ft. long, 3 in. broad, and 2 in. thick, weigh 240 lb., what will be the weight of 20 bars, each 6 ft. long, $2\frac{1}{2}$ in. broad, and $1\frac{1}{4}$ in. thick?

12. If 9 bricklayers can lay a wall 80 ft. long, 20 ft. high, and $1\frac{1}{2}$ ft. thick, in 15 days of 9 hr. each, in how many days of 10 hr. each can 12 bricklayers lay a wall 100 ft. long, 25 ft. high, and 2 ft. thick?

13. If 240 men, in 11 days of 8 hours each, dig a ditch 350 ft. long, 11 ft. wide, and $2\frac{1}{2}$ ft. deep, in how many days of 9 hours each will 48 men dig a ditch 500 ft. long, $16\frac{2}{3}$ ft. wide, and $3\frac{1}{2}$ ft. deep?

14. If 54 men, in 28 days of 10 hours each, dig a trench 352 yards long, $2\frac{1}{2}$ yards broad, and $1\frac{1}{2}$ yards deep, how long a trench $2\frac{3}{4}$ yards broad, and $1\frac{3}{4}$ yards deep, will 112 men dig in 25 days of $8\frac{1}{4}$ hours each?

15. If a regiment of 1025 soldiers consumes 11,500 pounds of bread in 15 days, how many pounds will 3 regiments of the same size consume in 12 days?

16. If the water that fills a vat, which is 8 feet long, 4 feet wide, and 5 feet deep, weighs 10,000 pounds, what will be the weight of the water required to fill a vat, which is 10 feet long, 5 feet wide, and 6 feet deep?

17. If 5 horses eat as much as 6 cattle, and 8 horses and 12 cattle eat 12 tons of hay in 40 days, how much hay will be needed to keep 7 horses and 15 cattle 65 days?

PARTITIVE PROPORTION.

438. The process by which a number is divided into parts, proportional to other given numbers, is called **Partitive Proportion.**

WRITTEN EXERCISES.

439. 1. Divide 240 into parts proportional to 3, 4, and 5.

EXPLANATION. — Since the parts are proportional to 3, 4, and 5, out of every 12 (the sum of 3, 4, and 5), there is a 3, a 4, and a 5. Consequently one part will be $\frac{3}{12}$ of 240, or 60, another will be $\frac{4}{12}$ of 240, or 80, and the other $\frac{5}{12}$ of 240, or 100.

Therefore the parts are 60, 80, and 100.

2. Divide $390 into parts proportional to $\frac{1}{2}$, $\frac{1}{3}$, and $\frac{1}{4}$.

EXPLANATION. — Since fractions have the ratios of their numerators when their denominators are the same, the fractions are changed to 12ths, and we have $\frac{6}{12}$, $\frac{4}{12}$, $\frac{3}{12}$.

Therefore the problem may be expressed thus : Divide $390 into parts proportional to 6, 4, and 3. This is solved in the same way as example 1.

3. Divide 420 into three parts which shall be to one another as 2, 5, and 7.

4. Divide 750 into five parts which shall be to one another as 1, 2, 3, 4, and 5.

5. Divide 468 into three parts, such that they shall be proportional to $\frac{1}{2}$, $\frac{1}{3}$, and $\frac{1}{4}$.

6. Divide $1596 into parts proportional to $\frac{2}{3}$, $\frac{3}{4}$, and $\frac{4}{5}$.

7. A man bought three farms for $26,150, and the prices paid for them were in the proportion of the fractions $\frac{4}{5}$, $\frac{5}{6}$, and $\frac{6}{7}$. What did he pay for each farm ?

8. A man bequeathed his property in such a way that his wife received $7 for every $5 received by each of his two sons and every $4 received by each of his three daughters. If his estate was worth $250,000, what was the sum bequeathed to each of the heirs ?

INVOLUTION.

440. 1. Of what number are 4 and 4 the factors? 5 and 5? 6 and 6? 3, 3, and 3? 4, 4, and 4? 5, 5, and 5?

2. What is the product of 6 used twice as a factor, or the *second power* of 6?

3. What is the *second power* of 7? Of 5? Of 9? Of 10? Of 12?

4. What is the *third* power of 2? Of 3? Of 4? Of 5?

5. What is the *second* power of $\frac{2}{3}$? Of $\frac{3}{4}$? Of $\frac{5}{6}$? Of $\frac{4}{5}$?

441. The product arising from using a number a certain number of times as a factor is a **Power** of the number.

442. The powers of a number are *named* from the number of times it is used as a factor.

Thus, 4 is the *second* power of 2; 9 the *second* power of 3; 8 the *third* power of 2; 27 the *third* power of 3.

The number itself is called its first power.

443. The number of times a number is used as a factor is indicated by a small figure, called an *Exponent*, written a little above and at the right of the number.

Thus, 3^2 means the *second* power of 3; 3^4 the *fourth* power of 3, etc.

Since the area of a square is the product of *two* equal factors, and the volume of a cube the product of *three* equal factors, the *second* power is called the *square*, and the *third* power the *cube*.

444. The process of finding the power of a number is called **Involution**.

324

WRITTEN EXERCISES.

445. **1.** Find the fourth power of 8.

SOLUTION.—$8 \times 8 \times 8 \times 8 = 4096$, the *fourth* power of **8.**

2. Find the second power of 13, 18, 21, 36.

3. Find the third power of 9, 15, 24, 42.

4. What is the square of 25? 32? 48? 66?

5. What is the cube of 22? 25? 54? 71?

6. What is the fourth power of 4? 6? 12? 19?

7. What is the third power of 23? 30? 43? 75?

8. What is the square of 45? 69? 86? 94?

9. What is the square of $\frac{2}{3}$? $\frac{4}{5}$? $\frac{6}{7}$? $\frac{5}{9}$?

10. What is the cube of $\frac{1}{2}$? $\frac{2}{3}$? $\frac{3}{4}$? $\frac{4}{5}$?

Raise the following to the powers indicated:

11. 85^2.	**16** 65^2.	**21.** $(1\frac{2}{13})^2$.	**26.** $(7\frac{1}{2})^2$.
12. 49^3.	**17.** $.75^2$.	**22.** $(2\frac{5}{35})^2$.	**27.** $(20\frac{1}{3})^2$.
13. 40^2.	**18.** $.05^3$.	**23.** $(4\frac{1}{61})^2$.	**28.** $(4.0\frac{1}{2})^2$.
14. 50^3.	**19.** $.004^2$.	**24.** $(\frac{8}{9})^3$.	**29.** $(3.50\frac{1}{2})^2$.
15. 102^2.	**20.** 3.05^3.	**25.** $(1\frac{7}{21})^3$.	**30.** $(5.02\frac{1}{4})^2$.

446. **1.** Find the *square* of 35 in terms of its tens and units.

$$35 = 30 + 5.$$
$$30 + 5$$
$$30 + 5$$
$$\overline{30^2 + 30 \times 5}$$
$$+ 30 \times 5 + 5^2$$
$$\overline{30^2 + 2(30 \times 5) + 5^2}$$

447. PRINCIPLE. — *The square of any number consisting of tens and units, is equal to the tens^2 + 2 times the tens $\times$ the units + the units^2.*

Thus, $25 = 20 + 5$, and $25^2 = 20^2 + 2(20 \times 5) + 5^2$.

The above principle is true into whatever two parts the number may be separated, and the principle stated in general terms would be, the square of any number consisting of two parts is equal to the first part^2 + 2 times the first part × the second + second part^2.

Thus, $14 = 8 + 6$, and $14^2 = 8^2 + 2(6 \times 8) + 6^2$.

Express in terms of their tens and units the square of the following numbers:

2. 54.	5. 47.	8. 74.	11. 39.
3. 71.	6. 89.	9. 95.	12. 44.
4. 68.	7. 26.	10. 82.	13. 67.

448. 1. Find the cube of 35 in terms of its tens and units.

$$35 = 30 + 5.$$

$$
\begin{array}{l}
30 + 5 \\
30 + 5 \\
\hline
30^2 + 30 \times 5 \\
\quad\; + 30 \times 5 + 5^2 \\
\hline
30^2 + 2(30 \times 5) + 5^2 \\
30 + 5 \\
\hline
30^3 + 2(30^2 \times 5) + \quad (30 \times 5^2) \\
\quad\; + \quad (30^2 \times 5) + 2(30 \times 5^2) + 5^3 \\
\hline
30^3 + 3(30^2 \times 5) + 3(30 \times 5^2) + 5^3 = 42875.
\end{array}
$$

449. PRINCIPLE. — *The cube of a number consisting of tens and units is equal to the tens^3 + 3 tens^2 × the units + 3 times the tens × units^2 + units^3.*

Thus, $25 = 20 + 5$, and $25^3 = 20^3 + 3(20^2 \times 5) + 3(20 \times 5^2) + 5^3$.

Express in terms of their tens and units the cube of the following numbers:

2. 27.	5. 43.	8. 46.	11. 66.
3. 36.	6. 51.	9. 55.	12. 58.
4. 29.	7. 44.	10. 64.	13. 75.

EVOLUTION.

450. 1. What are the two equal factors of 25? 36? 49?

2. What are the three equal factors of 8? 27? 64? 125?

451. One of the equal factors of a number is a **Root** of the number.

Thus, 4 is a root of 16 and 3 is a root of 27.

452. Roots are named in a manner similar to powers.

Thus, one of the *two* equal factors of a number is the *second* or *square* root; one of the three equal factors, the *third* or *cube* root; one of the *four* equal factors the *fourth* root, etc.

453. The process of finding the roots of numbers is called **Evolution.**

EVOLUTION BY FACTORING.

454. 1. What is the cube root of 4096?

EXPLANATION. — Since the cube root of a number is one of the three equal factors of it, the number 4096 is separated into its prime factors, and the product of one of the three equal sets of prime factors is the cube root. The prime factors are 2, 2, 2, 2, 2, 2, 2, 2, 2, 2, 2, 2, and 2, 2, 2, 2, is one of the three equal sets. Therefore $2 \times 2 \times 2 \times 2$ or 16 is the cube root of 4096.

2. Find the square root of 225, 1296, 2401.

3. Find the square root of 11025, 14400, 46656.

4. Find the cube root of 343, 1728, 15625.

5. Find the cube root of 19683, 32768, 74088.

6. Find the 4th root of 65536. The 5th root of 248832.

7. Find the 4th root of 331776. The 6th root of 2985984.

SQUARE ROOT.

$$1^2 = 1 \qquad 10^2 = 100 \qquad 100^2 = 10000$$
$$9^2 = 81 \qquad 99^2 = 9801 \qquad 999^2 = 998001$$

455. 1. How many figures are required to express the square of any number of *units?*

2. How does the number of figures required to express the second power of any number between 9 and 100 compare with the number of figures in the number?

3. How does the number of figures expressing the second power of any number between 99 and 1000 compare with the number of figures in the number?

4. If the second power of a number is expressed by 3 figures, how many orders of units are there in the number? If by 4, how many? By 5? By 7?

456. PRINCIPLES. — 1. *The square of a number is expressed by twice as many figures as is the number itself, or by one less than twice as many.*

2. *The orders of units in the square root of a number correspond to the number of periods of two figures each into which the number can be separated, beginning at units.*

The left-hand period may contain only one figure.

WRITTEN EXERCISES.

457. 1. What is the square root of 576, or what is the side of a square whose area is 576 square units?

$$576(20$$
$$20^2 = 400 \quad 4$$
$$2 \times 20 = 40)176 \ 24$$
$$(40 + 4) \times 4 = 176$$

EXPLANATION. — According to Prin. 2, Art. 456, the orders of units in the square root of any number may be determined by separating the number into periods of two figures each, beginning at units. Separating 576 thus, there are found to be two orders of units in the root, or it is composed of tens and units.

Since the square of tens is hundreds, 5 hundreds must be the square of at least 2 tens. 2 tens or 20 squared is 400, and 400 subtracted from 576 leaves 176, therefore the root, 20, must be increased by such an amount as will exhaust the remainder.

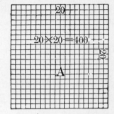

The square (A) already formed from the 576 square units is one whose side is 20 units, but inasmuch as the number of units was not exhausted, such additions must be made to the square as will exhaust the units and keep the figure a square. The necessary additions are two equal rectangles B and C, and a small square D.

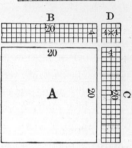

Since the square D is small, the area of the rectangles B and C is nearly 176 units. The area, 176 units, divided by the length of the rectangles, will give the width, which is 4 units. The width of the additions is 4 units, and the entire length, including the small square, is 44 units ; therefore the area of all the additions is 4 times 44 units, or 176 square units, which is equal to the entire number of units to be added. Therefore the side of the square is 24 units, or the square root of the number is 24.

2. Find the square root of 2809.

$$
\begin{array}{r|l}
 & 2809(53 \\
 & 25 \\
\hline
2 \times 50 = 100 & 309 \\
3 & \\
\hline
103 & 309 \\
\end{array}
$$

EXPLANATION. — Since the number can be separated into two periods, it is evident that the square root of the number is composed of tens and units. The number of tens in the root cannot be greater than 5. Writing the 5 tens in the root, squaring and subtracting from 2809, there is a remainder of 309.

According to Art. 447, *when the square of the tens has been subtracted,* the remainder is composed of 2 times the tens × the units + the square of the units. Therefore 309 is 2 times the tens × the units + the square of the units.

Since 2 times the tens × the units is much more than the square of the units, 309 is nearly two times the tens × the units. Therefore 309 divided by two times the tens, or 100, is approximately the units of the root. Dividing, the units are found to be 3.

Since 2 times the tens are to be multiplied by the units, and the units are to be multiplied by the units, or squared, and the results added, to abridge the process the units are added to 2 times the tens, and the result is multiplied by the units. Thus $100 + 3$ is multiplied by 3, making 309.

Therefore the square root of 2809 is 53.

Since any number may be regarded as composed of tens and units, its square root may be found in a similar manner.

Thus, $486 = 48$ tens $+ 6$ units; $3456 = 345$ tens $+ 6$ units.

3. Find the square root of 785.

```
 7·85 | 28.01785+
    4
48 | 385
     384
560 |  100
       000
5601 | 10000
       5601
56027 | 439900
        392189
        477110
        448216
        288940
        280135
```

EXPLANATION. — The first figure of the root is 2.

Regarding the 2 of the root as tens, and multiplying by 2, the first *partial divisor*, 40, is found. Dividing 385 by it, the second figure of the root is found, which is 8, and this added to 40 forms the *complete divisor* 48.

Regarding 28, the part of the root found, as tens, and multiplying by 2, the second *partial divisor*, 560, is found. Dividing 100 by it, the next figure of the root is found, which is 0, and this added to 560 gives 560 for the *complete divisor*. The other partial and complete divisors are found in the same way.

After a number of decimal places in the root has been found, a *few* more may be found by ordinary division, as shown in the example.

RULE. — *Separate the number into periods of two figures each, beginning at units.*

Find the greatest square in the left-hand period, and write its root for the first figure of the required root.

Square this root and subtract the result from the left-hand period, and annex to the remainder the next period for a dividend.

Double the root already found for a partial divisor, and by it divide the dividend, disregarding the right-hand figure. The quotient or quotient diminished will be the second figure of the root.

Annex to the partial divisor for a complete divisor the figure last found, multiply this divisor by the last figure of the root found, subtract the product from the dividend, and to the remainder annex the next period for the next dividend.

Proceed in this manner until all the periods have been used thus. The result will be the square root sought.

1. When the number is not a perfect square, annex periods of decimal ciphers and continue the process.

2. Decimals are pointed off into periods of two figures each, by beginning at tenths and passing to the right.

3. The square root of a common fraction is found by extracting the square root of both numerator and denominator separately, or by reducing it to a decimal and then extracting its root.

Extract the square root of the following:

4. 3025.	**8.** 13225.	**12.** 41616.	**16.** 1900.96.
5. 5476.	**9.** 14641.	**13.** 52441.	**17.** .514089.
6. 9604.	**10.** 21025.	**14.** 77284.	**18.** 97.8121.
7. 11881.	**11.** 23409.	**15.** 173056.	**19.** .001225.

20. 89 661961.   **23.** $\frac{1764}{2809}$.   **26.** $2450\frac{49}{196}$.

21. 2540.664025.   **24.** $\frac{46656}{117649}$.   **27.** $49117\frac{164}{256}$.

22. 282429536481.   **25.** $\frac{262144}{390625}$.   **28.** $\frac{55225}{784996}$.

Find the square root to five decimal places:

29. 18.	**33.** 127.	**37.** 7.25.	**41.** $12.6\frac{7}{8}$.
30. 35.	**34.** 245.	**38.** .526.	**42.** $25.0\frac{3}{4}$.
31. 47.	**35.** 370.	**39.** .031.	**43.** $.004\frac{2}{3}$.
32. 91.	**36.** 813.	**40.** 42.9.	**44.** $.000\frac{4}{9}$.

APPLICATIONS OF SQUARE ROOT.

458. Since the area of a square is the product of the two equal factors which represent its sides, it is evident that the length of a side may be found by finding the square root of the area.

1. A man owns a farm in the form of a square which contains 45 A. 25 sq. rd. How many rods in length or breadth is it?

2. What are the dimensions of a rectangular farm containing 80 acres, whose length is twice its breadth?

3. A general, attempting to draw his army of 8000 men into a square, found he had 256 men over. What was the number of men in rank and file?

4. A man, having a garden 324 yards square, extended it so as to make it 9 times as large. How many yards square was it then?

5. How much more will it cost, at $1.35 a rod, to fence a field in the form of a rectangle, 135 rods long and 60 rods wide, than to fence a field of equal area in the form of a square?

459. Since the square described upon the hypotenuse, or side opposite the right angle, of a right-angled triangle is equivalent to the sum of the squares upon the other two sides, it is evident:

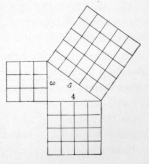

1st, *That the hypotenuse is equal to the square root of the sum of the squares of the other two sides.*

2d, *That the base or perpendicular is equal to the square root of the difference of the square of the hypotenuse and that of the other side.*

6. A rope attached to the top of a derrick 60 feet high, and drawn perfectly straight, reaches the ground 80 feet from the derrick. How long is the rope?

SOLUTION. — The sides about the right angle are 60 ft. and 80 ft. respectively, and we are to find the hypotenuse. By Art. 459, the hypotenuse is equal to the square root of the sum of the squares of the other two sides.

$$\therefore \ \sqrt{60^2 + 80^2} = 100, \text{ feet in length of the rope.}$$

7. Two rafters, each 24 feet long, meet at the ridge of a roof 12 feet above the body of the house. How wide is the house?

8. If a line 150 feet long will reach from the top of a fort to the opposite side of a river that is 85 feet wide, what is the height of the fort?

9. At $1.75 a rod, what will it cost to fence a triangular lot, one side of which, 40 rods in length, forms a right angle with another side 30 rods in length?

10. How far apart are the opposite corners of a square farm which contains 360 acres?

11. A tree, broken off 21 feet from the ground, and resting on the stump, touches the level ground 28 feet from the base of the stump. What was the height of the tree?

12. What is the distance from a lower corner to the opposite upper corner of a room 24 feet long, 18 feet wide, and 12 feet high?

13. There are two columns in the ruins of Persepolis left standing upright; one is 70 feet above the plane, and the other 50 feet above. In a straight line between these stands a small statue, 5 feet in height, the head of which is 100 feet from the summit of the higher, and 80 feet from the top of the lower column. What is the distance between the two columns?

SIMILAR SURFACES.

460. Figures which have the same form and differ only in size are **Similar Figures**.

The following truths regarding similar figures can be established by geometry:

461. PRINCIPLES. — 1. *Similar surfaces are to each other as the squares of their corresponding dimensions.*

2. *The corresponding dimensions of similar surfaces are to each other as the square roots of their areas.*

1. There are two circular gardens, one having a diameter of 8 rods and the other 32 rods. How do they compare in size?

SOLUTION. — Since the gardens are similar in form, their sizes or areas are to each other as the squares of the same dimensions in each; that is, as 8^2 is to 32^2, or as 64 is to 1024. Since 1024 is 16 times 64, the larger garden is, therefore, 16 times as large as the smaller.

2. A lady had a circular flower-bed 8 feet in diameter, and a similar one four times as large. What was the diameter of the larger bed?

3. A has a rectangular field 80 rods long and 60 rods wide. What will be the dimensions of a similar field containing $13\frac{1}{2}$ acres?

4. If a horse tied to a stake by a rope 7.13 rods in length can graze upon just one acre of ground, how long should the rope be to allow him to graze upon $6\frac{1}{2}$ acres?

5. If 6 gallons of water flow through a pipe 1 inch in diameter in a minute, how many gallons will flow through a pipe 4 inches in diameter in 5 minutes, when the stream moves with the same velocity?

6. A school-room contained two square blackboards whose sides were 3 ft. and 6 ft. respectively. How did they compare in area?

CUBE ROOT.

$1^3 = 1$	$10^3 = 1000$	$100^3 = 1000000$
$3^3 = 27$	$36^3 = 46656$	$361^3 = 47045881$
$9^3 = 729$	$99^3 = 970299$	$999^3 = 997002999$

462. 1. How many figures are required to express the cube of any number of *units?*

2. How does the number of figures required to express the cube of any number between 9 and 100 compare with the number of figures expressing the number ?

3. How does the number of figures expressing the cube of any number between 99 and 1000 compare with the number of figures expressing the number ?

4. If, then, the cube of a number is expressed by 4 figures, how many orders of units are there in the root ? If by 5 figures, how many ? If by 6 figures, how many ? If by 8 figures, how many ?

5. How may the number of figures in the cube root of a number be found ?

463. PRINCIPLES. — 1. *The cube of a number is expressed by three times as many figures as the number itself, or by one or two less than three times as many.*

2. *The orders of units in the cube root of a number correspond to the number of periods of three figures each into which the number can be separated, beginning at units.*

The left-hand period may contain one, two, or three figures.

464. If the tens of a number are represented by t and the units by u, the cube of a number consisting of tens and units will be the cube of $(t + u)$ or $t^3 + 3t^2u + 3tu^2 + u^3$, Art. 449.

Thus, $35 = 3$ tens $+ 5$ units, or $30 + 5$, and $35^3 = 30^3 + 3(30^2 \times 5) + 3(30 \times 5^2) + 5^3 = 42875$.

WRITTEN EXERCISES.

465. **1.** What is the cube root of 13824, or what is the edge of a cube whose solid contents are 13824 units?

$$13\cdot824(20+4=24$$

$$
\begin{array}{rl}
20^3 = & 8\,000 \\
3\times20^2 = 1200 & \overline{5\,824} \\
3\times4\times20 = 240 \\
4^2 = 16 \\
\hline
1456 & 5\,824
\end{array}
$$

EXPLANATION.—According to Prin. 2, Art. 463, the orders of units in the cube root of any number may be determined from the number of periods obtained by separating the number into periods containing three figures each, beginning at units. Separating the given number thus, there are two periods, or the root is composed of tens and units.

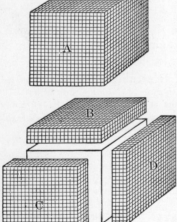

The tens in the cube root of the number cannot be greater than 2, for the cube of 3 tens is 27000. 2 tens, or 20 cubed, are 8000, which, subtracted from 13824, leave 5824; therefore the root, 20, must be increased by a number such that the additions will exhaust the remainder.

The cube (A) already formed from the 13824 cubic units is one whose edge is 20 units. The additions to be made, keeping the figure formed a perfect cube, are 3 equal rectangular solids, B, C, and D; 3 other equal rectangular solids, E, F, and G; and a small cube, H. Inasmuch as the solids, B, C, and D, comprise much the greatest part of the additions, their solid contents will be *nearly* 5824 cubic units, the contents of the addition.

Since the cubical contents of these three equal solids are nearly equal to 5824 units, and the superficial contents of a side of each of these solids are 20 × 20, or 400 square units, if we divide 5824 by 3 times 400, or 1200, since there are 3 equal solids, we shall obtain the thickness of the addition, which is 4 units.

Since all the additions have the same thickness, if their superficial contents, or area of each side, are multiplied by 4, the result will be the solid contents of these additions.

Besides the larger additions there are three others, E, F, and G, which are each 20 units long and 4 units wide, or whose surfaces have an area of 80 units each, or 240 units altogether; and a small cube whose sides have an area of 16 units. The sum of these areas, 1456, multiplied by 4, the thickness of the additions, gives the solid contents of the additions, which are 5824 units.

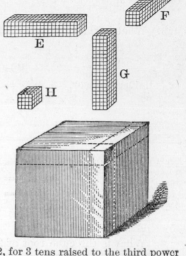

Therefore the edge of the cube is 24 units in length, or the cube root of 13824 is 24.

EXPLANATION. — In the same manner as before, it may be shown that the root of the number contains only tens and units. The tens cannot be greater than 2, for 3 tens raised to the third power is 27000. Cubing 2 tens and subtracting, there is left 5824.

This remainder contains 3 times the tens² × the units + 3 times the tens × the units², + the units³.

$$13 \cdot 824 \, (24$$

$$
\begin{array}{rl}
t^3 = 20^3 = & 8\ 000 \\
3\,t^2 = 20^2 \times 3 = 1200 & \overline{5\ 824} \\
3\,t \times u = (20 \times 4) \times 3 = 240 & \\
u^2 = 4 \times 4 = 16 & \\
3\,t^2 + 3\,tu + u^2 = \overline{1456} & \\
(3\,t^2 + 3\,tu + u^2) \times u = & 5\ 824
\end{array}
$$

Each of these parts contains the *units* as a factor, hence 5284 is the product of two factors, one of which is the units, and the other 3 times the tens² + 3 times the tens × the units + the units².

Since 3 times the tens² is much greater than the rest of the factor, if 5284 is divided by 3 times the tens², or 1200, the quotient will be the units or other factor. It is found to be 4.

The factor completed is therefore $3 \times 20^2 + 3 \times 20 \times 4 + 4^2$, which is equal to 1200 + 240 + 16, or 1456. This multiplied by 4 gives the product 5824. Therefore the cube root of the number is 24.

When the number consists of more than two orders of units, the root may be found in the same manner by considering each time the root already found as *tens* and the next order of the root as *units*.

2. What is the cube root of 48228544 ?

$$48 \cdot 228 \cdot 544 \ \lfloor \ 364$$

$3^3 =$		27
Partial divisor, $3 \times 30^2 =$	2700	21228
$3 \times 30 \times 6 =$	540	
$6^2 =$	36	
Complete divisor,	3276	19656
		1572544
Partial divisor, $3 \times 360^2 =$	388800	
$3 \times 360 \times 4 =$	4320	
$4^2 =$	16	
Complete divisor,	393136	1572544

3. What is the cube root of 22906304 ?

$$22 \cdot 906 \cdot 304 \ \lfloor \ 284$$

$2^3 =$		8
$3 \times 20^2 =$	1200	14906
$3 \times 20 \times 8 =$	480	
$8^2 =$	64	
	1744	13952
		954304
$3 \times 280^2 =$	235200	
$3 \times 280 \times 4 =$	3360	
$4^2 =$	16	
	238576	954304

When the number of figures in the root is more than two the following method materially abridges the process :

4. What is the cube root of 4 to 4 decimal places?

$$4 \,|\, 1.5874$$

$$
\begin{array}{rrr}
& & 1 \\
3 \times 10^2 = 300 & & 3000 \\
3 \times 10 \times 5 = 150 & & \\
u^2 = \quad\quad 5^2 = 25 \left.\right\} & & \\
3\,t^2 + 3\,tu + u^2 = \quad\quad 475 \left.\right\} & & 2375 \\
3\,tu + u^2 = \quad\quad 175 \left.\right) & & 625000 \\
3(t^2 + 2\,tu + u^2) = \quad 3 \times 150^2 = 67500 & & \\
3 \times 150 \times 8 = 3600 & & \\
8^2 = 64 \left.\right\} & & \\
71164 \left.\right\} & & 569312 \\
3664 \left.\right) & & 55688000 \\
3 \times 1580^2 = 7489200 & & \\
3 \times 1580 \times 7 = 33180 & & \\
7^2 = 49 \left.\right\} & & \\
7522429 \left.\right\} & & 52615003 \\
33229 \left.\right) & & 3072997000 \\
3 \times 15870^2 = 755565800 & & 3022263200 \\
\end{array}
$$

EXPLANATION. — Since the root of the number is not a whole number, periods of decimal ciphers are annexed, and the required number of decimal places found.

After two figures of the root have been found, the partial divisors may be found as follows : Add together 3 times the product of the tens by the units and the square of the units, then add this sum to the complete divisor, plus the square of the units, and the result, with two ciphers annexed, will be the next partial divisor.

Thus, in the example solved, to obtain the partial divisor for the third figure of the root add 150 and 25, and place their sum immediately below the complete divisor. Then add together 175, 475, and 25, and to the sum annex two ciphers. The result will be the next partial divisor.

After several decimal places have been found a *few* more may be found by ordinary division.

It will be seen by examining the solution that the numbers added together are equal to $3\,t^2 + 6\,tu + 3\,u^2$, or $3\,(t^2 + 2\,tu + u^2)$, that is, the sum is 3 times the square of the tens and units already found.

RULE. — *Separate the number into periods of three figures each, beginning at units.*

Find the greatest cube in the left-hand period, and write its root for the first figure of the required root.

Cube this root, subtract the result from the left-hand period, and annex to the remainder the next period for a dividend.

Take three times the square of the root already found, considered as tens, for a partial divisor, and by it divide the dividend. The quotient or the quotient diminished will be the second part of the root.

To this partial divisor add three times the product of the first part of the root, considered as tens, by the second part, and also the square of the second part. Their sum will be the complete divisor.

Multiply the complete divisor by the second part of the root, and subtract the product from the dividend.

Continue thus until all the figures of the root have been found.

1. When there is a remainder, after subtracting the last product annex periods of decimal ciphers, and continue the process. The figures of the root obtained after the ciphers are annexed will be decimals.

2. Decimals are pointed off into periods of three figures each, by beginning at tenths and passing to the right.

3. The cube root of a common fraction is found by extracting the cube root of both numerator and denominator separately, or by reducing it to a decimal and then extracting its root.

Extract the cube root of the following:

5. 54872.	10. 43614208.	15. 491916472984.
6. 175616.	11. 130323843.	16. 13312.053.
7. 405224.	12. 1865409391.	17. 28.094464.
8. 857375.	13. 4065356736.	18. .000166375
9. 3048625.	14. 95256152263.	19. .000001953125.

20. What is the cube root of 2 to four decimal places?

21. What is the cube root of 6 to five decimal places?

22. What is the cube root of $\frac{4}{9}$? $\frac{5832}{19683}$? $\frac{157464}{34965783}$?

APPLICATIONS OF CUBE ROOT.

466. 1. A cubical box contains 54,872 cubic inches. What is the length of each side?

2. What is the depth of a cubical cistern which contains 2744 cubic feet?

3. What is the number of square inches in one face of a cubical block whose contents are 185,193 cubic inches?

4. What are the dimensions of a cubical box which contains as much as a rectangular box 5 ft. 4 in. long, 4 ft. 6 in. wide, and 2 ft. 8 in. deep?

5. What must be the depth of a cubical bin that will contain exactly 1200 bushels?

6. A cubical cistern holds 400 barrels of water. How deep is it?

7. How much will it cost, at 35 cents per square yard, to plaster the bottom and sides of the cistern described in problem 6?

8. A bin that is just twice as long as it is wide or high holds 500 bushels of grain. What is its length?

9. Which has the greater surface, and how much; a cube whose solid contents are 4096 cubic feet, or a rectangular solid having the same contents, whose width is twice its height, and whose height is one third its length?

SIMILAR VOLUMES.

The truth of the following principles can be shown by geometry:

467. PRINCIPLES. — 1. *Similar solids are to each other as the cubes of their like dimensions. Hence,*

2. *The corresponding dimensions of similar solids are to each other as the cube roots of their volumes.*

1. If a globe 4 inches in diameter weighs 8 lb., what will be the diameter of a similar one that weighs 125 lb. ?

EXPLANATION.—Since the corresponding dimensions of similar solids are proportional to the cube roots of these volumes, we have the diameter of the smaller globe 4 inches : the diameter of the larger globe x :: the cube root of the weight of the smaller globe $\sqrt[3]{8}$: the cube root of the weight of the other globe $\sqrt[3]{125}$ (1). Extracting the cube root of 8 and 125, we have (2). Whence, solving, the diameter is 10 inches.

$$4 : x :: \sqrt[3]{8} : \sqrt[3]{125} \quad (1)$$
$$4 : x :: \quad 2 : \quad 5 \quad (2)$$
$$x = 10, \text{ inches in diam.}$$

2. There are two cubes whose dimensions are 4 inches and 16 inches respectively. The larger is how many times the smaller ?

3. If a ball 3 inches in diameter weighs 7 pounds, what will be the weight of a similar ball 5 inches in diameter ?

4. A cubical bin 5 feet long will hold 100.44 bushels. How much will a cubical bin 10 feet long hold ?

5. The height of a cubical vessel is 1 foot 6 inches. How high must another cubical vessel be to hold four times as much ?

6. If a globe of gold 1 inch in diameter is worth $120, what is the diameter of a globe of gold worth $6400 ?

7. If a man 5 ft. 6 in. high weighs 140 pounds, what is the weight of a man of similar build whose height is 6 ft. ?

8. There are two balls whose diameters are 4 inches and 5 inches respectively. What is the diameter of a ball whose contents are equal to them both ?

9. If a haystack 13 feet in diameter contains 17 tons, what is the diameter of a similar stack which contains 136 tons ?

10. A bushel measure is in the form of a cylinder $18\frac{1}{2}$ in. in diameter, and 8 in. deep. What will be the dimensions of a peck measure of similar shape ?

GENERAL REVIEW EXERCISES.

468. 1. Two boys have together 45 cents, but one has twice as much as the other. How many cents has each?

2. If a man can do $\frac{2}{5}$ of a piece of work in a day, how long will it take him to do one half of it?

3. If 5 men can do a piece of work in 12 days, how long will it take 8 men to do it?

4. A man bought sheep at $3 a head. Had he paid $5 a head they would have cost $16 more. How many did he buy?

5. In what time can 40 men do a piece of work that 50 men can do in 8 days?

6. A can do a piece of work in 3 days and B in $4\frac{1}{2}$ days. In what time can they together do it?

7. James and Henry can hoe a field in 5 days. James can do it alone in 9 days. In how many days can Henry hoe the field alone?

8. A can make a door in $\frac{2}{3}$ of a day, and B in $\frac{3}{4}$ of a day. How many doors can they together make in a day?

9. How long will it take A to finish a door after B has worked on it half a day?

10. A, B, and C can do a piece of work in 4 days. A can do it alone in 12 days, and B alone in 15 days. How long will it take C to do it alone?

11. If I lose $\frac{2}{7}$ of my money, and spend $\frac{4}{9}$ of the remainder, what part have I left?

343

12. Three boys, Peter, George, and Jacob, can do a piece of work in 3 days. Peter can do it alone in 12 days, and Peter and Jacob can do it in 8 days. How long will it take each of them to do it?

13. If I gain $\frac{1}{3}$ of a cent apiece by selling eggs at 8 cents a dozen, how much apiece will I gain by selling them at 10 cents a dozen?

14. If I sell my apples at 6 cents a dozen, I lose 15 cents; but if I sell them at 9 cents a dozen, I gain 12 cents. How many have I, and what did they cost me?

15. If $\frac{3}{4}$ of A's money equals $\frac{6}{7}$ of B's, what part of B's equals $\frac{7}{8}$ of A's?

16. Five times $\frac{2}{17}$ of a number is 14 less than the number. What is the number?

17. I sold a bureau to A for $\frac{1}{4}$ more than it cost me. He sold it for $6, which was $\frac{2}{5}$ less than it cost him. What did it cost me?

18. A man agreed to work 16 days for $24 and board, but he was to pay $1 a day for his board for every day he was idle. He received $14. How many days did he work?

19. B engaged to work 20 days for $40, and agreed to forfeit 1\frac{1}{2}$ for every day he was idle. How many days was he idle, if he received 29\frac{1}{2}$?

20. Two persons share $150 in the ratio of $\frac{1}{4}$ and $\frac{1}{6}$. What is the share of each?

21. A and B engaged in a business in which A invested $36 and B received $5 out of the $8 which they gained. How much did B invest?

22. Three persons are to share a certain sum of money in the ratio of $\frac{1}{3}$, $\frac{1}{4}$, and $\frac{1}{5}$. The second receives $9 more than the third. What is the share of each?

23. If a man can earn $\frac{5}{8}$ of a dollar in $\frac{3}{4}$ of a day, how much can he earn in $\frac{8}{9}$ of a day?

24. If $\frac{2}{3}$ of the value of a carriage is equal to $\frac{3}{4}$ of the value of a horse, and the value of the carriage is $20 more than the value of the horse, what is the value of each?

25. In an orchard $\frac{1}{3}$ of the trees bear apples, $\frac{1}{4}$ bear pears, and the remainder, 300, bear peaches. How many trees are there in the orchard?

26. A man can saw 2 cords of wood per day, or he can split 3 cords of wood when sawed. How much must he saw that he may be occupied the rest of the day in splitting it?

27. A man spent one half of his money and half a dollar for a coat, one half of what he had left and half a dollar for a hat, one half of what was left and half a dollar for shoes, and had a dollar left. How much had he at first?

28. A merchant, after selling from a cask of vinegar 15 gallons more than $\frac{1}{7}$ of the whole, found that he had left just 4 times as much as he had sold. How many gallons did the cask contain at first?

29. Three boys had together earned 150 cents. James had earned $\frac{1}{2}$ as much as John, and Henry $\frac{1}{4}$ as much as James and John. What sum had each earned?

30. A tree 129 feet high was broken in a storm. $\frac{3}{5}$ of the part broken off was equal to $\frac{5}{6}$ of the part standing. What was the length of each part?

31. Wheat sold at $1.50 per bushel pays a profit of one half the cost. If it is sold at $2 per bushel, what part of the cost will be gained?

32. If a merchant sells $\frac{3}{4}$ of an article for what $\frac{7}{8}$ of it cost, what is his gain per cent?

33. I sold some goods at a discount of 40%, and 10% off for cash. What was the total % discount?

34. If goods are bought at 80% discount, and 20% off for cash, what is the entire % discount?

35. Which is better, and how much, to buy goods at 25% discount and 10% off for cash, or to buy goods at 10% discount and 25% off for cash?

36. A wholesale merchant offered dress goods, marked at 50 cents per yard, at a discount of 20%, and 5% off for cash. At what price per yard did he offer them?

37. A man purchased a horse, giving in payment his note at 6%. At the end of 3 years and 6 months he found that he owed $42 interest. How much did the horse cost him?

38. A man wished to invest enough money in government bonds paying 4% interest annually to secure an income of $800. How many one-thousand-dollar bonds must he purchase?

39. What principal will amount to $1300 in 6 years, with interest at 5 %?

40. What principal will amount to $850 in 10 years, with interest at 7%?

41. If I had paid 8% less for my house than I did, it would have made a difference of $400 in the cost. What did it cost me?

42. A and B each had farms containing 240 acres. A purchased a certain number of acres from B and he then had 320 acres. What per cent of A's farm was B's after the purchase?

43. The retail price of some books was $1 per volume. If I bought them at a discount of 20% from the retail price, and sold them at the retail price, what per cent did I gain?

44. If goods are sold so that $\frac{5}{7}$ of the cost is received for half the quantity of goods, what is the gain per cent?

45. I asked 20% more for goods than they cost me, but sold them at 10% less than I asked for them. What per cent did I gain?

46. A sells a horse to B, gaining 20%, and B sells it to C for $150, and gains 25%. What did the horse cost A?

47. If a banker sells a sight draft on New Orleans for $5000 for $5012.50, what is the rate of exchange?

48. A pole which is 10 feet long casts a shadow 4 feet long, and at the same time the shadow of a steeple is 30 feet long. How high is the steeple?

49. Six times a number equals 5 times $\frac{5}{6}$ of the same number, plus 33. What is the number?

50. A man, being asked how many sheep he had, replied, "If I had 3 times as many as I have and 5 sheep, I would have 185." How many had he?

51. What time after 2 o'clock are the hour and minute hands of a clock together?

52. A person, being asked the time of day, replied that it was past noon, and that $\frac{3}{4}$ of the time past noon was equal to $\frac{3}{5}$ of the time to midnight. What was the time?

53. A, B, and C ate 8 loaves of bread. A furnished 3 loaves and B 5 loaves. C paid the others 24 cents for his share. How much money should A and B each receive?

54. How far may a person ride in a stage, going at the rate of 8 miles an hour, if he is gone 11 hours, and walks back at the rate of 3 miles an hour?

55. A yacht, whose rate of sailing is 12 miles an hour, sails down a river whose current is 4 miles an hour. How far may it go, if it is to be gone 15 hours?

56. A steamboat sailed $42\frac{1}{2}$ miles in $2\frac{1}{2}$ hours. How far did it sail in 20 minutes?

57. If 7 men can dig 32 rods of ditch in 1 day, how many men will be required to dig 96 rods in $\frac{3}{4}$ of a day?

58. I have pasturage for either 12 horses or 18 cows on my farm. If I have 6 cows, how many horses can I keep?

59. If it costs $ 50 to support 8 persons for $2\frac{1}{2}$ weeks, what will it cost to support 10 persons for 3 weeks ?

60. A is 25 years old and B is 4 years old. In how many years will A be four times as old as B ?

61. John is 20 years old, which is $\frac{5}{8}$ of his uncle's age. How long since his uncle was twice as old as John ?

62. Mr. A. is 35 years of age and his son is 10. How soon will the son be one half the age of the father ?

63. Ten years ago C was $\frac{1}{4}$ as old as D, but now he is $\frac{1}{3}$ as old. What is the age of each ?

64. A farmer one day bought a certain number of sheep for $ 100. By buying 10 additional sheep the next day at $1 less each, his bill for all was increased to $ 140. How many did he buy at first ?

65. A party of 8 hired a coach. If there had been 4 more the expense would have been reduced $ 1 for each person. How much was paid for the coach ?

66. A and B agree to do a piece of work for $ 15. A can do the work alone in 8 days; B can do it alone in 12 days. What should each receive ?

67. C and D do a piece of work for $ 59. C can do the whole work in $2\frac{1}{4}$ weeks, and B can do it in $2\frac{2}{3}$ weeks. How should the money be divided between them ?

68. A and B can do a piece of work in 10 days. A can do it alone in 15 days. They work together 4 days, after which B finishes the work. If they earn $ 30, how much should each receive ?

69. A farmer being asked how many apple trees he had, replied, "If I had 3 times as many and 5 trees more, I should have 1358." How many had he ?

70. A man bought a number of pigs for $ 36. Nine of them having died, he sold $\frac{2}{3}$ of the remainder for cost, and received $ 15. How many did he buy ?

71. A fox is 60 leaps ahead of a hound, and takes 4 leaps while the hound takes 3; but 1 of the hound's equals 2 of the fox's leaps. How many leaps must the hound take to catch the fox?

72. A fox has 120 rods the start of a hound. If the hound runs 30 rods while the fox runs 26, how far will the hound run before he overtakes the fox?

73. A hare is 70 leaps before a hound, and takes 5 leaps while the hound takes 3; but three of the hound's leaps equal 7 of the hare's. How many leaps will the hound take to catch the hare?

74. A teacher took some pupils on an excursion, and after expending 15 cents for each pupil, found that she had $2 left. If she had expended 20 cents for each, she would have had only $1 left. How many pupils were there?

75. A man bought a horse, a cow, and a sheep for a certain sum. The horse and the sheep cost 5 times as much as the cow, and the sheep and the cow cost $\frac{2}{7}$ as much as the horse. What did each cost, if the cow cost $30?

76. A lady had money enough to pay 15 cents a yard for some ribbon and have 50 cents left. If she had paid 25 cents a yard for it, she would have needed 50 cents more. How many yards were there, and how much money had she?

77. The head of a fish is 8 inches long. The tail is as long as the head and $\frac{1}{2}$ of the body, and the body is as long as the head and tail. What is the length of the fish?

78. A tree is broken into three pieces. The part standing is 8 ft. long. The top piece is as long as the part standing and $\frac{1}{4}$ of the middle piece, and the middle piece is twice as long as the other pieces. How high was the tree?

469. 1. The minuend is 21,870, and the remainder 6492. What is the subtrahend?

2. The quotient is 3217, the divisor 63, and the remainder 29. What is the dividend?

3. Multiply 7.64 by .000302.

4. Divide .0085604 by 2.07.

5. Simplify $\left(1\frac{3}{8} + \frac{5}{4} \text{ of } \dfrac{21}{11\frac{2}{5}} - \dfrac{\frac{5}{6}}{2\frac{1}{2}} \right) \div 2\frac{77}{114}.$

6. If $\frac{5}{6}$ of a yard of broadcloth costs \$3$\frac{3}{4}$, what will 5$\frac{3}{5}$ yards cost?

7. A farmer sold 7 firkins of butter, each containing 100 pounds, for 24 cents per pound, and 16 dozen eggs for 18 cents a dozen. He received in payment 50 pounds of sugar at 5$\frac{1}{2}$ cents per pound, 18 yards of cloth at \$1.37$\frac{1}{2}$ per yard, and the rest in money. How much money did he receive?

8. Half of A's money is equal to $\frac{3}{4}$ of B's, and A has \$18 more than B. How much has each?

9. How many yards of silk, $\frac{3}{8}$ of a yard wide, will it take to line 4$\frac{1}{4}$ yards of broadcloth 1$\frac{3}{8}$ yards wide?

10. How much must be paid for 3580 lb. of coal, at \$6.50 a ton?

11. A square lot, measuring on each side 36.5 yards, is inclosed by four lines of galvanized iron wire. Eight yards of this wire weigh a pound, and the wire cost 6 cents a pound. What did the wire fence cost?

12. A man bought $\frac{5}{16}$ of a section (a square mile) of land for \$2500. He sold $\frac{3}{5}$ of it at \$14.50 an acre, and the rest at \$15.75 an acre. How much did he gain?

13. Divide \$7.75 among 5 boys and 4 girls, and give each boy $\frac{3}{4}$ as much as each girl.

14. If a man takes 2 steps of 30 inches each, in 3 seconds, how long will it take him to walk 10 miles?

15. Three men engage to reap a field of wheat. A can do it in 12 days, B in 15 days, and C in 18 days. In what time can they do it together?

16. What will it cost to lay a pavement 40 feet long and 9 feet 6 inches wide, at 35 cents a square yard?

17. A boy bought a certain number of oranges at the rate of 5 for 6 cents, and sold them at the rate of 3 for 5 cents. He gained 70 cents. How many did he buy?

18. A man bequeathed $\frac{1}{3}$ of his estate to his wife, $\frac{1}{6}$ to each of three children, $\frac{1}{12}$ to his brother, and the rest, amounting to $1850, to a charitable institution. How much was his estate worth?

19. Mr. A bought 480 bushels of grain, consisting of wheat, oats, and corn, in the proportion of 3, 4, and 5. How many bushels of each did he buy?

20. How many acres are there in a rectangular piece of land, 8450 feet long and 3580 feet wide?

21. How many cords of wood are there in a pile 80 feet long, 5 feet high, and 4 feet wide?

22. A man invested $\frac{2}{5}$ of his capital in bank stock, $\frac{3}{4}$ of the remainder in real estate, and had $4260 left. What was his capital?

23. What must be the length of a plot of ground, if the breadth is $18\frac{3}{4}$ feet, that its area may contain 56 square yards?

24. If 14 ounces of wool make $2\frac{1}{4}$ yards of cloth 1 yard wide, how much will it take to make $6\frac{1}{2}$ yards $1\frac{1}{4}$ yards wide?

25. One fourth of a certain number is 132 more than $\frac{1}{6}$ of it. What is the number?

26. If to a certain number you add $\frac{1}{5}$ of itself and $\frac{1}{6}$ of itself, the sum will be 943. What is the number?

27. A paid $65 an acre for his farm, which was $\frac{5}{6}$ as much as B paid per acre for his farm of 160 acres. What was the cost of B's farm?

28. A man owns $\frac{3}{8}$ of a ship, and sells $\frac{2}{3}$ of his share for £1260. At this rate, what is the value of the ship in U. S. money?

29. If a train runs 30 miles per hour, what is its average speed per second?

30. A, B, and C hire a pasture for $155. A puts in 20 oxen for $5\frac{1}{2}$ months, B 8 oxen and 28 sheep for 6 months, and C 56 sheep for $6\frac{1}{2}$ months. If 2 oxen eat as much as 7 sheep, how much should each man pay?

31. What is the interest on a note for $460 for 3 yr. 5 mo. 23 da. at 5%?

32. A merchant sold a quantity of goods at a gain of 20%. If, however, he had purchased the goods for $60 less than he did, his gain would have been 25%. What did the goods cost?

33. A regiment of soldiers, consisting of 1100 men, was furnished with bread sufficient to last it 8 weeks, allowing each man 15 oz. per day. If $\frac{1}{9}$ of it was found to be unfit for use, how many ounces per day should each man receive so that the balance may last 8 weeks?

34. If 5 oxen or 7 horses will eat up the grass of a field in 60 days, in what time will 3 oxen and 4 horses eat it?

35. If I buy coal at $4 per ton on 4 months' credit, at what price must I sell it immediately to gain 20%, money being worth 6%?

36. A dealer bought flour for $900 cash, and sold it for $1080 on 6 months' credit, for which he received a note. If he should get the note discounted at a bank at 6%, what would be the gain on the flour? (Allow days of grace.)

37. A farmer was offered $1.45 per bushel for his wheat, but he determined to have it ground and sell the flour. It cost to take it to the mill $2\frac{1}{4}$ cents per bushel; the miller took $\frac{1}{8}$ for grinding; it took $4\frac{40}{30}$ bushels to make a barrel of flour; he paid 45 cents apiece for barrels, and it cost 25 cents per barrel commission to sell it. 75 barrels were sold for $550 and 25 barrels for $165. If the refuse was sold for $100, did he gain or lose, and how much per hundred barrels?

38. How many more feet of fencing will be required to inclose a rectangular field 80 rods long and 45 rods wide, than to inclose a square one of the same area?

39. What is the difference between the true and the bank discount of $360 due in 6 months at 6%? (No grace.)

40. An agent sells for a manufacturer goods to the amount of $1675.80, at a commission of 5%, and purchases for him raw material amounting to $3860, at a commission of $2\frac{1}{2}$%. What is the sum earned by the agent?

41. A carriage has its hind wheel $4\frac{1}{2}$ ft. high, and its fore wheel 4 ft. high. While the hind wheel is making 720 revolutions, how many does the fore wheel make?

42. An estate is divided among three heirs, A, B, and C, so that A has $\frac{5}{12}$ of the whole, and B has twice as much as C. It is found that A has 56 acres more than C. How large is the estate?

43. What is the present worth of a debt of $1200, due in 2 years and 3 months, without interest, money being worth 6%?

44. From your knowledge of circular measure and of the length of a degree of longitude at the equator, compute the circumference of the earth at the equator.

45. A and B in partnership gained $860, of which A's share was $500. B's stock was $1800. What was A's stock?

46. How many square inches are there in the entire surface of a cube whose edge is 17 inches?

47. A drover bought a certain number of horses for $2850. If he had bought 13 more, at $12 more each, they would have cost $4956. How many did he buy?

48. A man bought 20 bushels of wheat and 15 bushels of corn for $36, and 15 bushels of wheat and 25 bushels of corn for $32.50. What did he pay per bushel for each?

49. What should be the cost of 15 crates of berries, each containing $2\frac{3}{4}$ pecks, at $9\frac{1}{2}$ cents a quart?

50. What will be the expense of plastering a room 18 feet long, 15 feet wide, and 8 feet high, at $.30 a square yard, allowing 150 square feet for doors, windows, etc.?

51. For what sum must a note be drawn at 3 months to net $150, when discounted at 6%? (Allow days of grace.)

52. At $3\frac{1}{2}$ cents a foot, board measure, what is the cost of 5 pieces of sawed timber, each measuring 18 feet long, 1 foot 4 inches wide, and 11 inches thick?

53. A man wishes his son to have $3000 when he is 21 years of age. What sum must be deposited at the son's birth, in a savings bank which pays compound interest at the annual rate of 6%, so that the deposit shall amount to that sum when the boy becomes of age?

54. What is the entire surface of a cube, the contents of which are 15,625 cubic feet?

55. How many acres of land are there in a rectangular farm $\frac{1}{2}$ of a mile long and $\frac{1}{3}$ of a mile broad?

56. In what time will $300, at 6% simple interest, yield an amount of interest equal to the principal?

57. How far from the base of a building must a ladder 50 feet long be placed to reach a window 40 feet from the ground?

58. What will it cost to dig a cellar, 38 feet long, 30 feet wide, and 8 feet deep, at $.45 a cubic yard?

59. What must be the price paid for 5% stock so that it may yield the same rate of income as $4\frac{1}{2}$% stock at 96?

60. How many bushels of wheat will a bin hold that is 5 feet long, $4\frac{1}{2}$ feet wide, and 4 feet deep?

61. If $8000 worth of $4\frac{1}{2}$% stocks are sold at $87\frac{1}{2}$, and the proceeds are invested in 6% stock at $116\frac{2}{3}$, what will be the change in the income?

62. A, B, and C agree to build a house. A and B can do the work in 32 days, B and C in 28 days, and A and C in 26 days. How long will it take them to do it working together? How long will it take each to do it alone?

63. How many barrels of water will a rectangular tank contain which is $7\frac{1}{2}$ feet long, 4 feet wide, and $2\frac{3}{4}$ feet deep?

64. If 8 men spend $32 in 15 weeks, how much will 56 men, at the same rate, spend in a year?

65. If 12 men can build a wall 30 feet long, 6 feet high, and 3 feet thick, in 15 days, by working 12 hours per day, in what time will 60 men build a wall 300 feet long, 8 feet high, and 6 feet thick, when they work only 8 hours a day?

66. If a pipe $1\frac{1}{2}$ in. in diameter fills a cistern in 2 hours, how long will it require a pipe that is 3 in. in diameter to fill it, no allowance being made for the difference in friction?

67. A man sold two farms for $4800 each. On the one he gained 20%, and on the other he lost 20%. Did he gain or lose on the sale, and how much?

68. B owned 75 shares of stock in a building association, at $50 each. The association declared a dividend of 8%, payable in stock. How many shares did he then own?

69. Mr. W. bought 40 shares of stock, $50 each, at $2\frac{1}{2}$% discount. He sold $\frac{1}{4}$ of it at $\frac{1}{2}$% discount, and the rest at $1\frac{3}{4}$% premium. What was his gain?

70. A man traveled 3 days at the rate of 18 miles per day, 4 days at the rate of 22 miles per day, and 5 days at the rate of 28 miles per day. What was his average rate of travel per day?

71. A liveryman borrowed money at 6% to purchase a horse. The horse, which cost him $90, earned $1 a day, and the expense of keeping him each day was $\frac{1}{3}$% of the purchase price. At the end of a year the liveryman sold the horse for $70. How much did he gain, if the horse worked 312 days during the year?

72. A tank which holds 200 gallons can be filled by one pipe in 15 minutes and emptied by another pipe in 40 minutes. If the tank is empty and both are opened at the same time, how long will it take to fill it?

73. In the Centigrade and Fahrenheit thermometers the freezing points are 0° and 32° respectively, and the boiling points 100° and 212° respectively. When the temperature is 50° Fahrenheit, what temperature will the Centigrade thermometer indicate?

74. An agent sold goods at a commission of 5% through a broker who charged him 2%, and the agent's commission after paying the brokerage was $315. How much did the agent remit to his employer?

75. How much will be realized from the sale of a draft for $1200 sold at $\frac{1}{4}$% premium?

76. What will be the face of a 60-day draft purchased for $450, if the rate of exchange is $\frac{1}{8}$% premium and the rate of discount 6%? (Allow days of grace.)

77. A room is 18 feet long, 15 feet wide, and 9 feet high. What must be the length of a line extending from one of the lower corners to an opposite upper corner?

78. A and B together have $851. How much has each if $\frac{8}{19}$ of A's money equals $\frac{4}{9}$ of B's?

79. A detachment of 2000 soldiers was supplied with bread sufficient to last 12 weeks, allowing each man 14 ounces a day; but 105 barrels, containing 200 pounds each, were wholly spoiled. How much a day may each man eat, that the remainder may supply them 12 weeks?

80. Find the value of $(3.0005 \times .006) \div .0009$.

81. An agent sold a house at 2% commission. He invested the net proceeds of the sale in city lots, after deducting his commission of 3% for buying them, and found that his commissions amounted to $350. For how much was the house sold?

82. What is the area in acres of a rectangular field whose breadth is 65 ch. 20 l., and whose length is 70 ch. 18 l.?

83. A farmer mixed 10 bushels of oats, worth $.35 a bushel, 12 bushels of corn, worth $.60 a bushel, and 7 bushels of rye, worth $.78 a bushel. What was the average value of a bushel of the mixture?

84. In a mixture of gold and silver, weighing 64 ounces, there are 4 ounces of silver. How much gold must be added that there may be $\frac{3}{4}$ of an ounce of silver in 18 ounces of the mixture?

85. There is a circular park 250 rods in diameter, and within it is a circular lake 125 rods in circumference. What is the area of the park exclusive of the lake?

86. How many balls, 3 in. in diam., will weigh as much as a ball of the same material and density 9 in. in diam.?

87. A note, due in 4 months, dated March 4, was discounted May 15. For what time was it discounted? (Allow days of grace.)

88. A man bought a house for $2700. He repaired it for a tenant who agreed to pay him a yearly rent of $225, which was 15% less than the cost of repairing it. What was the entire cost of the house?

89. Three men took a contract to build a bridge for $32,525. The first had 80 men at work for 40 days, the second had 70 men at work for 45 days, and the third had 56 men at work for 50 days. The third received $500 for superintending the work. How much was each one's share of the contract price?

90. It cost $150 to support 4 grown persons and 3 children 8 weeks. What will it cost to support 3 grown persons and 8 children for the same time, if 3 children cost as much as 2 grown persons?

91. A man has real estate assessed at $3200, and personal property at $1280. If he pays a tax of $1\frac{3}{8}\%$, what is his total tax?

92. If a tax of $60 is paid on a factory valued at $12,000, what is the assessed valuation of a residence that is taxed 8.87\frac{1}{2}$ at the same rate?

93. What is the ad valorem duty, at 40%, upon a consignment of 425 dozen silk handkerchiefs, invoiced at 35 francs per dozen?

94. A merchant imported 40 pieces of carpet, each piece containing 56 square yards, invoiced at 3 s. 8 d. per square yard, upon which he paid a specific duty of 15 cents per square yard, and 30% ad valorem. What was the total amount of duty paid?

95. Two men were employed to build a wall. The first received $.87$\frac{1}{2}$ per day, and the second 1.12\frac{1}{2}$ per day. Each worked until he had earned $60. How many days did each labor?

96. If $300, placed at interest, yields an income of $18 in 9 months, how much must be placed at interest, at the same rate, to yield an income of $115 in 6 months?

97. A, B, and C entered into partnership. A advanced $1200, B, $900, and C, $850. A left his money in the business 8 months, B, 10 months, and C, 12 months. They gained $1296. To what share of the profit is each entitled?

98. A and B have the same income. A saves $\frac{1}{6}$ of his, but B, by spending $100 each year more than A, at the end of 5 years finds himself $240 in debt. What was the income of each?

99. A ladder 70 feet long is so planted as to reach a window 40 feet from the ground, on one side of the street, and without moving it at the foot, it will reach a window 30 feet high on the other side. What is the width of the street?

100. A father gave to his four sons $1200, which they were to divide so that each son should receive $60 more than his next younger brother. What was the share of the oldest?

101. A and B are on opposite sides of a circular pond which is 1380 feet in circumference. They walk around it, starting at the same time and in the same direction. A goes at the rate of 45 yards per minute, and B at the rate of 50 yards per minute. In what time will B overtake A, and how many times around the pond will he have traveled?

102. A father wishes to divide $1500 between his son and daughter, whose ages are 12 and 16 years, respectively, in such proportions that the share of each, being put at simple interest at 6%, will amount to the same sum when they reach the age of 21. What should each receive?

103. A, B, and C are to share $1200 in the proportion of 3, 4, and 5, respectively. B dies. How should the whole sum be divided between A and C?

104. A man bought a house, a store, and a lot. The lot cost $1650, the house and store $5\frac{2}{3}$ times as much as the lot, and the store cost $\frac{1}{4}$ as much as the house and lot. What was the cost of each?

105. At $75 an acre, and $1.50 a rod for fencing, what will it cost me to purchase and fence a field having two parallel sides 100 and 80 rods long, respectively, the distance between them being 70 rods, and the other two sides being equal?

106. A person in purchasing sugar found that if he bought sugar at 5 cents, he would lack 30 cents of having money enough to pay for it, so he bought sugar at $4\frac{1}{2}$ cents, and had 45 cents left. How many pounds did he buy?

107. What is the base of a triangular field whose area is 1 acre 65 sq. rods, and whose altitude is 18 rods?

108. What is the altitude of a triangular plot of ground whose area is $5\frac{1}{2}$ acres, and whose base is 44 rods?

109. A man sold a horse and carriage for $597, gaining by the sale 25% on the cost of the horse and 10% on the cost of the carriage. If $\frac{3}{4}$ of the cost of the horse equaled $\frac{2}{3}$ of the cost of the carriage, what was the cost of each?

110. A merchant bought cloth to the amount of $750, and silk goods to the amount of $500. On the cloth goods he gained 20% and on the silk he lost $16\frac{2}{3}\%$. How much did he gain?

111. If a house is bought for $2150, and sold again for $2365, what is the gain per cent?

112. A merchant sold a coat for $15.40, and gained 20%. How much would he have gained had he sold it for $16.50?

113. A owes B $1200, payable in 6 months, but at the end of 4 months he pays $400. How long after this payment is made will it be before the rest is equitably due?

114. A house is 38 feet from the ground to the eaves. How long must a ladder be to reach the eaves if its foot is placed 25 feet from the house?

115. A farmer had his sheep in three fields. $\frac{2}{3}$ of the number in the first field was equal to $\frac{3}{4}$ of the number in the second field, and $\frac{2}{3}$ of the number in the second field was $\frac{3}{4}$ of the number in the third field. If the entire number was 434, how many were there in each field?

116. If 9 men can mow 75 acres of grass in 6 days of $8\frac{1}{4}$ hours each, in how many days of 8 hours each can 15 men mow 198 acres?

117. A board is 18 feet long, 20 inches wide at one end, and tapers gradually until it is only 1 foot wide at the other end. It is 1 inch thick. How many board feet does it contain?

118. What is the compound interest of $ 1650 for 3 years at 6%, interest being compounded semi-annually?

119. In what time will $ 460.75 earn $ 95 interest when the rate is 6%?

120. What is the rate per cent per annum when $ 712 in 3 years 4 months earns $142.40?

121. A, B, and C in partnership gained $ 3192. A's stock was $ 5600, which was $1\frac{1}{3}$ times B's, and B's was $1\frac{1}{3}$ times C's. What was the gain of each?

122. D, E, and F engage to do a piece of work for $ 381. D sends 7 men 6 days, E sends 8 men 5 days, and F sends 5 men 9 days. What should each receive?

123. A's capital was in trade 9 months, B's 12 months, and C's 15 months. A's gain was $ 1125, B's $ 1200, and C's $1275. The whole capital was $18,600. What was the capital of each?

124. A man bought a farm for $ 2500 and sold it for $ 3000. If the buying and selling were done by a real estate agent, who charged 2% for each transaction, what per cent of the cost did the man gain?

125. The diameter of a circular plot for flowers is 8 feet. What must be the diameter of a similar plot which shall contain 6¼ times as much area?

126. The weight of oak ashes is $\frac{3}{100}$ of the weight of the wood consumed, and the weight of carbonate of potash contained in the ashes is .065 of the weight of the ashes. How many ounces of carbonate of potash are there in the ashes of 500 pounds of oak wood?

127. What is the G. C. D. of 3038, 5394, and 8308?

128. What is the L. C. M. of 42, 63, 49, 91, and 70?

129. A, B, and C together have $4750. How much has each if A has ¾ as much as B, and C ³⁄₇ as much as both A and B?

130. A speculator bought stock at 25% below par and sold it at 20% above par. He gained $1560. How much did he invest?

131. A carriage maker sold two carriages for $300 each. On one he gained 25%; on the other he lost 25%. Did he gain or lose by the sale? How much, and how much per cent?

132. New York is 74° 3′ west of Greenwich, England. What is the difference in time between the two places?

133. Paris is about 2° 20′ east of Greenwich. What is the difference in time between New York and Paris?

134. Which is the heavier, and how much, an ounce of lead or an ounce of gold?

135. A barn worth $900 was insured for ⅔ of its value for $3.75. What was the rate of insurance?

136. A ship worth $48,000, and its cargo valued at ¼ that amount, were insured for ⅔ of their value, at 1¼%. What was the cost of the insurance?

137. If a ladder, placed 8 feet from the base of a building 40 feet high, just reached the top, how far must it be placed from the base of the building that it may reach a point 10 feet from the top ?

138. The total net weight of 40 loads of hay was 56,724 pounds. What was the hay worth at $ 8.25 per ton ?

139. A load of four-foot wood is $3\frac{1}{2}$ feet high and $7\frac{1}{2}$ feet long. What must be paid for 3 such loads, when wood sells at $3.75 per cord ?

140. At the rate of $ 12,760 a mile, what will it cost to construct a railroad 5 miles, 28 rods, 2 yards long ?

141. If 1 bushel 3 pecks of wheat are sown to the acre, how much land can be sown with the contents of a bin 4 feet long, 3 feet wide, and $2\frac{1}{2}$ feet deep, filled with wheat ?

142. John and Charles can do a piece of work in 45 days, and Charles can do $\frac{4}{5}$ as much as John. In what time can each do the work alone ?

143. A, B, and C pasture an equal number of cattle upon a field of which A and B are the owners, A of 9 acres and B of 15 acres. If C pays $ 24 for his pasturage, how much should A and B each receive ?

144. A and B engaged to do a piece of work for $ 385. A worked $\frac{3}{4}$ as many days as B, plus 5 days, and received $ 175. How many days did each work ?

145. A note for $ 100 was due on Sept. 1st, but on Aug. 11th the maker proposed to pay as much in advance as would allow him 2 months after Sept. 1st to pay the balance. How much must be paid Aug. 11th, money being worth 6% ?

146. A and B in partnership gained $ 1200. A owned $\frac{2}{5}$ of the stock, plus $ 500, and gained $ 600. What was the entire stock ?

147. $360. MOBILE, ALA., June 24, 1892.

Three months after date, for value received, I promise to pay D. C. Morgan, or order, Three Hundred Sixty Dollars, with interest at 6%.

A. B. HENRY.

This note was discounted at a bank at 6%, July 15, 1892. What were the proceeds?

148. A hollow sphere whose diameter is 6 inches weighs $\frac{1}{8}$ as much as a solid sphere of the same material and diameter. How thick is the shell?

149. A train started on a trip of 245 miles at 35 miles an hour, but after having gone 140 miles it was delayed 20 minutes. If it finished the trip at the rate of 30 miles an hour, how much behind time was it?

150. Twenty per cent of a barrel of oil leaked out. What per cent must be gained on the remainder that a gain of 10% may be realized on the cost of the oil?

151. How much alloy must be mixed with 2 lb. 2 oz. 15 pwt. 19 gr. of pure gold, to make gold 18 carats fine?

152. A and B traded with equal sums of money. A gained a sum equal to $\frac{1}{5}$ of his capital, and B lost $220. B then had $\frac{1}{2}$ as much as A. How much capital had each at first?

153. A man invested $\frac{3}{4}$ of his money in a foundry, expended $\frac{2}{5}$ of what he had left in building a house, and still had $4671. How much money had he at first?

154. If in selling cloth $\frac{3}{4}$ of the gain is equal to $\frac{3}{16}$ of the selling price, for how much will $3\frac{1}{3}$ yards sell that cost $5 per yard?

155. A teacher agreed to teach 9 months for 562\frac{1}{2}$ and his board. At the end of the term, on account of two months' absence caused by sickness, he received only 409\frac{1}{2}$. What was his board worth per month?

156. A person after spending $40 more than .6 of his money had $60 less than .42⅔ of it left. How much money had he at first?

157. What is the greatest number which will divide 27, 48, 90, and 174, and leave the same remainder in each case?

158. The gross earnings of a mill were $365,816.92. The entire expenses exclusive of repairs were $318,214.84; the repairs were .06 of the earnings. If the net profits were divided equally among 8 shareholders, what was the share of each?

159. A grain dealer expended a certain sum of money in the purchase of wheat, 1½ times as much in the purchase of barley, and twice as much for oats. He sold the wheat at a profit of .05 of the cost, the barley at a profit of .08, the oats at a profit of .1, receiving for all the grain $9740. What did he pay for each kind of grain?

160. I wish to raise $550 by having my note discounted at a bank for 2 mo. 15 da. at 6%. What must be the face of the note? (Allow days of grace.)

161. A farmer sold a team of horses for $440, but did not receive his pay for them until 1 yr. 8 mo. after the sale. He had at the same time a cash offer of $410 for them. Did he gain or lose by the sale and how much, money being worth 6%?

162. A weight of 240 pounds, suspended on a pole 4 feet in length, the point of suspension being 6 inches from the middle, is carried by two men, the ends of the pole resting on their shoulders. How much of the weight is borne by each man?

163. A and B invested equal sums in business. A gained a sum equal to 25% of his stock, and B lost $225. A's money at this time was double that of B's. What amount did each invest?

164. A owned two farms for the better of which he asked 50% more than for the other. Not finding a purchaser, he reduced the price of the better $33\frac{1}{3}\%$, and the price of the other 20%, and sold them both for $5580. What was the price asked for each?

165. A merchant bought a bill of goods amounting to $3257 on a credit of 3 months, but was offered a discount of $2\frac{1}{2}\%$ for cash. How much would he have gained by paying cash, money being worth 7%?

166. Which is better for me, to buy 6% bonds at 72%, or to invest my money in mortgages bearing 8%? How much better is it?

167. A machine shop was insured at an annual rate of 3%, the premium paid being $750. For how much was it insured?

168. A merchant bought broadcloth at a discount of 25% from the marked price, receiving besides a discount of 5% for cash. If he sold it at an advance of 10% on the marked price, what was his gain per cent?

169. A commission merchant received 35,000 bushels of oats, which he sold at 32 cents per bushel. He was instructed to invest the proceeds, together with $4000 cash sent him, in prints at $5\frac{1}{2}$ cents per yard. If his commission both for buying and for selling was 2%, how many yards of prints did he buy?

170. I find that I owe A 50% more than I owe C, and B $33\frac{1}{3}\%$ more than I owe A. Now if I owe B $800 more than I do C, how much is my indebtedness to each?

171. A started in business with a capital of $4000, and at the end of 5 years he was joined by B with a capital of $5000. Three years later they were joined by C with a capital of $6000. If at the end of 15 years after the commencement of business the profits, which amounted to $18,240, were divided, how much was each one's share?

172. How many shares of stock, at $113\frac{1}{4}$, can a broker purchase for me with $22,675, brokerage $\frac{1}{8}\%$?

173. I am offered 6% stock at 84, and 5% stock at 72. Which investment is preferable, and how much ?

174. I am desirous of securing an income of $6\frac{1}{2}\%$ or 7% on my investments. Can I do it by purchasing 5% stock at 75% ? What will be the rate of income ?

175. I have, as the net proceeds of a consignment of goods sold by me, $3816.48, which the consignor desires me to remit by draft at 2 months. If the rates of exchange are $\frac{3}{4}\%$ premium, and the rate of interest 6%, what will be the face of the draft ? (Allow days of grace.)

176. A man bought a horse and a carriage, paying twice as much for the horse as for the carriage. He sold them both for $662, receiving 15% more for the horse, and 8% more for the carriage than they cost him. What did they each cost him ?

177. A man sold 500 acres of land, receiving in payment $\frac{2}{3}$ of the value in cash, and the rest in a note due in 3 months without interest. He immediately discounted the note at a bank at 6%, paying $57.50 discount. What was the price of the land per acre ? (Allow days of grace.)

178. How many slates will be required to cover a roof, each side of which is 34 feet 9 inches long and 16 feet wide, allowing 4 slates to cover a square foot; and what will they cost at the rate of $4.75 per C ?

179. An article was sold at a price which was $\frac{1}{4}$ above cost. If the cost had been $\frac{4}{5}$ of what it really was and the selling price had remained the same, the gain would have been $6.75. How much did the article cost ?

180. Three men bought a grindstone 20 inches in diameter. How much of the diameter must each grind off so as to share the stone equally, making no allowance for the eye ?

AVERAGE OF PAYMENTS.

470. **1.** How long may $1 be kept to balance the use of $5 for 2 months? $6 for 3 months? $10 for 4 months?

2. How long may $10 be kept to balance the use of $6 for 5 months? $8 for 10 months? $12 for 5 months?

3. I owe B two equal debts, one due in 3 months and the other in 6 months. When may I pay both at one payment?

4. If I pay $20 3 months before it is due, how long after it is due may I keep $30 to balance it?

5. If I owe $20 due in 4 months and $40 due in 6 months, at what time are both debts equitably due?

471. Finding the equitable time for discharging, by one payment, sums due at different times is **Averaging Payments.**

472. The date at which the debts may be equitably discharged by a single payment is the **Average Time.**

473. The time that must elapse before the debt becomes due is the **Term of Credit.**

474. The time that must elapse before the debts due at different times may be equitably discharged by a single payment is the **Average Term of Credit.**

475. When the terms of credit begin at the same date.

1. A. T. Stewart & Co. sold a bill of goods upon the following terms: $400 cash, $300 due in 2 months, and $400 due in 4 months. At what time might the whole indebtedness be equitably discharged by a cash payment?

368

EXPLANATION. —

$400 for 0 mo. = $1 for —————.

300 for 2 mo. = $1 for 600 mo.

400 for 4 mo. = $1 for 1600 mo.
_____   _____

$1100   2200 mo.

2200 mo. ÷ 1100 = 2 mo.   Average term of credit.

Since $400 was to be paid in cash, there was no term of credit for that sum. Since $300 was to be paid in 2 months, the use of that sum for 2 months is equal to the use of $1 for 600 months; and the use of $400 for 4 months is equal to the use of $1 for 1600 months. Hence, the credit of the whole debt, $1100, is equal to the credit of $1 for 2200 months, or $1100 for $\frac{1}{1100}$ part of 2200 months, which is 2 months, the average term of credit.

RULE. — *Multiply each debt by its term of credit, and divide the sum of the products by the sum of the debts. The quotient will be the average term of credit.*

Disregard fractional parts of a day that are less than $\frac{1}{2}$, and consider $\frac{1}{2}$ of a day or more as a whole day.

2. Find the average term of credit of a bill of goods amounting to $2300, on the following terms: $300 cash, $1200 due in 3 months, and the balance due in 4 months.

3. Marshall Field sold a bill of goods payable as follows: $500 in 1 month, $500 in 2 months, and $800 in 4 months. What was the average term of credit?

4. Whitney & Co. sold a bill of lumber on the following terms: $1500 cash, $3000 payable in 30 days, and $2000 payable in 90 days. What was the average term of credit?

5. Thurber, Whyland & Co. sold to F. N. Burt a bill of goods amounting to $2400, payable as follows: $\frac{1}{3}$ in 30 days, $\frac{1}{2}$ the remainder in 60 days, and the balance in 4 months. What was the average term of credit?

6. Mr. Birge bought a bill of goods amounting to $3000, payable as follows: $\frac{1}{4}$ in 3 months, $\frac{1}{4}$ in 2 months, and the rest in 4 months. What was the average term of credit?

476. When the terms of credit begin at different dates.

1. Find the average time of payment of the following bills : February 10, 1891, $400 due in 2 months; March 15, 1891, $350 due in 3 months; and April 12, 1891, $300 due in 3 months.

$400 due April 10.   400

350 due June 15. $350 \times 66 = 23100$

300 due July 12. $300 \times 93 = 27900$

————   ————

1050   51000

51000 da. $\div$ 1050 $= 48\frac{12}{21}$ days.

April 10 $+$ 49 days $=$ May 29, average term.

EXPLANATION. — Adding to the date of the purchase of each bill its term of credit, we obtain the time when it is due, and so we have $400 due April 10, $350 due June 15, $300 due July 12.   The average time when the bills will be due will be either after the earliest date, or before the latest date, and so we may select either of these dates from which to compute the average time.   Selecting the earliest date, we find that $350 was due 66 days after that time, and $300 was due 93 days thereafter.   Averaging, as in Art. 475, we find the term of credit to be $48\frac{12}{21}$ days, and since the fraction $\frac{12}{21}$ is greater than $\frac{1}{2}$, the term of credit is considered to be 49 days.   This, added to April 10, gives May 29, the average time of payment.

RULE. — *Select the earliest date at which any debt becomes due for the standard date, and find how long after that date the other amounts become due.*

Find the average term of credit by multiplying each debt by the number of days from the standard date, and dividing the sum of the products by the sum of the debts.

Add the average term of credit to the standard date, and the result will be the average term of payment.

Instead of the *earliest* date, the *first of the month* may be used.

2. What is the average time at which the following bills become due : Feb. 1, 1887, $200 on 1 mo. credit; March 10, 1887, $500 on 3 mo. credit; April 12, 1887, $275 on 2 mo credit; and May 1, 1887, $400 on 4 mo. credit?

3. A merchant owes bills dated as follows: Jan. 1, 1892, $500 due in 2 mo.; Jan. 15, 1892, $850 due in 3 mo.; Feb. 20, 1892, $375 due in 3 mo.; and, Feb. 28, 1892, $650 due in 4 mo. What will be the average time of payment?

4. A merchant purchased goods of Cragin Bros. & Co. as follows: Sept. 10, 1891, $300 on 4 mo. credit; Oct. 15, 1891, $400 on 6 mo. credit; Nov. 1, 1891, $750 on 2 mo. credit; and Nov. 15, 1891, $300 on 1 mo. credit. What was the average time of payment?

5. Messrs. J. Richards & Son bought goods from George C. Buell & Co. as follows: Sept. 1, 1891, $600 on 3 mo. credit; Oct. 3, 1891, $400 on 4 mo. credit; Oct. 20, 1891, $250 on 2 mo. credit; and, Nov. 10, 1891, $375 on 1 mo. credit. What was the average time of payment?

6. Stevens & Shepard bought goods from the Russell Irwin Manufacturing Co. as follows: Dec. 10, 1891, a bill of $460 on 4 mo. credit; Jan. 5, 1892, a bill of $200 on 3 mo. credit; Jan. 30, 1892, a bill of $200 on 4 mo. credit; and, Feb. 25, a bill of $900 on 2 mo. credit. What was the average time of payment?

7. Bought goods of Carson, Pirie & Co. as follows: Jan. 25, 1892, $850 on 4 mo. credit; Feb. 15, 1892, $600 on 3 mo. credit; March 20, 1892, $500 on 4 mo. credit; and, April 10, 1892, $960 on 2 mo. credit. What was the average time of payment?

8. May 1, 1892, Mr. S. purchased goods to the amount of $2400 on the following terms: ¼ payable in cash, ¼ payable in 2 mo., and the balance in 6 mo. When may the whole be equitably paid by one payment?

9. A bookseller sold $1800 worth of books upon the following terms: ⅓ of the amount in cash, $600 payable in 6 months, $300 in 9 months, and the rest in a year. What was the average time of payment?

AVERAGE OF ACCOUNTS.

477. **1.** What should be the date of a note given to settle the following account?

| *Dr.* | | | | | | H. R. GOODRICH. | | | *Cr.* |

1892.						1892.				
May	5	To Mdse.			50 00	May	15	By Cash	25 00	
June	7	" "	2 mo.		140 00	June	10	" Draft, 10 da.	100 00	
June	21	" "	1 "		150 00	June	30	" "	100 00	

PROCESS.   (*By Products.*)

Due.		Amount.	Days.	Product.	Paid.		Amount.	Days.	Product.
May	5	$ 50	94	4700	May	15	$ 25	84	2100
Aug.	7	140	0		June	23	100	45	4500
July	21	150	17	2550	June	30	100	38	3800
		340		7250			225		10400
		225							7250
		115			$3150 \div 115 = 27\frac{50}{115}$				3150

Aug. 7 + 27 days = Sept. 3, the average time.

EXPLANATION. — From the dates at which the various amounts become due, we select the latest, which is Aug. 7, for the assumed time of settlement, and multiply each amount by the number of days intervening between that date and the time when each item of the account becomes due. The debit side of the account shows there is due $ 340 and the use of $ 1 for 7250 days, and the credit side shows that $ 225 has been paid, and that the debtor is entitled to the use of $ 1 for 10,400 days, if the time of settlement is Aug. 7. Subtracting the amounts, there is shown to be $ 115 due, and the debtor is entitled to the use of $ 1 for 3150 days. Therefore, he should not be required to pay the account until the time when the use of $ 115 is equal to the use of $ 1 for 3150 days, which is 27 days. Hence, the note should be dated 27 days after Aug. 7, or Sept. 3.

2. When should interest begin on the following account?

Dr. JAMES HOWARD, *in acc't with* HIRAM SIBLEY. *Cr.*

1892.				1892.			
Apr.	10	To Mdse.	$ 150	Apr.	12	By Cash	$ 250
Apr.	30	" "	400	May	1	" "	200
May	16	" "	100	June	7	" "	400
June	24	" "	500				

3. What should be the date of a note given to settle the following account?

Dr. S. DANDRIDGE & Co. *Cr.*

1892.					1892.			
Jan.	1	To Mdse., 1 mo.	$ 500	Feb.	3	By Cash	$ 500
Jan.	20	" " 3 "	850	Feb.	28	" "	200
Feb.	15	" " 2 "	1500	May	15	" Draft, 1 mo.	1200
Apr.	3	" " 4 "	2500				

4. When should interest begin on the following account?

Dr. WHITNEY & MYERS. *Cr.*

1892.					1892.			
Feb.	1	To Mdse.	$ 1800	Feb.	20	By Cash	$ 3000
Mar.	15	" " 1 mo.	3000	May	18	" Accept'ce, 2 mo.	8000
Mar.	20	" " 4 "	4800				
Apr.	3	" " 4 "	6000				

5. What will be the cash balance of the following account, Jan. 1, 1892, interest at 6%?

Dr. HENRY G. SWINBURNE. *Cr.*

1891.					1891.			
July	10	To Mdse., 2 mo.	$ 500	July	20	By Cash	$ 400
Aug.	1	" " 3 "	700	Aug.	20	" "	1000
Sept.	8	" " 1 "	800				
Sept.	20	" " 2 "	600				

SAVINGS BANK ACCOUNTS.

478. Savings Banks receive small sums of money on deposit and pay the depositors compound interest, either monthly, quarterly, or semi-annually.

479. The interval between the dates at which interest is paid is called an **Interest Term.**

The interest term in most banks is three months, beginning Jan. 1, Apr. 1, July 1, and Oct. 1. Banks whose interest term is one month usually begin the interest term on the first day of each month; those whose term is six months, usually on Jan. 1 and July 1.

480. Depositors are at liberty to deposit money at any time and generally to draw it out at their pleasure, but interest is computed only upon the sum that has been on deposit during the whole of the interest term.

481. PRINCIPLE. — *Interest is added at the end of every interest term on the smallest balance on deposit during the entire term.*

1. The smallest balance on deposit at any time during the term is the smallest balance on deposit during the entire term.

2. In examples in this book no interest is computed upon the cents in the balance, and in the interest any fractional part of a cent is dropped. However, the usage of banks on these points varies.

482. Depositors in savings banks are given a bank-book in which all deposits and amounts drawn out are recorded.

WRITTEN EXERCISES.

483. **1.** What will be the balance due on the following account on Apr. 1, 1891, interest being allowed quarterly at 4% ?

Deposited Jan. 12, 1890, $75; May 10, $150; Sept. 1, $20; Jan. 1, 1891, $130.

Drew out Mar. 5, 1890, $30; Aug. 16, $50; Dec. 1, $48.

Dates.	Deposited.	Drew out.	Interest.		Balance.	
1890						
Jan. 12	75				75	
Mar. 5		30			45	
Apr. 1			00	00	45	
May 10	150				195	
July 1				45	195	45
Aug. 16		50			145	45
Sept. 1	20				165	45
Oct. 1			1	45	166	90
Dec. 1		48			118	90
1891						
Jan. 1	130		1	18	250	08
Apr. 1			2	50	252	58

EXPLANATION. — The statement is an exhibit of the condition of the account at any day and at the end of each interest term.

At the end of the first interest term, no interest was allowed because no part of the deposits was in the bank during the entire term.

The smallest balance during the second quarter was $45. The interest upon it ($.45) added to the previous balance gives the balance July 1, etc.

The balance due Apr. 1, 1891, was $252.58.

Make out statements and find the balance due on each of the following accounts :

2. What will be the balance due on the following account on Jan. 1, 1891, interest being allowed semi-annually, at 4%?

Deposited June 4, 1889, $175; Nov. 1, $150; Feb. 24, 1890, $200; Sept. 10, $56.

Drew out Sept. 14, 1889, $65; July 25, 1890, $120; Dec. 3, $80.

3. What will be the balance due on the following account on Jan. 1, 1892, interest being allowed monthly at 4%?

Deposited Jan. 1, 1890, $36.50; Mar. 17, $25.38; Aug. 1, $84.72; June 11, 1891, $50; Nov. 16, $40.78.

Drew out Sept. 16, 1890, $36.16; Jan. 27, 1891, $13.48; Mar. 1, $17.50.

PROGRESSIONS.

484. **1.** How does each of the numbers 2, 4, 6, 8, 10, 12, compare with the number that follows it?

2. How may each of the numbers 4, 6, 8, etc., be obtained from the one that precedes it?

3. How does each of the numbers 2, 5, 8, 11, 14, 17, compare with the number that follows it? How with the one that precedes it?

4. Write in succession some numbers beginning with 3 having a *common difference* of 2.

5. Write a *series* of numbers beginning at 4, and having a common difference of 4.

6. Write a series of numbers beginning with 25, and decreasing by the common difference 4.

7. How does each of the numbers 2, 4, 8, 16, 32, etc., compare with the one that follows it? How may each be obtained from the one that precedes it?

8. Write a series of numbers beginning with 2, and increasing by a common multiplier 3.

9. Write a series of numbers beginning with 5, and increasing by a common multiplier 5.

485. Numbers in succession, each derived from the preceding according to some fixed laws, are called a **Series**.

486. The first and last terms of a series are called the *extremes*, the intervening terms the *means*.

Thus, in the series 2, 4, 6, 8, 10, the numbers 2 and 10 are the extremes and the others are the means.

487. A series in which the numbers increase regularly from the first term is called an **Ascending Series.**

Thus, 2, 5, 8, 11, 14, 17, 20, etc., is an ascending series.

488. A series in which the numbers decrease regularly from the first term is called a **Descending Series.**

Thus, 48, 24, 12, 6, 3, is a descending series.

ARITHMETICAL PROGRESSION.

489. A series of numbers which increase or decrease by a constant *common difference* is an **Arithmetical Progression.**

Thus, 5, 9, 13, 17, 21, etc., is an arithmetical progression of which the common difference is 4.

490. 1. The first term of an arithmetical series is 3 and the common difference is 2. What is the 7th term?

PROCESS.

Com. diff., $2 \times 6 = 12$

First term, $3 + 12 = 15$, the 7th term.

EXPLANATION.—Since the common difference is 2, the second term is equal to the first plus *once* the common difference, the third term is equal to the first plus *twice* the common difference, the fourth term is equal to the first term plus *three times* the common difference. Hence, the seventh term will be equal to the first term plus *six times* the common difference, which is 15.

RULE. — *Any term of an arithmetical progression is equal to the first term, increased or diminished by the common difference multiplied by a number one less than the number of terms.*

2. A boy agreed to work for 50 days at 25 cents the first day, and an increase of 3 cents per day. What were his wages the last day?

3. A body falls $16\frac{1}{12}$ feet the first second, 3 times as far the second second, 5 times as far the third second. How far will it fall the seventh second?

4. An arithmetical series has 1000 terms, the first term of which is 75 and the common difference 5. What is the last term?

5. The first term is 10 and the common difference 5. What is the 10th term? Prove it.

6. The first term is 6 and the common difference is 8. What is the 25th term?

7. Find the sum of an arithmetical series of which the first term is 2. the common difference 3, and the number of terms 7.

$2 + (6 \times 3) = 20$
$2 + 20 = 22$
$22 \div 2 = 11$
$11 \times 7 = 77$

EXPLANATION. — By examining the series 2, 5, 8, 11, 14, 17, 20, it is evident that the average term is 11, for if half the sum of any two terms equidistant from the extremes is found, it will be 11, and in general in any arithmetical progression the average term is equal to half the sum of the extremes or any two terms equidistant from the extremes. Since the first term is 2 and the common difference 3, the last term is found by the previous rule to be 20. The sum of the extremes is therefore 22, which, divided by 2, gives the average term. And since there are 7 terms, the sum will be 7 times the average term, or 77.

RULE. — *To find the sum of an arithmetical series: Multiply half the sum of the extremes by the number of terms.*

8. What is the sum of an arithmetical series composed of 50 terms, of which the first term is 2 and the common difference 3?

9. What is the sum of a series in which the first term is $\frac{1}{10}$, the common difference $\frac{1}{10}$, and the number of terms 100?

10. A man walked 15 miles the first day, and increased his rate 3 miles per day for 10 days. How far did he walk in the eleven days?

11. How many strokes does a clock strike in 12 hours?

12. A person had a gift of $100 per year from his birth until he became 21 years old. These sums were deposited in a bank and drew simple interest at 6%. How much was due him when he became of age?

13. What is the sum of the series in which the first term is $\frac{1}{2}$, the common difference $\frac{1}{4}$, and the number of terms 100?

GEOMETRICAL PROGRESSION.

491. A series of numbers which increase or decrease by a constant *multiplier* or *ratio* is called a **Geometrical Progression.**

Thus 5, 10, 20, 40, 80, etc., is a geometrical progression, of which the multiplier or ratio is 2.

WRITTEN EXERCISES.

492. 1. The first term of a geometrical series is 3 and the multiplier or ratio is 2. What is the 5th term?

$2^4 = 16$

$3 \times 16 = 48$

EXPLANATION. — Since the multiplier is 2, the second term will be 3×2, the third $3 \times 2 \times 2$ or 3×2^2, the fourth $3 \times 2^2 \times 2$ or 3×2^3, and the fifth $3 \times 2^3 \times 2$ or 3×2^4, that is, the *fifth* term is equal to the first term multiplied by the ratio raised to the *fourth* power.

RULE. — *Any term of a geometrical progression is equal to the first term, multiplied by the ratio raised to a power one less than the number of the term.*

2. The first term of a geometrical progression is 10, and the ratio 3. What is the 6th term?

3. The first term of a geometrical progression is 10, the ratio 4, and the number of terms 6. What is the 6th term?

4. If a farmer should hire a man for 10 days, giving him 5 cents for the first day, 3 times that sum for the second day, and so on, what would be his wages for the last day?

5. If the first term is $100 and the ratio 1.06, what is the 6th term? Or, what is the amount of $100 at compound interest for 5 years at 6%?

6. What is the amount of $520 for 6 years, at 5% compound interest?

7. What is the sum of a geometrical series, of which the first term is 5, the ratio 3, and the number of terms 5?

$5 \times 81 = 405$, the 5th term.

$\dfrac{3 \times 405 - 5}{3 - 1} = 605$, the sum.

EXPLANATION.— Since in this series the first term is 5, the ratio 3, and the number of terms 5, their sum may be obtained by the following process, which illustrates the formation of the rule:

$$\begin{array}{ll} \text{Series} & 5 + 15 + 45 + 135 + 405 \\ \text{3 times Series} & \underline{\quad 15 + 45 + 135 + 405 + 1215} \\ \text{2 times Series} & = 1215 - 5 \\ \text{Series} & = \dfrac{1215 - 5}{2} \end{array}$$

RULE. — *The sum of a geometrical series is equal to the difference between the first term, and the product of the last term by the ratio, divided by the difference between the ratio and 1.*

Or, since the last term is equal to the first term multiplied by the ratio raised to a power one less than the number of terms,

The sum of a geometrical series is found by dividing the difference between the first term and the first term multiplied by the ratio raised to the power equal to the number of the terms by the difference between the ratio and 1.

8. The extremes of a geometrical progression are 4 and 1024, and the ratio is 4. What is the sum of the series?

9. The extremes are $\frac{1}{5}$ and $\frac{343}{135}$ and the ratio is $2\frac{1}{3}$. What is the sum of the series?

10. What is the sum of the series in which the first term is 2, the last term 0, and the ratio $\frac{1}{2}$; or what is the sum of the infinite series 2, 1, $\frac{1}{2}$, $\frac{1}{4}$, $\frac{1}{8}$, $\frac{1}{16}$, $\frac{1}{32}$, etc. ?

11. The extremes of a geometrical progression are $\frac{1}{10}$ and $\frac{15625}{4096}$, and the ratio is $1\frac{1}{4}$. What is the sum of the series?

12. If a child should receive 1 cent at birth, 2 cents on the second birthday, 4 cents on the third, etc., how much would he be worth when 21 years of age?

PROBLEMS IN COMPOUND INTEREST.

493. To find the principal, when the compound interest, the time, and the rate are given.

1. What principal at 6% compound interest will produce $2372.544 interest in 10 years?

$1.790848 − $1 = $.790848.   EXPLANATION. — By geomet-
$2372.544 ∴ .790848 = $3000.   rical progression, or by the com-
                                pound interest table on page
272, the amount of $1 at compound interest for the given time at the given rate is found to be $1.790848. That sum less $1 gives $.790848, the compound interest of $1 for the given time at the given rate. Then, $2372.544 ÷ .790848 = $3000, the principal.

2. What principal at 6% compound interest will produce $3150 interest in 8 years?

3. What principal at 5% compound interest will produce $2896 interest in 12 years?

4. What principal at 7% compound interest will produce $3600 interest in 15 years? At 4% in 20 years?

494. To find the rate, when the principal, compound interest, and time are given.

1. At what rate per cent will $500 yield $203.55 compound interest in 7 years?

$203.55 ÷ 500 = $.4071.   EXPLANATION. — Since $203.55 is the
                             compound interest of $500 for 7 years,
$\frac{1}{500}$ of that sum will be the compound interest of $1 for the same time. By referring to the compound interest table, opposite 7 years, we find the amount $1.4071, or the interest $.4071, in the 5% column. Therefore, the rate is 5%.

2. At what rate per cent will $1000 yield $503.63 compound interest in 7 years?

3. At what rate per cent will $1200 yield $721.2384 compound interest in 12 years?

4. What is the rate per cent when $1800 yields $901.314 compound interest in 6 years?

5. What is the rate per cent when $2000 yields $4344.338 compound interest in 15 years?

495. To find the time when the principal, the compound interest, and rate are given.

1. In what time will $600 amount to $1200 at 7% compound interest?

$1200 ÷ 600   = $2.

$2. − $1.967151 = $.032849

$1.967151 × .07 = $.137701

$\frac{32849}{137701}$ yr. = 2 mo. 26 da.

∴ The time = 10 yr. 2 mo. 26 da.

EXPLANATION. — Since $600 amounts to $1200 at 7% in a certain time, $1 in the same time and at the same rate, will amount to $\frac{1}{600}$ of $1200, or $2. By the compound interest table, $1 at 7% will in 10 yr. amount to $1.967151, and in 11 yr. to $2.104852, consequently the time must be between 10 and 11 yr. The interest of $1.967151 for a year at 7% is $.137701, and the difference between $2 and $1.967151 is $.032849. Since the interest of $1.967151 for a year is $.137701, to earn $.032849 will require $\frac{32849}{137701}$ of a year, or 2 mo. 26 da. Therefore the time is 10 yr. 2 mo. 26 da.

2. In what time will $400 amount to $1000, at 6% compound interest?

3. In what time will $750 amount to $1500, at 5% compound interest? Or, in how long a time will any sum double itself at 5%?

4. In what time will $960 amount to $2000, at 7% compound interest?

5. In what time will $1300 amount to $2500, at 6% compound interest?

6. In what time will $3200 amount to $4800, at 4% compound interest?

ANNUITIES.

496. A definite sum of money payable at the end of equal periods of time is an **Annuity**.

Properly speaking, an annuity is a sum payable annually, but sums payable at intervals of quarter-years, half-years, or other periods, are also called annuities.

497. An annuity which continues forever is called a Perpetual **Annuity** or **Perpetuity**.

498. An annuity which commences at a definite time, and continues for a definite time, is called a **Certain Annuity**.

499. An annuity whose commencement or continuance, or both, depend upon some contingent event, as the death of some person, is called a **Contingent Annuity**.

500. An annuity upon which the payments were not made when they were due is called an **Annuity in Arrears** or **Forborne**.

501. The **Amount** or **Final Value** of an annuity is the sum of all the payments, increased by the interest of each payment, from the time it becomes due until the annuity ceases.

502. A sum of money, which, upon being put at interest for the given time at the given rate, will be equal to the amount of the annuity, is the **Present Value** of the annuity.

503. Annuities are sometimes computed at **Simple Interest** and sometimes at **Compound Interest**.

504. Annuities at Simple Interest.

1. What is the amount of an annuity of $500, unpaid for 5 yr., at 6%?

$l = \$500 + \$ \ 30 \times 4 = \$ \ 620$

$s = \dfrac{\$500 + \$620}{2} \times 5 = \$2800$

EXPLANATION. — Since the annuity was unpaid for 5 yr., the first payment will draw interest from the end of the first year until the time of payment, or 4 yr.; the second payment will draw interest for 3 yr.; the third payment, for 2 yr.; the fourth payment, for 1 yr. Hence, these sums form an arithmetical progression, the first term of which is $500, the common difference, the interest of $500 for 1 yr., or $30, and the number of terms, 5. The sum of this series will be the amount due.

2. What is the present worth of an annuity of $2500 to remain unpaid for 6 years, interest at 6%?

$17,250 = Amount of annuity.

$17,250 ÷ 1.36 = $12,683.82

EXPLANATION.—The amount due at the end of 6 years would be $17,250.

Since this sum is not payable for 6 years, the present worth of it is found by dividing by the amount of $1 for the given time at the given rate.

3. What is the amount of an annuity of $800, unpaid for 4 years, at 6%?

4. What is the amount of an annuity of $960, payable semi-annually, at 6%, but unpaid for 4 years?

5. What is the present worth of an annuity of $1500, to remain unpaid for 8 years, at 6%?

6. Mr. L. has an annuity of $1800, payable quarterly. If it remains unpaid for 3 years 9 months, what will be the amount due at 8%?

7. A house was rented for $45 a month for $2\frac{1}{2}$ years. What sum would pay the entire rent in advance if it was not due until the lease expired, interest at 6%?

505. Annuities at Compound Interest.

1. What is the amount of an annuity of $200 which is 20 years in arrears, compound interest at 6%?

$$\frac{\$200 \times (1.06^{20}-1)}{1.06-1} = \$7357.12$$

EXPLANATION. — The payment now due is $200; the payment 1 year in arrears is $200 × 1.06; the payment 2 years in arrears is $200 × 1.06 × 1.06, or $200 × 1.06², the payment 3 years in arrears is $200 × 1.06³.

Thus it appears that the sums unpaid form a geometrical series, of which the first term is $200, the ratio 1.06, and the number of terms 20. The sum of this series is $7357.12, the amount of the annuity.

1. In finding the value of 1.06²⁰, or similar expressions, use the compound interest table on page 272.

2. The amount of an annuity at *simple* interest is the sum of an arithmetical series; the amount of an annuity at *compound* interest is the sum of a geometrical series.

2. What is the amount of an annuity of $225, which is 6 years in arrears, compound interest at 7%?

3. What is the amount of an annuity of $300, which is 9 years in arrears, compound interest at 6%?

4. What is the amount of an annuity of $450, in arrears for 15 years, compound interest at 5%?

5. What is the amount of an annuity of $650, in arrears for 10 years, the interest being compounded semi annually, at 6%?

6. A young man spends $50 a year for tobacco. What will this amount to in 20 years, at 6% compound interest?

7. What is the present value of an annuity of $800 for 6 years, compound interest at 5%?

SUGGESTION. — Divide the amount of the annuity by the amount of $1, at compound interest, for the given time and rate.

8. What is the present worth of an annuity of $480 for 12 years, compound interest at 6%?

9. A man purchased an annuity of $600 a year for 15 years, at 6% compound interest. What did it cost him?

DIVISORS AND MULTIPLES.

COMMON DIVISORS.

506. 1. What numbers will exactly divide 12? 15? 20?

2. What numbers will exactly divide both 12 and 15? 15 and 20? 24 and 48? 63 and 72?

3. What numbers will exactly divide both 12 and 24? What is the largest number that will exactly divide them?

4. What is the largest number that will exactly divide both 15 and 30? 16 and 32? 16 and 24? 24 and 32?

5. Name all the divisors common to 15 and 30.

6. Name all the *prime* divisors or factors common to 15 and 30?

7. How is the greatest divisor common to 15 and 30 found from the prime factors of those numbers?

8. What is the greatest divisor common to 24 and 30?

9. How is the greatest divisor common to 24 and 30 obtained from the prime factors of those numbers?

507. A number that is an exact divisor of two or more numbers is called a **Common Divisor** of the numbers.

508. The greatest number that is an exact divisor of two or more numbers is called the **Greatest Common Divisor** of the numbers.

Thus 12 is the greatest common divisor of 12 and 24.

509. PRINCIPLE. — *The greatest common divisor of two or more numbers is the product of all their common prime factors.*

WRITTEN EXERCISES.

510. 1. What is the greatest common divisor of 42, 63, and 126?

$42 = 2 \times 3 \times 7$

$63 = 3 \times 3 \times 7$

$126 = 2 \times 3 \times 3 \times 7$

$3 \times 7 = 21$

EXPLANATION. — Since the greatest common divisor is equal to the product of all the prime factors common to the given numbers, we separate the numbers into their prime factors. The only common prime factors are 3 and 7; hence, their product, 21, is the greatest common divisor of the given numbers.

$$\begin{array}{r|rrr} 7 & 42 & 63 & 126 \\ 3 & 6 & 9 & 18 \\ \hline & 2 & 3 & 6 \end{array}$$

The common prime factors may be found readily by dividing the numbers by the prime factors successively, until the quotients contain no common factor.

2. 24, 120.	**8.** 135, 225.	**14.** 36, 42, 54.
3. 33, 154.	**9.** 232, 493.	**15.** 48, 60, 96.
4. 42, 252.	**10.** 210, 350.	**16.** 120, 210, 345.
5. 60, 270.	**11.** 330, 495.	**17.** 216, 360, 432.
6. 56, 126.	**12.** 352, 384.	**18.** 42, 63, 126, 189.
7. 112, 168.	**13.** 840, 1260.	**19.** 126, 210, 294, 402.

511. Sometimes the numbers cannot be readily factored. In such cases the following method is employed:

1. What is the greatest common divisor of 35 and 168?

$$\begin{array}{r} 35)\overline{168}(4 \\ \underline{140} \\ 28)\overline{35}(1 \\ \underline{28} \\ 7)\overline{28}(4 \\ \underline{28} \end{array}$$

EXPLANATION. — The greatest common divisor cannot be greater than the smaller number; therefore 35 will be the greatest common divisor if it is exactly contained in 168. By trial it is found that it is not an exact divisor of 168, since there is a remainder of 28. Therefore 35 is not the greatest common divisor.

Since 168 and 140, which is 4 times 35, are each divisible by the greatest common divisor (Art. 106, 11), their difference, 28, must be divisible by the greatest common divisor, therefore the greatest common divisor cannot be greater than 28. 28 will be the greatest common divisor if it is exactly contained in 35; since if it is contained in 35, it will be contained in 140 (Art. 106, 11), and in 28 *plus* 140, or 168. By trial we find that it is not an exact divisor of 35, for there is a remainder of 7. Therefore 28 is not the greatest common divisor.

Since 28 and 35 are each divisible by the greatest common divisor, their difference, 7, must contain the greatest common divisor (Art. 106, 12); therefore the greatest common divisor cannot be greater than 7. 7 will be the greatest common divisor if it is exactly contained in 28; since if it is contained in itself and 28, it will be contained in the sum, 35, and also in 168, which is the sum of 28 and 4 times 35, or 140. By trial we find that it is an exact divisor of 28. Hence 7 is the greatest common divisor.

RULE. — *Divide the greater number by the less, and if there is a remainder, divide the less number by it, then the preceding divisor by the last remainder, and so on, till nothing remains. The last divisor will be the greatest common divisor.*

If more than two numbers are given, find the greatest common divisor of any two, then of this divisor and another of the given numbers, and so on. The last divisor will be the greatest common divisor.

Find the greatest common divisor of

2. 252, 280. 5. 756, 1575. 8. 146, 365, 219.

3. 323, 425. 6. 1008, 1036. 9. 225, 315, 420.

4. 432, 936. 7. 1088, 1632. 10. 462, 882, 546.

Reduce the following fractions to their lowest terms by finding the greatest common divisor of their terms:

11. $\frac{84}{196}$. 14. $\frac{216}{288}$. 17. $\frac{219}{730}$. 20. $\frac{825}{1375}$.

12. $\frac{115}{210}$. 15. $\frac{228}{399}$. 18. $\frac{324}{807}$. 21. $\frac{1287}{1551}$.

13. $\frac{168}{182}$. 16. $\frac{336}{576}$. 19. $\frac{961}{1178}$. 22. $\frac{1792}{1832}$.

23. A farmer wishes to put 336 bushels of wheat and 576 bushels of corn into the least number of bins possible of uniform size, without mixing the two kinds of grain. How many bushels must each bin hold?

COMMON MULTIPLES.

512. **1.** Name some numbers that are exactly divisible by 2. By 3. By 4. By 2, 3, and 4.

2. What is the smallest number that is exactly divisible by each of the numbers 2, 3, and 4 ?

3. What is the least number that will contain 10 and 15 ?

4. What common prime factors have 10 and 15? What factor occurs in 10 that does not occur in 15? What factor is found in 15 that is not found in 10 ?

5. What are all the different prime factors of 10 and 15 ?

6. How may the least number that will contain 10 and 15 be formed from their prime factors ?

What is the least number that will exactly contain

7. 3, 6, and 9 ?	**12.** 2, 3, 5, and 6 ?
8. 3, 5, and 6 ?	**13.** 3, 4, 5, and 6 ?
9. 4, 8, and 12 ?	**14.** 3, 6, 8, and 12 ?
10. 7, 14, and 28 ?	**15.** 4, 8, 12, and 15 ?
11. 4, 6, and 10 ?	**16.** 5, 6, 10, and 12 ?

513. A number that will exactly contain another number is a **Multiple** of that number.

514. A number that will exactly contain each of two or more numbers is a **Common Multiple** of those numbers.

515. The least number that will exactly contain each of two or more numbers is their **Least Common Multiple.**

516. PRINCIPLE. — *The least common multiple of two or more numbers is equal to the product of the largest number multiplied by the prime factors of the other numbers not found in the largest number.*

WRITTEN EXERCISES.

517. 1. Find the least common multiple of 30, 28, and 60.

$30 = 2 \times 3 \times 5$
$28 = 2 \times 2 \times 7$
$60 = 2 \times 2 \times 3 \times 5$
$2 \times 2 \times 3 \times 5 \times 7 = 420$

EXPLANATION. — To find the prime factors of the other numbers which are not found in the largest number, all the numbers must be separated into their prime factors. The prime factors of the largest number are 2, 2, 3, and 5, and the factor of the other numbers not included in these factors is 7. Therefore, the product of 2, 2, 3, 5, and 7 is the least common multiple of the numbers.

2	30	28	60
2	15	14	30
3	15	7	15
5	5	7	5
	1	7	1

$2 \times 2 \times 3 \times 5 \times 7 = 420$

EXPLANATION. — By dividing the given numbers by any prime number that will exactly divide two or more of them, until quotients are found that are prime to each other, and then finding the product of these divisors and the last quotients, the least common multiple of the numbers is found.

In finding the least common multiple of numbers, all numbers that are factors of other given numbers, may be disregarded.

Thus, the common multiples of 4, 8, 16, 32, 64, 80, and 128 are the same as the common multiples of 80 and 128.

Find the least common multiple of

2. 16, 20, 48, 60.
3. 18, 21, 27, 36.
4. 20, 35, 40, 45.
5. 36, 40, 48, 126.
6. 7, 11, 91, 13.
7. 45, 75, 135, 180.
8. 96, 126, 72, 56.

9. 126, 36, 48, 66.
10. 16, 60, 140, 210.
11. 57, 36, 231, 330.
12. 126, 140, 154, 280.
13. 48, 117, 54, 312.
14. 63, 72, 84, 105.
15. 132, 144, 288, 324.

518. When the prime factors of the given numbers cannot be discovered by inspection, they may be found by the method of finding the greatest common divisor under such circumstances.

16. Find the least common multiple of 255 and 357.

255)357(1
   255
   ─────
   102)255(2
      204
      ─────
      51)102(2
        102

∴ The G. C. D. is 51.

51)255 357
   ─────────
    5   7

$51 \times 5 \times 7 = 1785$.

EXPLANATION. — Since the factors of the numbers cannot be discovered by inspection, the greatest common divisor of the numbers is found to be 51.

Dividing each of the given numbers by 51, the quotients 5 and 7 are obtained which are prime to each other. Therefore $51 \times 5 \times 7$, or 1785, is the least common multiple of the numbers.

Find the least common multiple of

17. 315, 420.	**20.** 468, 923.	**23.** 777, 1110.
18. 448, 512.	**21.** 432, 936.	**24.** 2310, 3150.
19. 560, 616.	**22.** 720, 868.	**25.** 2520, 2772.

26. Find the contents of the smallest vessel that may be filled by using a 3-quart, a 4-quart, a 5-quart, or a 6-quart measure.

27. What is the shortest length that can be measured by either of four measures which are respectively 10 in., 15, in., 27 in., and 30 in. long?

28. A can walk round a race-course in 12 min., B in 15 min., and C in 18 min. If they start together and keep walking each at his own rate, how many minutes will elapse before they are all three together at the starting-point, and how many times will each have made the circuit?

29. A lady desires to purchase a quantity of cloth that can be cut without waste into parts 4, 5, or 6 yards long. What is the least number of yards that she can buy for that purpose?

GREATEST COMMON DIVISOR OF FRACTIONS.

519. 1. Give several fractions which are contained in $\frac{3}{4}$ an integral number of times.

2. What relation do the numerators of these divisors bear to the numerator of $\frac{3}{4}$?

3. What relation do the denominators of these divisors bear to the denominator of $\frac{3}{4}$?

4. Find several fractions which are common divisors of $\frac{3}{4}$ and $\frac{3}{8}$. Of $\frac{4}{5}$ and $\frac{2}{3}$. Of $\frac{6}{7}$ and $\frac{3}{14}$. Of $\frac{3}{4}$ and $\frac{2}{5}$.

5. What relation do the numerators of these common divisors bear to the numerators of the fractions which they divide?

6. What relation do the denominators of these common divisors bear to the denominators of the fractions?

7. Since the fraction which will exactly divide the given fractions is greatest when its numerator is as large as possible, and its denominator as small as possible, how are the terms of the *greatest common divisor* of fractions obtained from the terms of the fractions?

520. PRINCIPLE. — *The greatest common divisor of two or more fractions in their lowest terms is the greatest common divisor of their numerators divided by the least common multiple of their denominators.*

WRITTEN EXERCISES.

521. Find the greatest common divisor of :

1. $\frac{3}{4}, \frac{5}{6}, \frac{7}{8}$.

2. $\frac{10}{21}, \frac{25}{28}, \frac{15}{49}$.

3. $\frac{24}{25}, \frac{18}{175}, \frac{27}{35}$.

4. $3\frac{1}{5}, 1\frac{5}{7}, \frac{24}{35}$.

5. $4\frac{2}{5}, 2\frac{3}{15}, 3\frac{2}{25}$.

6. $3\frac{1}{2}, 9\frac{1}{3}, \dfrac{2\frac{1}{3}}{4}$.

7. The sides of a triangular lot are $115\frac{1}{2}$ feet, $128\frac{1}{3}$ feet, and $134\frac{3}{4}$ feet long. How many rails of the greatest length possible will be needed to fence it, the rails lapping 6 inches at each end, and the fence to be 7 rails high?

LEAST COMMON MULTIPLE OF FRACTIONS.

522. **1.** Give several fractions or integers which will contain $\frac{1}{8}$ an integral number of times $\frac{1}{4}$, $\frac{1}{16}$, $\frac{3}{8}$, $\frac{3}{4}$, $\frac{5}{16}$.

2. What relation do the numerators of these multiples bear to the numerators of the given fractions?

3. What relation do the denominators of these multiples bear to the denominators of the given fractions?

4. Find several common multiples of $\frac{1}{8}$ and $\frac{1}{4}$. Of $\frac{3}{8}$ and $\frac{3}{4}$. Of $\frac{1}{8}$ and $\frac{3}{4}$.

5. What relation do the numerators of these common multiples bear to the numerators of the fractions which they contain?

6. What relation do the denominators of these common multiples bear to the denominators of the fractions which they contain?

7. Since the number that will exactly contain the given fractions is least when its numerator is as small as possible and its denominator as large as possible, how are the terms of the *least common multiple* of fractions obtained from the terms of the fractions?

523. PRINCIPLE. — *The least common multiple of two or more fractions in their lowest terms is the least common multiple of their numerators divided by the greatest common divisor of their denominators.*

WRITTEN EXERCISES.

524. Find the least common multiple of:

1. $\frac{5}{8}$, $\frac{3}{4}$, $\frac{7}{12}$.   3. $\frac{9}{24}$, $\frac{7}{82}$, $\frac{22}{18}$.   5. $\frac{63}{100}$, $1\frac{37}{75}$, $2\frac{22}{25}$.

2. $\frac{7}{24}$, $\frac{35}{36}$, $\frac{49}{60}$.   4. $2\frac{2}{3}$, $3\frac{5}{9}$, $4\frac{4}{15}$.   6. $11\frac{1}{9}$, $14\frac{2}{7}$, $33\frac{1}{3}$.

7. The pendulum of one clock makes 25 beats in 28 seconds, and that of another clock 30 beats in 34 seconds. If the clocks are started at the same moment, when first after starting will the clocks beat together again?

CIRCULATING DECIMALS.

525. 1. When a cipher is annexed to a number, by what is the number multiplied? After the cipher has been annexed, by what numbers can the number be divided by which it could not be divided before?

2. Since the only new factors by which a number multiplied by 10 can be divided are 2 and 5, when a common fraction in its lowest terms is being reduced to a decimal, if the denominator contains only the factors 2 or 5, will the division be exact or not?

3. If the denominator contains other factors besides 2 or 5, what can be said of the division?

4. If any fraction, as $\frac{1}{7}$, is reduced to a decimal by annexing ciphers to the numerator and dividing by the denominator, how many possible remainders can there be?

5. Since in each instance the remainder with a cipher annexed forms the new dividend, and since there can be but 6 different dividends, what may be concluded regarding the repetition of the decimal figures?

6. What, then, may be inferred regarding the repetition of the decimal figures in any infinite decimal?

526. A decimal that contains a definite number of decimal places is called a **Finite Decimal.** A decimal that never terminates is called an **Infinite Decimal.**

527. An infinite decimal having a figure or set of figures repeated indefinitely is called a **Circulating Decimal.**

528. The figure or set of figures repeated in an infinite or circulating decimal is called the **Repetend.**

Thus, the common fraction $\frac{1}{3}$ is expressed by .3333 + etc.; the fraction $\frac{1}{7}$ by .142857142857 + etc. In the first fraction the *repetend* is 3; in the second 142857.

A repetend is indicated by placing a dot over the repeated figure; or over the first and last figures of the set that is repeated.

Thus, .333 + is written $.\dot{3}$; .142857142857 + is written $.\dot{1}4285\dot{7}$; .1666 + is written $.1\dot{6}$.

529. A decimal expressed wholly by a repetend is called a **Pure Circulating Decimal.**

Thus, .3333 + and .142857142857 + are pure circulating decimals.

530. A decimal expressed only in part by a repetend is called a **Mixed Circulating Decimal.**

Thus, .1666 + etc., .4535353 + are mixed circulating decimals.

531. PRINCIPLES. — 1. *Any fraction in its lowest terms whose denominator contains no other prime factors besides 2 or 5 can be reduced to a finite decimal.*

2. *Any fraction in its lowest terms whose denominator contains other prime factors besides 2 or 5 will produce a circulating decimal.*

EXERCISES.

532. Tell by inspection which fractions will produce finite decimals and which circulating decimals.

1. $\frac{3}{4}$.	4. $\frac{7}{10}$.	7. $\frac{5}{6}$.	10. $\frac{3}{8}$.	13. $\frac{7}{20}$.
2. $\frac{2}{3}$.	5. $\frac{3}{7}$.	8. $\frac{7}{8}$.	11. $\frac{1}{3}$.	14. $\frac{4}{11}$.
3. $\frac{3}{5}$.	6. $\frac{5}{9}$.	9. $\frac{2}{5}$.	12. $\frac{2}{9}$.	15. $\frac{5}{12}$.

16. Reduce $\frac{1}{9}$ to a decimal. $\frac{2}{9}$. $\frac{3}{9}$. $\frac{4}{9}$.

17 Reduce $\frac{1}{99}$ to a decimal. $\frac{5}{99}$. $\frac{35}{99}$. $\frac{71}{99}$.

18. Reduce $\frac{1}{999}$ to a decimal. $\frac{7}{999}$. $\frac{73}{999}$. $\frac{757}{999}$.

533. **To reduce a repetend to a common fraction.**

1. To what common fraction is .1111+ or $.\dot{1}$ equal? .5555+ or $.\dot{5}$? .7777+ or $.\dot{7}$? (Art. 532, Ex. 16.)

2. To what common fraction is .010101+ or $.\dot{0}\dot{1}$ equal? .050505+ or $.\dot{0}\dot{5}$? .373737+ or $.\dot{3}\dot{7}$?

3. To what common fraction is .001001+ or $.\dot{0}0\dot{1}$ equal? .007007+ or $.\dot{0}0\dot{7}$? .356356+ or $.\dot{3}5\dot{6}$?

534. PRINCIPLE. — *The denominator of a pure circulating decimal is as many 9's as there are figures in the repetend.*

EXERCISES.

535. Express as common fractions :

1. $.\dot{3}$.	4. $.\dot{3}2\dot{4}$.	7. $.\dot{6}4\dot{2}$.	10. $.\dot{3}63\dot{6}$.
2. $.\dot{1}\dot{4}$.	5. $.\dot{3}7\dot{8}$.	8. $.\dot{9}6\dot{3}$.	11. $.\dot{0}026\dot{1}$.
3. $.\dot{1}2\dot{3}$.	6. $.\dot{0}4\dot{5}$.	9. $.\dot{9}80\dot{1}$.	12. $.\dot{9}8601\dot{3}$.

13. Express as common fractions, $.0\dot{6}3\dot{5}$ and $.5\dot{3}4\dot{7}$.

$$.0\dot{6}3\dot{5} = \tfrac{635}{9990} = \tfrac{127}{1998}.$$

EXPLANATION. — If the decimal were $.\dot{6}3\dot{5}$, its value as a common fraction would be $\tfrac{635}{999}$. But since the repetend begins one place to the right of the decimal point, its value is $\tfrac{1}{10}$ of $\tfrac{635}{999}$. Therefore $.0\dot{6}3\dot{5} = \tfrac{1}{10}$ of $\tfrac{635}{999}$ or $\tfrac{635}{9990}$.

$$.5\dot{3}4\dot{7} = .53\tfrac{47}{99} = \tfrac{53}{100} + \tfrac{47}{9900} = \tfrac{5294}{9900} = \tfrac{2647}{4950}.$$

Express as common fractions :

14. $.16\dot{5}$.	17. $.5\dot{6}3\dot{5}$.	20. $.0\dot{8}1\dot{5}$.	23. $.09\dot{5}6\dot{3}$.
15. $.25\dot{6}$.	18. $.2\dot{0}4\dot{5}$.	21. $.5\dot{6}2\dot{2}$.	24. $.00\dot{9}86\dot{7}$.
16. $.32\dot{7}$.	19. $.3\dot{5}7\dot{2}$.	22. $.3\dot{1}5\dot{6}$.	25. $.985\dot{3}7\dot{5}$.

SCALES OF NOTATION.

536. The ratio by which numbers increase or decrease is termed a **Scale**.

The ordinary scale of notation for integers is decimal, but it is possible to express numbers in many other scales.

537. The number of units required to make one of the next higher order is called the **Radix** of the scale.

Thus 10 is the radix of the decimal scale, 12 of the duodecimal.

SCALES.

Name.	Radix.	Name.	Radix.
Binary	2	Septenary	7
Ternary	3	Octary	8
Quaternary	4	Nonary	9
Quinary	5	Decimal	10
Senary	6	Undenary	11
		Duodecimal	12

NOTATION.

538. In expressing numbers in any uniform scale, as many characters must be employed as there are units in the radix of the scale, and one of the characters must be 0.

To express numbers in scales higher than the decimal, new characters must be employed. Thus, t may be used to represent 10 and e to represent 11, etc.

539. Inasmuch as the names of the orders of units used in expressing numbers are adapted to the decimal scale, numbers in other scales should be read by naming the number of units of each order.

Thus, 342 in the *quinary* scale should be read : *quinary scale*, 3 *units of the third order*, 4 *of the second, and* 2 *of the first.*

WRITTEN EXERCISES.

540. 1. Write in the quinary scale the numbers corresponding to the numbers from 1 to 13 in the common or decimal scale.

EXPLANATION. — Since the radix of the scale is 5, the characters employed are 1, 2, 3, 4, 0.

Since 5 units of any order are equal to 1 of the next higher order, the numbers including 5 will be expressed by 1, 2, 3, 4, 10.

Since 6 is equal to 1 unit of the second order and 1 of the first order it is written 11 ; since 7 is equal to 1 unit of the second order and 2 of the first it is written 12.

Expressing the numbers from 1 to 13 in accordance with the law just illustrated, they are 1, 2, 3, 4, 10, 11, 12, 13, 14, 20, 21, 22, 23.

Write the numbers corresponding to the numbers from 1 to 20 in the common or decimal scale :

2. In the quaternary scale.   **6.** In the nonary scale.

3. In the octary scale.   **7.** In the undenary scale.

4. In the senary scale.   **8.** In the septenary scale.

5. In the ternary scale.   **9.** In the binary scale.

541. To change from the decimal to another scale.

1. Change 58375 from the decimal to the senary scale.

$$
\begin{array}{r|l}
6 & 58375 \\
\hline
6 & 9729 + 1 \\
\hline
6 & 1621 + 3 \\
\hline
6 & 270 + 1 \\
\hline
6 & 45 + 0 \\
\hline
6 & 7 + 3 \\
\hline
& 1 + 1
\end{array}
$$

EXPLANATION. — By dividing by 6, we obtain the number of units of the second order and the number of units of the first order remaining.

By continuing to divide by 6, the number of units in the successive orders is obtained and the number of units remaining after division. It is thus found that 58375 when expressed in the *senary* scale contains 1 unit of the *seventh* order, 1 of the *sixth*, 3 of the *fifth*, etc., or the number is expressed by 1130131_6.

For convenience in notation the radix of the scale is indicated by a small subscript figure.

2. Express in the quinary scale, 3824, 5861, and 3843.

3. Express in the septenary scale, 5163, 6842, and 4276.

4. Express in the quaternary scale, 3947, 5439, and 3854.

5. Express in the duodecimal scale, 6193, 8427, and 6958.

542. To change from any scale to the decimal scale.

1. Express 3432_5 in the decimal scale.

$$
\begin{array}{r}
3432 \\
5 \\
\hline
19 \\
5 \\
\hline
98 \\
5 \\
\hline
492
\end{array}
$$

EXPLANATION. — Since each higher unit is equal to 5 of the next lower order, 3 units of the fourth order are equal to 15 of the third, and adding 4, the number of the third order given, we obtain 19, the number of the third order.

Proceeding in the same manner, until the number of units of the first order is obtained, the number in the decimal scale is 492.

Change the following to the decimal scale:

    2. 5867_9; 23123_4; 34254_6; 52364_7.

    3. 3432_5; $231t5_{11}$; 41324_5; 41342_6.

    4. 6735_8; $3819e_{12}$; 34514_7; $268te_{12}$.

543. Arithmetical processes in any scale.

The processes are performed in the same manner as in the decimal scale. The student must simply bear in mind each time the number of units of each order required to make one of the next higher order.

    1. Add 3123_5, 4124_5, 3243_5, 4233_5.

    2. Add 5243_7, 6231_7, 5634_7, 3543_7.

    3. Add 4384_9, 5276_9, 8346_9, 7436_9.

    4. Subtract 34562_7 from 62456_7.

    5. Subtract 41375_8 from 73245_8.

    6. Multiply 3424_5 by 234_5.

PROOFS.

FUNDAMENTAL PROCESSES.

544. The proofs given under addition, subtraction, multiplication, and division are the most practical and reliable that can be given. A briefer method, however, has been discovered, which may be employed as a test of accuracy.

545. Method by casting out the nines.

It has been discovered that when the number of 9's in a number is found, the remainder is equal to the sum of the digits of the number, or the sum with the 9's omitted.

Thus, $743 = 700 \div 9 + 40 \div 9 + 3$; and the remainders in each instance correspond with the digits which express the number. Hence the sum of the digits $7 + 4 + 3$, or 14, or (with the 9 omitted) 5 is the number remaining after the 9's have been found.

546. The method of proof by casting out the 9's is based upon the presumption, that when the *remainders* in the results agree with the remainders in numbers, from which the results were obtained, the work is correct.

PROOF OF ADDITION.

547. 1. Prove that $893 + 296 + 452 + 368 = 2009$.

$$893 = 2$$
$$296 = 8$$
$$452 = 2$$
$$368 = 8$$
$$\overline{2009 = 2}$$

EXPLANATION. — The 9's in the first addend are a certain number and 2 units remaining; in the second, a certain number and 8 units; in the third, a certain number and 2 units; in the fourth, a certain number and 8 units. The sum of the units remaining is 20, or casting out the 9's from that sum it is 2. The remainder after casting out the 9's in the sum 2009 is also 2. Hence, the work is *probably* correct.

400

It should be borne in mind, however, that this is not an accurate test of correctness, for the same excess of nines will be obtained in whatever order the figures are arranged.

PROOF OF SUBTRACTION.

548. Prove that $18945 - 9326 = 9169$.

$$18945 = 0$$
$$9326 = 2$$
$$\overline{9619} = \overline{7}$$

EXPLANATION. — Casting out the 9's from the minuend there is 0 for a remainder. Casting out the 9's from the subtrahend there is a remainder of 2, 2 subtracted from a unit of the next higher order, or 9, leaves a remainder of 7. Casting out the 9's from the remainder there is also a remainder of 7. Hence the result is presumed to be correct.

PROOF OF MULTIPLICATION.

549. Prove that $718 \times 28 = 20104$.

$$718 = 7$$
$$28 = 1$$
$$\overline{20104} = \overline{7}$$

EXPLANATION. — Casting out the 9's from the multiplicand the remainder is 7. Casting out the 9's from the multiplier, the remainder is 1. The product of these remainders is 7, and it is the same as the remainder after the 9's have been cast out from the product. Hence the work is probably correct.

PROOF OF DIVISION.

550. Prove that $8232 \div 21 = 392$.

$$\overset{3}{21})\overset{6}{8232}(\overset{5}{392}$$

EXPLANATION. — Casting the 9's out of the *divisor* and *quotient*, the remainders are 3 and 5 respectively. Their product is 15, from which, when the 9's are cast out, the remainder is 6. This number corresponds with the remainder in the dividend after the nines have been cast out of it ; and the work is presumed to be correct, since the divisor multiplied by the quotient is equal to the dividend.

$$643)5926431(9216 \quad \text{Rem. } 543.$$

EXPLANATION. — The product of the divisor by the quotient, plus the remainder is equal to the dividend. Casting the 9's out of the divisor the remainder is 4 ; casting them out of the quotient the remainder is 0. The product of 4 and 0 is 0 ; to which is added the excess of 9's in the remainder which is 3. The number remaining after casting out the 9's from the dividend is 3, therefore since the results agree, the work is presumed to be correct.

DIVISION BY FACTORS.

551. 1. What are the factors of 32? 25? 64? 96?

2. If a number is divided by 8, by what must the quotient be divided that the number may be divided by 16?

3. If a number is divided by 8 and the quotient by 6, by what is the number divided?

4. What factors may be used to divide a number by 36?

5. What factors may be used to divide a number by 48?

6. Divide 5683 by 32, using factors.

4	5683
2	1420 . . . 3
4	710
	177 . . . 2

$3 + (2 \times 8) = 19$ true Rem.

$177\frac{19}{32}$ Quotient.

EXPLANATION. — 32 is equal to 4 × 2 × 4. Dividing 5683 by 4 gives a quotient of 1420 *fours* and 3 units remaining.

Dividing 1420 *fours* by 2 gives a quotient of 710 *eights.* Dividing 710 *eights* by 4 gives a quotient of 177 *thirty-twos* and 2 *eights* remainder.

The first partial remainder is 3 *units*, and the second, 2 *eights*, or 16; hence, the entire remainder is 3 + 16, or 19, and the quotient is $177\frac{19}{32}$.

RULE. — *Divide the dividend by one factor of the divisor, the quotient thus obtained by another factor, and so continue until all the factors have been used successively as divisors.*

If there are remainders, multiply each remainder by all the preceding divisors except the one that produced it. The sum of these products will be the true remainder.

Divide, using factors:

7. 1704 by 24.   11. 1288 by 56.   15. 3275 by 56.

8. 4725 by 15.   12. 3528 by 72.   16. 3276 by 27.

9. 5740 by 28.   13. 3824 by 32.   17. 4104 by 45.

10. 1428 by 42.   14. 2184 by 49.   18. 7304 by 24.

MEASUREMENT OF SOLIDS.

552. A surface such that a straight line joining any two points of it lies wholly in the surface is a **Plane Surface**.

553. A surface no part of which is a plane surface is a **Curved Surface**.

554. A plane figure bounded by straight lines is a **Polygon**.

555. The length of the lines that bound a figure is its **Perimeter**.

556. Anything that has length, breadth, and thickness is a **Solid** or **Body**.

The plane surfaces or planes which bound a solid are called its *faces*, and their intersections, its *edges*.

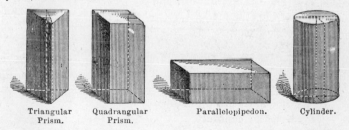

Triangular Prism.   Quadrangular Prism.   Parallelopipedon.   Cylinder.

557. A solid whose two ends are equal polygons, parallel to each other, and whose sides are parallelograms, is a **Prism**.

Prisms, from the form of their bases, are named *triangular, quadrangular, pentagonal,* etc.

403

558. A regular solid bounded by a uniformly curved surface, and having for its ends two equal circles, parallel to each other, is a **Cylinder**.

The face of any section of a cylinder parallel to the base is a circle equal to the base.

559. A solid whose base is a polygon and whose faces are triangles, meeting at a point called the vertex, is a **Pyramid**.

560. A solid, whose base is a circle and whose surface tapers uniformly to a point called the vertex, is a **Cone**.

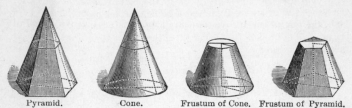

Pyramid.   Cone.   Frustum of Cone.   Frustum of Pyramid.

561. The portion remaining after the top has been cut off from a pyramid or cone by a plane parallel to the base, is a **Frustum** of a pyramid or cone.

562. A solid, every point of whose surface is equally distant from a point within, called the center, is a **Sphere**.

563. A straight line passing through the center, and terminating in the surface of a sphere at both ends, is its **Diameter**.

564. One half the diameter, or the distance from the center to the surface of a sphere, is its **Radius**.

Sphere.

565. The greatest distance around a sphere is its **Circumference**.

566. The perpendicular distance from the highest point of a solid to the plane of the base is its **Altitude**.

SURFACE OF SOLIDS.

567. All the surface of a solid except its base or bases is called the **Lateral Surface**.

The *entire* surface includes the area of the bases also.

WRITTEN EXERCISES.

568. To find the lateral surface of a prism or cylinder.

It is evident that if a prism or cylinder were 1 inch high, its lateral surface would contain as many square units of surface as there were units in the perimeter of the base; and if it were 2 inches, 3 inches, or 4 inches high, the lateral surface would contain 2, 3, or 4 times the number of units in the perimeter of the base. Hence the following rule:

RULE. — *Multiply the perimeter of the base by the altitude.*

1. What is the lateral surface of a cylinder whose diameter is 2 feet, and whose length is 5 feet?

2. What is the lateral surface of a quadrangular prism whose sides are each $2\frac{1}{2}$ feet, and whose height is 4 feet?

3. What is the lateral surface of a triangular prism whose sides are each 6 feet, and whose altitude is 8 feet?

4. What is the entire surface of a cylinder which is 5 feet in length, and whose base is 2 feet in diameter?

569. To find the lateral surface of a pyramid or cone.

It is evident that the lateral surface of any pyramid is composed of triangles, and the lateral surface of a cone may also be assumed to be made up of an infinite number of triangles. The bases of these triangles form the perimeter of the solid, and their height is the slant height of the solid. Hence the following rule:

RULE. — *Multiply the perimeter of the base by one half the slant height.*

1. What is the lateral surface of a quadrangular pyramid whose base is 15 feet square, and whose slant height is 18 feet?

2. What is the lateral surface of a cone whose diameter at the base is 12 feet, and whose slant height is 20 feet?

3. What is the lateral surface of a cone whose base is 20 feet in diameter, and whose slant height is 20 feet?

4. What is the cost of painting a church steeple, the base of which is an octagon 6 feet on each side, and whose slant height is 80 feet, at $.30 per square yard?

5. How many feet of lateral surface are there on a cone, the base diameter of which is 6 feet, and whose slant height is 9½ feet?

6. How many feet of lateral surface are there on a pyramid whose base is 10 feet square, and whose slant height is 20 feet?

7. How many feet of lateral surface are there on a cone whose base is 8 feet in diameter, and whose slant height is 6 feet?

8. What is the lateral surface of a cone whose base is 10 feet in diameter, and whose slant height is 10 feet?

570. **To find the lateral surface of a frustum of a pyramid or cone.**

It is evident that the lateral surface of a frustum of a pyramid is composed of trapezoids, the sum of whose parallel sides forms the perimeter of the bases, and whose altitude is the slant height of the frustum; and the lateral surface of a cone may be assumed to be made of an infinite number of trapezoids. Hence the following rule:

RULE. — *Multiply half the sum of the perimeter of the two bases by the slant height.*

1. How many feet of lateral surface are there in the frustum of a cone whose slant height is 8 feet, the diameter of whose lower base is 12 feet and of the upper base 8 feet?

2. What is the lateral surface of the frustum of a pyramid, the slant height of which is 25 feet, whose lower base is 40 feet square, and whose upper base is 20 feet square?

3. What did it cost, at $.15 per square yard, to paint the lateral surface of a vat which was 10 feet in diameter at the bottom and 8 feet at the top, the slant height of which was 12 feet?

4. What is the lateral surface of a vat, the base of which is 9 feet square, whose top is 8 feet square, and whose slant height is 10 feet?

5. What will be the cost of covering the outside surface, including the bottom of such a vat with sheet metal at 8 cents per square foot?

571. To find the convex surface of a sphere.

The convex surface of a sphere is computed, according to geometrical principles, by the following rules.

RULE. — 1. *Multiply the diameter by the circumference.*

2. *Multiply the square of the diameter by 3.1416.*

1. What is the convex surface of a sphere whose diameter is 15 inches?

2. What is the convex surface of a spherical cannon-ball 8 inches in diameter?

3. What is the convex surface of a base-ball whose circumference is 9⅛ inches?

4. What is the convex surface of a sphere whose circumference is 12 feet?

VOLUME OF SOLIDS.

572. The **Volume** of any body is the number of solid units it contains.

WRITTEN EXERCISES.

573. To find the volume of a prism or cylinder.

It is evident that if a prism or cylinder were 1 inch high, it would contain as many cubic inches as there were square inches in the area of the base; and if it were 2 inches, 3 inches, or 4 inches high, the volume would be 2 or 3 or 4 times as much. Hence the following rule:

RULE. — *Multiply the area of the base by the altitude.*

1. What are the solid contents of a prism whose base is 12 inches square and whose height is 2 feet?

2. What is the volume of a cylinder whose diameter is $1\frac{1}{2}$ feet and whose length is 4 feet?

3. What will be the cost of a piece of timber 20 feet long, 18 inches wide, and 12 inches thick at $.30 per cubic foot?

4. What was the capacity in bushels of a square bin, the base of which was 8 feet square, and the height of which was 9 feet on the inside?

5. How many gallons of water will a vat in the form of a cylinder hold, whose inside dimensions are — base 8 feet in diameter, height 7 feet.

6. How much would the wheat be worth at $1.85 per bushel, which would just fill a bin the base of which is 15 feet square, and the height of which is 12 feet?

574. To find the volume of a pyramid or cone.

It can be shown by geometry that a pyramid or cone is one third of a prism or cylinder of the same base and altitude. Hence the following rule :

RULE. — *Multiply the area of the base by one third of the altitude.*

1. What are the solid contents of a cone, the diameter of whose base is 6 feet, and whose altitude is 9 feet ?

2. What are the solid contents of a pyramid whose base is 30 feet square and whose altitude is 60 feet ?

3. If a cubic foot of granite weighs 165 pounds, what is the weight of a granite cone the diameter of whose base is 6 feet, and whose altitude is 8 feet ?

4. What is the weight of a marble pyramid whose base is 4 feet square and whose altitude is 8 feet, if a cubic foot of marble weighs 171 pounds ?

575. To find the volume of a frustum of a pyramid or cone.

It can be shown by geometry that the frustum of a pyramid or cone is equal to three pyramids or cones, having for their bases, respectively, the upper base of the frustum, its lower base, and a mean proportional between the two bases. Hence the following rule :

RULE. — *To the sum of the areas of the two ends add the square root of the product of these areas, and multiply the result by one third of the altitude.*

1. What is the volume of a frustum of a pyramid the lower base of which is 20 feet square, the upper base 10 feet square, and the altitude 20 feet ?

2. What are the solid contents of the frustum of a cone whose upper base is 5 feet in diameter, whose lower base is 8 feet in diameter, and whose altitude is 7 feet ?

3. A tree was 3 feet in diameter at the butt, and its diameter at a height of 40 feet was 1 foot. What were the cubical contents of that portion of the tree?

4. A vat whose inside measurements were as follows — diameter of the bottom 12 feet, diameter of the top 10 feet, height 9 feet — was filled with water. How many gallons did it contain?

576. **To find the volume or contents of a sphere.**

A sphere may be regarded as composed of pyramids whose bases form the surface of the sphere, and whose altitude is the radius of the sphere. Hence the following rule:

RULE. — 1. *Multiply the convex surface by one third of the radius;* or,

2. *Multiply the cube of the diameter by .5236.*

1. The diameter of a sphere is 5 feet. How many cubic feet does it contain?

2. Find the contents of a sphere whose diameter is 8 feet.

3. The circumference of a sphere is 9.4248. What are its cubical contents?

4. A cubic foot of cast-iron weighs about 450 pounds. What is the weight of a cannon-ball whose diameter is 18 inches?

5. What are the cubical contents of a spherical vessel the diameter of which is 2½ feet?

6. How many cubic feet are there in a spherical body whose diameter is 25 feet?

7. If a cubic inch of water weighs 252.96 gr., and iron is 7.21 times as heavy as water, what will be the weight of a six-inch cannon ball?

METRIC SYSTEM OF WEIGHTS AND MEASURES.

———•◦•———

577. The **Metric System** of weights and measures is used by most of the civilized nations of the world except the United States and Great Britain and some of her colonies. It has also been legalized by the United States government.

578. The unit of length is the *meter*, and from it the other units, viz. : surface, volume, capacity, and weight are derived.

1. The length of the meter was intended to be one ten-millionth of the distance from the equator to the poles, but subsequent calculations have shown it to be a very little less than that.

2. The system derives its name from the *meter*, because all the units of measure in the system are derived from it.

3. The system has a decimal notation.

579. From the standard units other denominations are formed by the use of prefixes derived from the Latin and the Greek.

Deci means 10th.	Deka means 10.
Centi means 100th.	Hekto means 100.
Milli means 1000th.	Kilo means 1000.
	Myria means 10000.

Thus, decimeter, $\frac{1}{10}$ of a meter ; dekameter, 10 meters.

580. The following tables give all the denominations, but many of them are not in common use. Those usually employed in business or science are indicated by bold-faced type.

Abbreviations beginning with a *small letter* indicate a *fractional part* of the standard unit; those beginning with a *capital* denote a *multiple* of the unit.

411

METRIC TABLES.

MEASURES OF LENGTH.

581. The unit of length is the meter.

TABLE.

10 **Millimeters** (^{mm})	= 1 **Centimeter** (^{cm})	= .3937079 in.
10 Centimeters	= 1 Decimeter (^{dm})	= 3.937079 in.
10 Decimeters	= 1 **Meter** (^{m})	= 39.37079 in.
10 Meters	= 1 Dekameter (^{Dm})	= 32.80899 ft.
10 Dekameters	= 1 Hektometer (^{Hm})	= 19.92781 rd.
10 Hektometers	= 1 **Kilometer** (^{Km})	= .621382 mi.
10 Kilometers	= 1 Myriameter(^{Mm})	= 6.21382 mi.

MEASURES OF SURFACE.

582. The units of surface are squares whose dimensions are the corresponding linear units; hence it requires 10 times 10, or 100, of a given denomination to make one of the next higher.

TABLE.

100 Sq. Millimeters	= 1 **Sq. Centimeter**	= .155+ sq. in.
100 Sq. Centimeters	= 1 Sq. Decimeter	= 15.5+ sq. in.
100 Sq. Decimeters	= 1 **Sq. Meter**	= 1.196+ sq. yd.
100 Sq. Meters	= 1 Sq. Dekameter	= 119.6034 sq. yd.
100 Sq. Dekameters	= 1 Sq. Hektometer	= 2.47114 **A.**
100 Sq. Hektometers	= 1 **Sq. Kilometer**	= 247.114 A. = .3861 sq. mi.

1. In measuring small areas the unit is the sq. meter.

2. In measuring land, the square meter is called a *centare* (^{ca}), the square dekameter an *are* (^{a}) and the square hektometer a *hektare* (^{Ha}).

MEASURES OF VOLUME.

583. The units of volume are cubes whose dimensions are the corresponding linear units; hence it requires 1000 of a given denomination to make one of the next higher.

TABLE.

1000 Cu. Millimeters $(^{cu\ mm})$ = 1 **Cu. Centimeter** $(^{cu\ cm})$.
1000 Cu. Centimeters = 1 Cu. Decimeter $(^{cu\ dm})$.
1000 Cu. Decimeters = 1 Cu. Meter $(^{cu\ m})$.

1. In measuring volumes the principal unit is the cubic meter.

2. In measuring wood, the cubic meter is called a *stere*, $\frac{1}{10}$ of a cubic meter a *decistere*, etc.

3. A cubic meter is equal to 1.308 cubic yards.

MEASURES OF CAPACITY.

584 The unit of capacity in both liquid and dry measure is the *liter*, and it contains a volume equal to a cube whose edge is a *decimeter*.

TABLE.

		LIQUID.	DRY.
10 Milliliters $(^{ml})$ = 1 **Centiliter** $(^{cl})$	= .6102 cu. in.	
10 Centiliters = 1 Deciliter $(^{dl})$	= .845 gi.	
10 Deciliters = 1 **Liter** $(^{l})$	= 1.0567 qt.	.908 qt.
10 Liters = 1 Dekaliter $(^{Dl})$	= 2.6417 gal.	1.135 pk.
10 Dekaliters = 1 **Hektoliter** $(^{Hl})$	= 26.417 gal.	2.8375 bu.
10 Hektoliters = 1 Kiloliter $(^{Kl})$	= 264.17 gal.	

MEASURES OF WEIGHT.

585. The unit of weight is the *gram*, and its weight is the weight of a cubic centimeter of distilled water at its greatest density.

TABLE.

		AVOIRDUPOIS.
10 **Milligrams** $(^{mg})$ = 1 **Centigram** $(^{cg})$	=	.15432 + gr.
10 Centigrams = 1 Decigram $(^{dg})$	=	1.54324 + gr.
10 Decigrams = 1 **Gram** $(^{g})$	=	15.43248 + gr.
10 Grams = 1 Dekagram $(^{Dg})$	=	.35273 + oz.
10 Dekagrams = 1 Hektogram $(^{Hg})$	=	3.52739 + oz.
10 Hektograms = 1 **Kilogram** $(^{Kg})$	=	2.20462 + lb.
10 Kilograms = 1 Myriagram $(^{Mg})$	=	22.04621 + lb.
10 Myriagrams = 1 Quintal $(^{Q})$	=	220.46212 + lb.
10 Quintals = 1 **Tonneau** $(^{T})$	=	2204.62125 + lb.

REDUCTION.

586. A denominate number in the metric system can be reduced to higher or lower denominations by the removal of the decimal point.

1. In measures of volume, since it requires 1000 of each denomination to make one of the next higher, the decimal point must be removed three places.

2. In measures of surfaces, since it requires 100 of each denomination to make one of the next higher, the decimal point must be removed two places.

3. In other measures remove the decimal point one place.

EXERCISES.

587. 1. Reduce 15675^{cm} to kilometers.

2. Reduce $7560^{sq\,m}$ to ares.

3. Write 6734^{cl} as liters; as hektoliters.

4. Write 43628^{mg} as grams; as kilograms.

5. Write $.75^{cu\,m}$ as liters; as hektoliters.

6. Write $876.37^{sq\,cm}$ as square meters; as ares.

7. What is the weight of $230.5^{cu\,cm}$ of water?

A cubic centimeter of water weighs 1 gram.

8. What is the weight in dekagrams of $.045^{cu\,m}$ of water?

9. What is the weight in kilograms of 13^{Hl} of water?

10. How much will a cubic meter of water weigh in kilograms? Express the same quantity of water in liters.

11. What is the amount of 65750.75^{l} of water in cubic meters? What is its weight in kilograms?

A milliliter of water weighs 1 gram.

12. What will 60^{l} of mercury weigh, mercury being 13.5 times as heavy as water?

The weight of any substance compared with the weight of an equal bulk of water is called its *specific gravity*. The sp. gr. of mercury is 13.5.

13. Find the weight in grams of a cubic decimeter of iron (sp. gr. 7.21).

14. What is the weight in kilograms of a cubic meter of ice (sp. gr. 0.92)?

15. Which is the cheaper and how much, to buy cloth at $ 3 per meter, or at $ 2.90 per yard ?

16. How many ares are there in a rectangular field 62^m long and 43.6^m wide ?

17. How much carpet a meter in width, is required to carpet a room 5.3 meters long and 4.2 meters wide ?

18. How many liters of water are there in a tank 2.6^m long, 2^m wide, and 6^{dm} deep ?

19. How long must a pile of wood be, to contain 12 steres, if it is 3.5 meters high and 3.8 meters wide ?

20. A barrel of flour contains 196 pounds. How many kilograms or kilos does it weigh ?

21. A bin is 3 meters square and 2.5 meters high. How many hektoliters of wheat will it hold ?

22. What weight of mercury will a vessel contain whose capacity is 25$^{cu\ cm}$?

23. A tank is 4^m long, 36^{dm} wide, 76^{cm} deep. How many liters of water will it hold ?

24. A vat is 6.4^m long, 3^m wide, and 2.8^m deep. How long will it take a water-pipe to fill the vat, if 2.9^{Dl} flow into it per minute?

25. A platform bears a weight of 60 pounds per square foot. What is the weight in kilograms per square meter ?

26. A man bought 360 bu. of wheat at $ .95 a bushel, and sold it at $ 2.95 a hektoliter. How much did he gain ?

27. The dimensions of a box are 3.5^m, 1.8^m, and 0.8^m. What are the contents in cubic yards ?

28. A room is 5.2 meters long, 4.5 meters wide, and 3.2 meters high. What will be the cost of plastering it at 35 cents per square meter ?

29. How much will a merchant receive for 3.68^{Hl} of wine, if he sells it at $ 2.50 per gallon ?

30. What is the weight in kilograms of 2583 $^{cu\ cm}$ of water ?

31. How much will 4 tons of coal cost at $ .75 per quintal ?

32. Reduce 20 lb. 8 oz. Avoirdupois to hektograms.

33. How many revolutions will be made by a wheel 9 ft. in circumference in passing over a distance of one kilometer ?

34. Which is the larger and how much, a cask which holds 21^{Dl} or one which holds 43 gallons ?

35. Change 10 hektograms to pounds Avoirdupois weight; Troy weight.

36. Find the weight in grams of a gallon of water.

37. What price per pound is equivalent to $ 2.20 per kilogram ?

38. A square foot is what part of a square meter ?

39. How many centares are there in a garden plot 10 feet square ?

40. The specific gravity of granite is 2.9. What is the weight of a block 50^{cm} long, 25^{cm} wide, 12^{cm} thick, in kilograms ? in pounds ?

41. What is the weight in kilograms of a cubic foot of water ?

42. How many meters are there in 2 mi. 40 rd. 12 ft. ?

43. How many gallons are there in 24 dekaliters ?

44. A man bought 50^{Kg} of sugar for $ 5.51. How much did he pay per pound ?

45. How many gallons will a cistern contain which is 3^m square and 2^m deep ?

46. What price per bushel is equivalent to $ 6.60 per hektoliter ?

47. If the specific gravity of copper is 8.8, what is the weight in hektograms of a cubic decimeter of the metal ?

48. If a bushel of oats weighs 32 pounds, what is the weight in kilograms of 40 bu. ?

49. If a body weighs 7.35^{Kg} in air and 4.41^{Kg} in water, what is its specific gravity ?

50. What is the weight in dekagrams of 44 cubic decimeters of zinc, if the specific gravity is 6.86 ?

51. A cask of olive oil containing 2^{Hl} cost $ 36.32. What was paid per quart for the oil ?

52. If a silver dollar weighs $412\frac{1}{2}$ grains, how many grams does it weigh ?

53. If a quire of paper is $.588^{cm}$ thick, what is the thickness in millimeters of a single sheet ?

54. What is the value of 20 qt. of sulphuric acid at $2\frac{1}{2}$ cents a pound, if the specific gravity is 1.841 ?

55. A rectangular vessel is 5^m long, 9^{dm} wide and 3^m deep. Find its capacity in cubic meters. What is the weight of distilled water at its greatest density that it will hold.

56. A liter is .264 of a gallon. How many grams will a gill of water make ?

57. A rectangular cistern is known to hold 25^{Hl}. If its length is 2^m, its breadth 1.5^m, what is its depth ?

58. An importer bought silk at $ 1.15 per meter and sold it at a profit of 20% per yard. How much did he get for it per yard ?

59. Mercury is $13\frac{1}{2}$ times as heavy as water, or its specific gravity is 13.5. How many pounds will a vessel hold whose capacity is $35^{cu\ cm}$?

60. A man paid 800 francs for 100 liters of wine. What price did he pay for it per gallon ?

61. A cubical block of silver whose dimensions are 2^{dm} was sold at $20\cent$ per dekagram. If the specific gravity of silver is 10.5, for how much did it sell ?

62. If alcohol is .8 as heavy as water, how many pounds Avoirdupois will $1250^{cu\ cm}$ of alcohol weigh ?

TABLES OF DENOMINATE NUMBERS.

MEASURES OF EXTENSION.

588. Measures of Extension are used in measuring lengths, distances, surfaces, and solids.

589.   LINEAR MEASURE.

TABLE.

12 Inches (in.)	= 1 Foot	. . . . ft.
3 Feet	= 1 Yard	. . . . yd.
$5\frac{1}{2}$ Yards or $16\frac{1}{2}$ ft.	= 1 Rod	. . . . . rd.
320 Rods	= 1 Mile	. . . . mi.

$$\begin{array}{ccccc} \text{mi.} & \text{rd.} & \text{yd.} & \text{ft.} & \text{in.} \\ 1 = & 320 = & 1760 = & 5280 = & 63360. \end{array}$$

Scale. — 320, $5\frac{1}{2}$, 3, 12.

The following are also used:

3 Barleycorns	= 1 Inch. Used by shoemakers.
4 Inches	= 1 Hand. Used to measure the height of horses.
6 Feet	= 1 Fathom. Used to measure depths at sea.
3 Feet	= 1 Pace. ⎫ Used in pacing distances.
5 Paces	= 1 Rod. ⎭
8 Furlongs	= 1 Mile.
1.15 Statute Miles	= 1 Geographical, or Nautical Mile.
3 Geographical Miles	= 1 League.
60 Geographic Miles ⎫	= 1 Degree ⎰ of Latitude on a Meridian, or
69.16 Statute Miles ⎭	⎱ of Longitude on the Equator.

1. The length of a degree of latitude varies. 69.16 miles is the average length, and is that adopted by the United States Coast Survey.

2. The *standard unit* of length is identical with the imperial yard of Great Britain.

3. The standard yard, under William IV., was declared to be fixed by dividing a pendulum which vibrates seconds in a vacuum, at the level of the sea, at 62° Fahrenheit, in the latitude of London, into 391,393 equal parts, and taking 360,000 of these parts for the yard.

The following denominations also occur: The *span* = 9 inches; 1 *common cubit* (the distance from the elbow to the end of the middle finger) = 18 inches; 1 *sacred cubit* = 21.888 inches.

590. SQUARE MEASURE.

TABLE.

144 Square Inches (sq. in.) = 1 Square Foot . . . sq. ft.
9 Square Feet   = 1 Square Yard . . . sq. yd.
$30\frac{1}{4}$ Square Yards   = 1 Square Rod . . . sq. rd.
160 Square Rods   = 1 Acre . . . . . . A.
640 Acres   = 1 Square Mile . . . sq. mi.

sq. mi.	A.	sq. rd.	sq. yd.	sq. ft.	sq. in.
1 =	640 =	102400 =	3097600 =	27878400 =	4014489600.

Scale.—640, 160, $30\frac{1}{4}$, 9, 144.

1. The term *perch* or *pole* is sometimes used instead of *rod*. The *rood*, 40 perches, is found in old title deeds and surveys.

2. Plastering, ceiling, etc., are commonly estimated by the *square yard;* paving, glazing, and stone-cutting, by the *square foot;* roofing, flooring, and slating by the *square* of 100 *feet.*

591. CUBIC MEASURE.

TABLE.

1728 Cubic Inches (cu. in.) = 1 Cubic Foot . . . cu. ft.
27 Cubic Feet   = 1 Cubic Yard . . . cu. yd.
128 Cubic Feet   = 1 Cord . . . . . C.

cu. yd.	cu. ft.	cu. in.
1 =	27 =	46656.

Scale. — 27, 1728.

1. A cord of wood or stone is a pile 8 ft. long, 4 ft. wide, and 4 ft. high.

2. A *perch* of stone or masonry is $16\frac{1}{2}$ ft. long, $1\frac{1}{2}$ ft. thick, and 1 ft. high, and contains $24\frac{3}{4}$ cu. ft.

3. A *cubic yard* of earth is considered a *load.*

4. Brick-work is commonly estimated by the thousand bricks.

5. Brick-layers, masons, and joiners commonly make a deduction of one half the space occupied by windows and doors in the walls of buildings.

6. In computing the contents of walls, masons and brick-layers multiply the entire distance around on the outside of the wall by the height and thickness. The corners are thus measured twice.

7. A cubic foot of distilled water at the maximum density, at the level of the sea, and the barometer at 30 inches, weighs $62\frac{1}{2}$ lb. or 1000 oz. Avoirdupois.

592.   SURVEYORS' LINEAR MEASURE.

TABLE.

7.92 Inches	= 1 Link	. . .	l.
25 Links	= 1 Rod .	. . .	rd.
4 Rods or 100 Links	= 1 Chain	. . .	ch.
80 Chains	= 1 Mile	. . .	mi.

$$\begin{array}{ccccc} \text{mi.} & \text{ch.} & \text{rd.} & \text{l.} & \text{in.} \\ 1 & = 80 & = 320 & = 8000 & = 63360. \end{array}$$

Scale.— 80, 4, 25, 7.92.

1. The Linear Unit commonly employed by *surveyors* is *Gunter's Chain*, which is 4 rods or 66 feet.

2. An *Engineers' Chain*, used by civil engineers, is 100 feet long, and consists of 100 links.

593.   SURVEYORS' SQUARE MEASURE.

TABLE.

| 625 Square Links = 1 sq. rd. | 10 Square Chains = 1 acre. |
| 16 Square Rods = 1 sq. chain. | 640 Acres   = 1 sq. mi. |

$$\begin{array}{ccccc} \text{sq. mi.} & \text{A.} & \text{sq. ch.} & \text{sq. rd.} & \text{sq. l.} \\ 1 & = 640 & = 6400 & = 102400 & = 64000000. \end{array}$$

Scale. — 640, 10, 16, 625.

In some parts of the country a *Township* contains 36 square miles, or is 6 miles square. A square mile of land is also called a *section*.

---

1. In Texas, New Mexico, and other Spanish sections of the United States, the Spanish land measures are still in use. The unit of length is the vara, equal in Texas to $33\frac{1}{3}$ inches, in California to 33 inches, and in Mexico to 32.9927 inches. Counting $33\frac{1}{3}$ inches to the vara, 108 varas = 100 yards, and 1900.8 varas = 1 mile.

2. Land is measured in square varas, labors, and square leagues.

1000000 Square Varas = 1 Labor	= 177.136 Acres.
25 Labors	= 1 Square League = 4428.4 Acres.
1 Acre	= 5645.376 Square Varas.

Reduce to square varas :

| **1.** 1.77136 A. | **3.** 5 labors. | **5.** 2 sq. leagues. |
| **2.** 5314.08 A. | **4.** 10 labors. | **6.** 19 sq. leagues. |

Reduce to acres :

| **7.** 5000000 sq. varas. | **9.** 5 sq. leagues. | **11.** 250 labors. |
| **8.** 16936.18 sq. varas. | **10.** 15 labors. | **12.** 25 sq. leagues. |

MEASURES OF CAPACITY.

LIQUID MEASURE.

594. **Liquid Measure** is used in measuring liquids.

TABLE.

4 Gills (gi.)	= 1 Pint . . .	pt.
2 Pints	= 1 Quart . . .	qt.
4 Quarts	= 1 Gallon . . .	gal.

gal. qt. pt. gi.
1 = 4 = 8 = 32

Scale. — 4, 2, 4.

1. In determining the capacity of *cisterns, reservoirs,* etc., $31\frac{1}{2}$ gallons are considered a barrel (bbl.), and 2 barrels, or 63 gallons, a hogshead (hhd.). In *commerce,* however, the barrel and hogshead are not fixed measures.

2. *Casks* of large size, called tierces, pipes, butts, tuns, etc., do not hold any fixed quantity. Their capacity is usually marked upon them.

3. The *standard gallon* of the United States contains 231 cubic inches, and will hold a little over $8\frac{1}{3}$ lb. of distilled water. The *imperial gallon,* now adopted by Great Britain, contains 277.274 cu. in., or 10 lb. of distilled water, temperature 62° Fahr., the barometer standing at 30 inches.

4. The *beer gallon* is not now in use. It contained 282 cubic inches.

DRY MEASURE.

595. **Dry Measure** is used in measuring grain, roots, fruit, etc.

TABLE.

2 Pints (pt.)	= 1 Quart . . .	qt.
8 Quarts	= 1 Peck . . .	pk.
4 Pecks	= 1 Bushel . . .	bu.

bu. pk. qt. pt.
1 = 4 = 32 = 64

Scale. — 4, 8, 2.

1. In measuring grain, seeds, or small fruits, the measure must be *even full* or *stricken.* In measuring large fruits or coarse vegetables, corn in the ear, etc., the measure should be heaped at least six inches.

2. Five stricken bushels are considered equal to 4 heaped bushels. The stricken bushel is now little used, except to ascertain capacities.

3. The *Winchester bushel* is the standard unit in the United States. In form it is a cylinder, $18\frac{1}{2}$ in. in diameter, and 8 in. deep, and contains 2150.42 cu. in. The Winchester bushel was discarded by Great Britain in 1826, and the *imperial bushel* was substituted. It contains 2218.192 cu. in.

4. A pint, quart, or gallon, dry measure is more than the same quantity, liquid measure; for a quart, dry measure, is $\frac{1}{32}$ of a bushel, or $\frac{1}{32}$ of 2150.4 cu. in., which is about $67\frac{1}{5}$ cu. in., while a quart liquid measure is $\frac{1}{4}$ of 231 cu. in., or $57\frac{3}{4}$ cu. in.

	Cu. In. in One Gal.	Cu. In. in One Qt.	Cu. In. in One Pt.	Cu. In. in One Gi.
Liquid Meas.	231	$57\frac{3}{4}$	$28\frac{7}{8}$	$7\frac{7}{32}$
Dry Meas.	$268\frac{4}{5}$	$67\frac{1}{5}$	$33\frac{3}{5}$	$8\frac{2}{5}$

MEASURES OF WEIGHT.

AVOIRDUPOIS WEIGHT.

596. Avoirdupois Weight is used in measuring all coarse and heavy articles, as hay, grain, groceries, coal, etc., and the metals, *except gold and silver.*

TABLE.

16 Ounces (oz.)	= 1 Pound	lb.
100 Pounds	= 1 Hundred-weight .	cwt.
20 Hundred-weight	= 1 Ton	T.

T.		cwt.		lb.		oz.
1	=	20	=	2000	=	32000

Scale.—20, 100, 16.

1. In weighing coal at the mines and in levying duties at the United States Custom House, the *long* ton of 2240 lb. is sometimes used.
2. The ounce is considered as 16 *drams.*
3. The unit is the *pound.* It contains 7000 grains.

The following denominations are also used:

14 lb.	= 1 Stone.
100 lb. Butter	= 1 Firkin.
100 lb. Grain or Flour	= 1 Cental.
100 lb. Dried Fish	= 1 Quintal.
100 lb. Nails	= 1 Keg.
196 lb. Flour	= 1 Barrel.
200 lb. Pork or Beef	= 1 Barrel.
280 lb. Salt at N. Y. Works	= 1 Barrel.

In states that regulate the weight of a bushel, the following are the statutory weights:

Wheat, 60 lb.   *Rye*, 56 lb., except in Cal. 54 lb. ; in La. 32 lb.

Corn, shelled, 56 lb., except in Cal. 52 lb.   *Corn in the ear*, 70 lb., except in Miss. 72 lb. ; in O. 68 lb. ; in Ind. after Dec. 1 and in Ky. after May 1, following the time of husking it, 68 lb.

Oats, 32 lb., except in Ida. and Or. 36 lb. ; in Md. 26 lb. ; in N. J. and Va. 30 lb.   *Barley*, 48 lb., except in Or. 46 lb. ; in Ala., Ga., Ky., Pa., 47 lb.; in Cal. 50 lb.; in La. 32 lb.

Buckwheat, 52 lb., except in Cal. 40 lb.; in Conn., Me., Mass., Mich., Miss., N. Y., Pa., Vt., Wis., 48 lb.; in Ida., N. D., Okl., Or., S. D., Tex., Wash., 42 lb. ; in Kan., Minn., N. J., N. C., O., Tenn., 50 lb.; in Ky. 56 lb.

Clover seed, 60 lb., except in N. J. 64 lb.   *Timothy seed*, 45 lb., except in Ark. 60 lb. ; in N. D., S. D., 42 lb.

Bran, 20 lb.   *Corn meal*, 50 lb., except in Ala., Ark., Ga., Ill., Miss., N. C., Tenn., 48 lb.   *Potatoes*, 60 lb., except in Md., Pa., Va., 56 lb.   *Coal*, 80 lb., except in Ky., Pa., 76 lb.

Peas, 60 lb.   *Beans*, 60 lb., except in Me. 62 lb. ; in Mass. 70 lb.

TROY WEIGHT.

597. **Troy Weight** is used in weighing gold, silver, and jewels.

TABLE.

24 Grains (gr.) = 1 Pennyweight . . . **pwt.**
20 Pennyweights = 1 Ounce . . . . . **oz.**
12 Ounces = 1 Pound . . . . . **lb.**

lb.   oz.   pwt.   gr.
1 = 12 = 240 = 5760

Scale. — 12, 20, 24.

1. In weighing diamonds, pearls, and other jewels, the unit commonly employed is the *carat*, which is equal to 4 carat grains, or 3.168 Troy grains.

2. The term *carat* is also used to express the fineness of gold, and means $\frac{1}{24}$ part. Thus, gold that is 18 carats fine is $\frac{18}{24}$ gold, and $\frac{6}{24}$ alloy.

3. The *standard unit* of weight is the *Troy pound*. It is equal to the weight of 22.7944 cu. in. of distilled water at its maximum density, the barometer being at 30 inches. It is identical with the Troy pound of Great Britain.

APOTHECARIES' WEIGHT.

598. Apothecaries' Weight is used by apothecaries and physicians in weighing medicines for prescriptions.

TABLE.

20 Grains (gr.)	= 1 Scruple . . .	sc., or ϴ
3 Scruples	= 1 Dram	dr., or ʒ
8 Drams	= 1 Ounce . . .	oz., or ℥
12 Ounces	= 1 Pound . . .	lb., or ℔

lb. oz. dr. sc. gr.
1 = 12 = 96 = 288 = 5760

Scale. — 12, 8, 3, 20.

1. In writing prescriptions, physicians express the number in Roman characters, using j instead of i final. They also write the symbol first; thus: ℥v, ʒvj, ϴij.

2. Medicines are bought and sold in large quantities by Avoirdupois weight.

1 lb. Avoirdupois = 7000 gr.   1 lb. $\left\{\begin{array}{l}\text{Troy and}\\\text{Apothecaries'}\end{array}\right\}$ = 5760 gr.

1 oz.   "   = 437½ gr.   1 oz.   "   = 480 gr.

3. It will be observed that the pound is identical with the Troy pound, as are also the ounce and the grain, though the ounce is differently divided.

APOTHECARIES' LIQUID MEASURE.

599. Apothecaries' Liquid Measure is used in compounding and measuring liquid medicines.

TABLE.

60 Drops (gtt.) or minims (♏)	= 1 Fluid drachm . .	fʒ.
8 Fluid drachms	= 1 Fluid ounce . . .	f℥.
16 Fluid ounces	= 1 Pint	O.
8 Pints	= 1 Gallon	*Cong.*

Cong. O. f℥. fʒ. ♏.
1 = 8 = 128 = 1024 = 61440

Scale. — 8, 16, 8, 60.

The abbreviation *Cong.* is from the Latin *congius*, a gallon. A pint being one eighth of a gallon the abbreviation for it is *O.*, from the Latin *octavus*, one eighth.

MEASURES OF TIME.

600. The following are the ordinary divisions of time:

60 Seconds (sec.)	= 1 Minute	min.
60 Minutes	= 1 Hour	hr.
24 Hours	= 1 Day	da.
7 Days	= 1 Week	wk.
365 Days	= 1 Year	yr.
366 Days	= 1 Leap Year	yr.
100 Years	= 1 Century	cen.

cen.	yr.	mo.	da.	hr.	min.	sec.
1 =	100 =	1200 =	36500 =	876000 =	52560000 =	3153600000.

Scale. — 100, 365, 24, 60, 60.

1. In most business computations 30 days are considered a month, and 12 months a year. For many purposes 4 weeks constitute a month.

2. The common year contains 52 weeks and 1 day, the leap year 52 weeks and 2 days. Hence, commonly, each year begins one day later in the week than did the preceding year, but the year succeeding leap year begins *two* days later.

3. The time required for the earth to revolve around the sun is one year, which is 365 days 5 hr. 48 min. 49.7 sec., or very nearly 365¼ days. Instead of reckoning this part of a day each year, it is disregarded, and an addition is made when this amounts to *one day*, which is very nearly every fourth year. This addition of one day is made to the month of February. Since the part of a day that is disregarded when 365 days are considered as a year, is a *little less than one quarter of a day*, the addition of one day every fourth year is a little too much, and, to correct this excess, addition is made to only every fourth centennial year. With this correction the error does not amount to much more than a day in 4000 years. Therefore,

Centennial years exactly divisible by 400, *and other years exactly divisible by* 4, *are* **Leap Years.**

4. The reckoning of time among the ancients was very inaccurate. This was owing to their ignorance of astronomy, and also to changes that were made from time to time for political reasons. The calendar was reformed by Julius Cæsar, 46 B.C., who made the year consist of 365¼ days, adding one day every fourth year. In 1582, the error in the calendar established by him had increased to 10 days; that is, too much time had been reckoned as a year, until the civil year was 10 days behind the solar year. To correct this error, Pope Gregory XIII. decreed that 10 days should be stricken from the calendar, that the day following the 3d day of October, 1582, should be made the 14th, and that henceforth only those centennial years should be leap years which are divisible by 400.

5. Most Catholic countries adopted the Gregorian Calendar soon after it was established. Great Britain did not adopt it until 1752, when the error amounted to 11 days. By Act of Parliament, the 3d of September was called the 14th. The civil year by the same act was made to commence on the 1st of January, instead of the 25th of March, as was previously the case.

6. Dates reckoned by the Julian calendar are called Old Style (O.S.), and those reckoned by the Gregorian calendar are called New Style (N.S.). Russia still reckons dates according to Old Style. The *difference* now amounts to 12 days.

The year begins with the month of January, and ends with the month of December.

The months, their names, and the number of days in each, are as follows:

January,	31 da.	. .	Jan.	July,	31 da.	. . July.
February,	28 or 29 da.		Feb.	August,	31 da.	. . Aug.
March,	31 da.	. .	Mar.	September,	30 da.	. . Sept.
April,	30 da.	. .	Apr.	October,	31 da.	. . Oct.
May,	31 da.	. .	May.	November,	30 da.	. . Nov.
June,	30 da.	. .	June.	December,	31 da.	. . Dec.

CIRCULAR OR ANGULAR MEASURE.

601. **Circular or Angular Measure** is used to measure arcs of circles and angles, in determining latitude, longitude, direction, the position of vessels at sea, etc.

602. That part of the circumference which is included between the lines which form the angle is the **Measure of the Angle.**

TABLE.

60 Seconds (˝) = 1 Minute . . . ′
60 Minutes   = 1 Degree . . . °
360 Degrees   = 1 Circumference . **Cir.**

Cir.　°　　　′　　　　″
1 = 360 = 21600 = 1296000

Scale. — 360, 60, 60.

1. A **Quadrant** is $\frac{1}{4}$ of a circumference, or 90°; a **Sextant** is $\frac{1}{6}$ of a circumference, or 60°.

2. The length of a degree of longitude on the earth's surface at the Equator is 69.16 miles.

3. In astronomical calculations 30° are called a **Sign,** and there are therefore 12 signs in a circle.

MEASURES OF VALUE.

603. The common measure of value is **Money.**

It is also called *Currency,* and is of two kinds, viz. : *coin* and *paper* money.

604. Stamped pieces of metal having a value fixed by law are **Coin** or **Specie.**

605. Notes and bills issued by the Government and banks, and authorized to be used as money, are **Paper Money.**

606. All moneys which, if offered, legally satisfy a debt are a **Legal Tender.**

UNITED STATES MONEY.

607. The *unit* of United States or Federal money is the *Dollar.*

TABLE.

10 Mills (m.) = 1 Cent . . ct.	10 Dimes = 1 Dollar. . $
10 Cents = 1 Dime . . d.	10 Dollars = 1 Eagle . . E.

Scale. — Decimal.

1. The dollar mark is probably a combination of U. S., the initials of the words "United States."

2. The *coins* of the United States are —

Gold : The double-eagle, eagle, half-eagle, quarter-eagle, and one-dollar piece.

Silver : The dollar, half-dollar, quarter-dollar, and the ten-cent piece.

Nickel : The five-cent piece.

Bronze : The one-cent piece.

There are various other coins of the United States in circulation, but they are not coined now.

The denominations dimes and eagles are rarely used, the dimes being regarded as cents, and the eagles as dollars.

3. The *unit of value* is the dollar. Its *standard weight* in gold is 25.8 gr.

4. The *standard purity* of the gold and silver coins is by weight 9 parts of pure metal and 1 part alloy.

The alloy of gold coins consists of silver and copper; the silver, by law, is not to exceed one tenth of the alloy.

The alloy of silver coins is pure copper.

The nickel coins consist of one fourth nickel and three fourths copper.

The cent is composed of 95 parts copper and 5 parts tin and zinc.

5. All gold coins are a legal tender for any amount ; silver coins *less* than $1 are legal tender for any amount not exceeding $10 in any one payment ; nickel and bronze coins, for any amount not exceeding 25 cents in any one payment.

CANADA MONEY.

608. The currency of Canada is decimal, and the *table* and *denominations* are the same as those of United States money. English money is, however, still used to some extent.

1. The coins of Canada are for the most part of the same denominations as those of the United States, except the gold coins, which are the sovereign and half-sovereign.

2. Canadian coins are not received at their full face value in many parts of the United States. The half-dollar pieces are taken for only 40 cents, the quarter-dollar pieces for only 20 cents, etc.

ENGLISH OR STERLING MONEY.

609. English money is the currency of Great Britain. The *unit* is the *Pound* or *Sovereign*.

TABLE.

4 Farthings (far.) = 1 Penny . . . *d.*
12 Pence = 1 Shilling . . *s.*
20 Shillings = $\left\{ \begin{array}{l} \text{1 Pound, or} \\ \text{1 Sovereign} \end{array} \right\}$. £

£   *s.*   *d.*   far.
1 = 20 = 240 = 960

Scale. — 20, 12, 4.

1. Farthings are commonly written as fractions of a penny. Thus, 7 pence 3 farthings is written $7\frac{3}{4} d.$; 5 pence 1 farthing, $5\frac{1}{4} d.$

2. The value of £1 or sovereign is $4.8665 in American gold, and the other coins have their proportionate values.

3. The coins of Great Britain in general use are —

Gold : Sovereign, half-sovereign, and guinea, which is equal to 21 shillings.

Silver : The crown (equal to 5 shillings), half-crown, florin (equal to 2 shillings), shilling, six-penny and three-penny pieces.

Copper : Penny and half-penny.

FRENCH MONEY.

610. In France the currency is *decimal*. The *unit* is the *Franc*.

TABLE.

10 Centimes (ct.) [pronounced *son-teems*] = 1 Decime . . dc.
10 Decimes [pronounced *des-seems*] = 1 Franc . . . fr.

Scale. — Decimal.

1. The value of the franc, as determined by the Secretary of the Treasury, is $.193 in United States money.

2. The coins of France are of gold, silver, bronze, and copper. The gold coins are the *hundred, forty, twenty, ten,* and *five* franc pieces ; the silver coins are the *five, two,* and *one* franc pieces ; also the *fifty* and *twenty-five* centime pieces. The bronze coins are the *ten, five, two,* and *one* centime pieces. There are also copper coins in *ten* and *five* centime pieces.

GERMAN MONEY.

611. German money is the legal currency of the German Empire.

TABLE.

100 Pfennigs = 1 Mark.

Scale. — Decimal.

1. The unit is the *mark.* Its value is $.2385 in United States money.

2. The coins of the German Empire are of gold, silver, nickel, and copper. The gold coins are the 20-mark piece, the 10-mark piece, and the 5-mark piece. The silver coins are the *two* and *one* mark pieces; the nickel coins are the *ten* and *five* pfennig pieces; and the copper coins are the *two* and *one* pfennig pieces.

COUNTING.

612. The following denominations are used in counting some classes of articles:

TABLE.

12 Things = 1 Dozen . . . . . doz.
12 Dozen = 1 Gross . . . . . gr.
12 Gross = 1 Great Gross . . . G. gr.

Scale. — Duodecimal.

Two things are often called a *pair*, and twenty things a *score;* as a *pair* of birds, a *score* of years.

STATIONERS' TABLE.

613. The denominations used in the paper trade are:

| 24 Sheets = 1 Quire. | 2 Reams = 1 Bundle. |
| 20 Quires = 1 Ream. | 5 Bundles = 1 Bale. |

Bale Bundles Reams Quires Sheets
 1 = 5 = 10 = 200 = 4800

Scale. — 5, 2, 20, 24.

The terms *folio, quarto, octavo,* applied to books, indicate the number of leaves into which a sheet of paper is folded. Thus, when a sheet of paper is folded into 2, 4, 8, 12, 16, 18, or 24 leaves, the forms are called respectively, folio, 4to or quarto, 8vo or octavo, 12mo, 16mo, 18mo, and 24mo.

INTEREST AND PARTIAL PAYMENTS.

VERMONT RULES.

614. The *Vermont* statutes contain the following provisions regarding the computation of time and rates of interest :

SEC. 12. The word "month" shall mean a calendar month; and the word "year" shall mean a calendar year, ...

SEC. 26. When time is to be reckoned from a day or date, or an act done, such day, date, or day when such is done shall not be included in the computation.

SEC. 2301. The rate of interest, or the sum allowed for the forbearance or use of money, shall be six dollars for one hundred dollars for one year, and at the same rate for a greater or less sum, and for a longer or shorter time, ...

The rule and custom in Vermont, in commercial transactions, in the banks, and in the courts, in computing interest, is to consider a calendar month whether it contains 28, 29, 30, or 31 days as one twelfth of a year; a day, or any number of days up to thirty, as so many thirtieths of a month.

When it is required to find the time between two dates less than a calendar month apart, count the actual number of days.

Thus, from January 28, 1895, to February 1, 1895, is four days; from February 28, 1895, to March 1, 1895, is one day; from February 28, 1892, to March 1, 1892, is two days, February in that year having 29 days.

The custom and the law relating to the time when a note matures and to the amount due at its maturity are illustrated by the following examples :

A note dated January 28, 1895, for $100, payable one month after date, with interest, became payable February 28, 1895 (31 days after date), and the amount due was $100.50.

A note dated January 29, 1895, for $100, payable one month after date, with interest, became payable February 28, 1895 (30 days after date), and the amount due was $100.50.

A note dated January 30, 1895, for $100, payable one month after date, with interest, became payable February 28, 1895 (29 days after date), and the amount due was $100.50.

A note dated January 31, 1895, for $100, payable one month after date, with interest, became payable February 28, 1895 (28 days after date), and the amount due was $100.50.

A note dated January 31, 1895, for $100, payable 30 days after date, with interest, became payable on March 2, 1895, and the amount due was $100.50.

A note was dated January 1, 1895, for $100, payable on demand, with interest. It was paid January 31, 1895; the amount due was $100.50, (30 days).

A note was dated January 1, 1895, for $100, payable on demand, with interest. It was paid February 1, 1895; the amount due was $100.50, (a calendar month).

A note was dated February 1, 1895, for $100, payable on demand, with interest. It was paid February 28, 1895; the amount due was $100.45, (27 days).

A note was dated February 1, 1895, for $100, payable on demand, with interest. It was paid March 1, 1895; the amount due was $100.50, (a calendar month).

A note dated January 1, 1895, payable 31 days after date, with interest, became payable on February 1, 1895, and the holder was entitled to interest for one month and one day.

The Vermont statutes contain the following provisions relating to the modes of computing the indebtedness upon notes, bills, or other similar obligations:

FIRST, When the note or debt draws simple interest.

SEC. 2302. *On notes, bills, or other similar obligations, payable on demand or at a specified time, with* INTEREST, *when payments are made, such payments shall be applied: first, to liquidate the interest accrued at the time of such payments; and second, to extinguish the principal.*

[It will be observed that this rule is similar to the United States Rule (Art. 361).]

SECOND, When the note or debt draws annual interest.

SEC. 2303. *When such obligations are payable on demand or at a specified time, with* INTEREST ANNUALLY, *the annual interest that remains unpaid shall bear simple interest from the time it becomes due to the time of final settlement; but if in any year, reckoning from the time such annual interest began to accrue, payments are made, the amount of such payments at the end of such year, with interest thereon from the time of payment, shall be applied: first, to liquidate the simple interest accrued from the unpaid annual interest; second, to liquidate the annual interests due; and third, to extinguish the principal.*

WRITTEN EXERCISES.

1. $2000.   BARRE, VT., July 15, 1885.

On demand, for value received, I promise to pay to the order of William D. Hudson, two thousand dollars, with interest annually.

                                                SAMUEL S. SPURR.

Indorsed as follows: Dec. 10, 1886, $500; Aug. 15, 1887, $20; Feb. 15, 1888, $25; Nov. 12, 1890, $20; Dec. 12, 1891, $575. How much was due April 18, 1892?

Solution.

	(1) Int. on unpaid yearly int.	(2) Unpaid yearly int.	(3) Principals.
Principal July 15, 1885,			$ 2000.00
Int. on prin. to July 15, 1887 (2 yr.),		$ 240.00	
Int. on $ 120 yearly int. unpaid for 1 yr.,	$ 7.20		
Total int. due July 15, 1887,	$ 247.20		
Am't of 1st pay't July 15, 1887 (7 mo. 5 da.), $ 517.92			
Bal. applied to liquidate principal ($ 517.92 − $ 247.20),			270.72
Principal (balance due) July 15, 1887,			$ 1729.28
Int. on prin. to July 15, 1888 (1 yr.),		$ 103.76	
Am't of 2d pay't to July 15, 1888 (11 mo.),	$ 21.10		
Am't of 3d pay't to July 15, 1888 (5 mo.),	25.63		
Sum of pay'ts applied to liquidate yearly int.,		46.73	
Bal. of unpaid yearly int. July 15, 1888,		57.03	
Principal July 15, 1888,			$ 1729.28
Int. on prin. to July 15, 1891 (3 yr.),		$ 311.27	
Int. on $ 103.76, the yearly int. on prin. for (2 yr. + 1 yr.) 3 yr.,	$ 18.68		
Yearly int. hitherto unpaid,		57.03	
Int. on bal. of unpaid yearly int., $ 57.03, for 3 yr.,	10.27		
Total int. upon unpaid yearly int.	28.95		
Total unpaid yearly int.,		368.30	
Am't of 4th payment to July 15, 1891 (8 mo. 3 da.), applied to liquidate int. upon unpaid yearly int.,	20.81		
* Bal. of int. upon unpaid yearly int.,	8.14		
Principal July 15, 1891,			$ 1729.28
Int. on prin. to April 18, 1892 (9 mo. 3 da.),	$ 78.68		
Unpaid yearly int. July 15, 1891,	368.30		
Int. upon $ 368.30 unpaid yearly int. to April 18, 1892,	$ 16.76		
* Bal. of int. upon unpaid yearly int.,	8.14		
Total int. due upon unpaid yearly int.,		24.90	
Total int. due at time of settlement,			471.88
Am't of note at time of settlement,			2201.16
Am't of pay't to Apr. 18, 1892 (4 mo. 6 da.),			587.08
Sum due Apr. 18, 1892,			$ 1614.08

* No interest is paid upon the interest upon unpaid yearly interest.

2. A note dated June 6, 1890, was given for $ 2250, with annual interest at 6%. Aug. 10, 1892, a payment of $ 1000 was indorsed. What amount was due Jan. 1, 1894 ?

3. $800.   BENNINGTON, VT., Jan. 30, 1888.

On demand, I promise to pay the bearer eight hundred dollars, for value received, with interest annually at 6%.   CHAS. H. SMITH.

The interest on the above note was regularly paid and indorsed for 3 years.   What was due Jan. 30, 1894 ?

4. A note for $1000, given Oct. 5, 1891, bearing annual interest at 6%, was indorsed as follows: Dec. 17, 1891, $100 ; June 25, 1892, $200 ; Nov. 14, 1893, $150.   What remained due Jan. 1, 1895 ?

5. At Rutland, Vt., a note for $500 was given Sept. 10, 1886, to be paid on demand, interest annually at 6%.   The following indorsements were made : April 1, 1888, $20 ; July 1, 1889, $25 ; March 19, 1891, $200.   What amount remained due after the last payment ?

6. Find the amount due July 1, 1889, on a note for $1250, dated July 1, 1885, annual interest 6%, and indorsed as follows : March 6, 1887, $250 ; June 1, 1888, $400 ; Dec. 13, 1888, $50 ; May 1, 1889, $125.

7. A note of $1500, payable on demand with 6% interest, payable annually, given Feb. 1, 1880, was indorsed as follows : Jan. 1, 1884, $100 ; Jan. 13, 1886, $40 ; Oct. 1, 1886, $900 ; Feb. 1, 1888, $400. What amount remained due after the last payment ?

8. Find the amount due on the following note July 1, 1891 :
$3000.   VERGENNES, VT., April 1, 1888.

On demand, I promise to pay to the bearer three thousand dollars, for value received, interest annually at 6%   THOMAS HALL.

Indorsements : Nov. 5, 1888, $300 ; Jan. 4, 1890, $100 ; Aug. 20, 1890, $1000.

NEW HAMPSHIRE RULE.

The law of New Hampshire for computing the indebtedness upon a note or other obligation when partial payments have been made is the same as the Vermont rule, with the following additional provision:

If, however, at the date of any payment there is no interest except the accruing annual interest, and the payment, or payments, do not exceed the annual interest at the end of the year, deduct the payment, or payments, without interest on the same.

1. On a note for $2500, given at Nashua, N.H., Oct. 1, 1888, with interest payable annually at 6%, the following payments were made: June 1, 1890, $500; Mar. 17, 1891, $87.94; Dec. 1, 1893, $1000. How much was due Apr. 1, 1895?

SOLUTION.

	Int. on unpaid yearly int.	Unpaid yearly int.	Principals.
Principal,			$2500.00
Int. on prin. to Oct. 1, 1890 (2 yr.),		$300.00	
Int. on $150, yearly int. on prin. for 1 yr.,	$9.00		
Total int. due Oct. 1, 1890,	$309.00		
Amt. of 1st paym't to Oct. 1, 1890,	$510.00		*
Bal. applied to liquidate principal ($510.00 — $309.00),			201.00
Principal Oct. 1, 1890,			$2299.00
Int. on prin. to Oct. 1, 1891,		$137.94	
Second pay't *without int.*, because less than int. due, applied to liquidate int.,		87.94	
Unpaid yearly int. Oct. 1, 1891,		50.00	
Principal Oct. 1, 1891,			$2299.00
Int. on prin. to Oct. 1, 1894 (3 yr.),		$413.82	
Int. on $137.94, the yearly int. on prin. for (2 yr. + 1 yr.) 3 yr.,	$24.83		
Unpaid yearly int. Oct. 1, 1891,		50.00	
Int. on unpaid yearly int. to Oct. 1, 1894 (3 yr.),	9.00		
Total unpaid yearly int.		$463.82	
Total int. upon unpaid yearly int.,	$33.83		
Total int. due Oct. 1, 1894,	$497.65		
Am't of pay't Oct. 1, 1894,	$1050.00		
Bal. applied to liquidate the principal ($1050.00 — $497.65),			$552.35
Principal Oct. 1, 1894,			$1746.65
Int. on prin. to Apr. 1, 1895,			52.40
Sum due Apr. 1, 1895,			$1799.05

2. On a note for $2000, given at Concord, N.H., Apr. 1, 1883, with interest annually at 6%, the following payments were made: July 1, 1885, $300; June 1, 1886, $35; Dec. 1, 1887, $500. How much was due Feb. 1, 1889?

3. On a note for $3600, given at Manchester, N.H., Feb. 10, 1886, with interest annually at 6%, the following payments were made: Dec. 10, 1886, $100; Aug. 10, 1888, $600; Sept. 10, 1890, $350. How much was due Mar. 10, 1892?

CONNECTICUT RULE.

The Connecticut court rule for computing the indebtedness upon a note or other obligation, when partial payments have been made, is :

Compute the interest to the time of the first payment, if that be one year or more from the time the interest commenced; add it to the principal, and deduct the payment from the sum total.

If there be after payments made, compute the interest on the balance due to the next payment, and then deduct the payment as above; and in like manner from one payment to another, till all the payments are absorbed, provided the time between one payment and another be one year or more.

But if any payment be made before one year's interest hath accrued, then compute the interest on the principal sum due on the obligation for one year, add it to the principal, and compute the interest on the sum paid, from the time it was paid, up to the end of the year; add it to the sum paid, and deduct that sum from the principal and interest added as above.

If any payments be made of a less sum than the interest arisen at the time of such payment, no interest is to be computed but only on the principal sum for any period.

1. On a note for $ 650, given at Hartford, Conn., June 12, 1890, with interest at 6 %, the following payments were made : July 1, 1891, $ 116.20; Apr. 10, 1892, $ 61.50 ; Feb. 12, 1893, $ 12.10 ; Aug. 20, 1893, $ 110. How much was due Dec. 21, 1893 ?

SOLUTION.

Principal	$ 650.00
Int. to July 1, 1891 (1 yr. 19 da.)	41.06
Amount	$ 691.06
First payment	116.20
New principal	$ 574.86
Int. to July 1, 1892 (second payment being made less than 1 yr. from previous payment)	34.49
Amount	$ 609.35
Am't of 2d pay't from Apr. 10 to July 1, 1892 (2 mo. 21 da.)	62.33
New principal	$ 547.02
Amount to July 1, 1893 (1 yr.)	579.84
Third payment draws no interest, being less than int. due	12.10
New principal	$ 567.74
Amount Dec. 21, 1893 (5 mo. 20 da.)	583.83
Amount of last payment at settlement (4 mo. 1 da.)	112.22
Balance due Dec. 21, 1893	$ 471.61

2. On a note for $1000, given at New Haven, Conn., Feb. 1, 1890, with interest at 6%, the following payments were made: Apr. 1, 1891, $80; Aug. 1, 1891, $30; Oct. 1, 1892, $10; Dec. 1, 1892, $600; May 1, 1893, $200. How much was due Oct. 1, 1893?

3. On a note for $1000, given at Middletown, Conn., Mar. 9, 1890, with interest at 6%, the following payments were made: Nov. 19, 1890, $204; Mar. 3, 1892, $50; June 15, 1893, $600; Nov. 1, 1893, $85. How much was due Jan. 1, 1894?

TAXES.

In Vermont, public revenues are derived from taxes laid on the business of certain corporations, such as railroads, insurance companies, savings banks, etc., from certain licenses and fees, from fines, from collateral inheritance taxes, and largely from *direct taxes* laid upon real and personal property and polls.

The method of computing direct taxes in Vermont varies a little from that adopted in many states. It is as follows:

1. A list of the real estate and personal property, together with a poll list, which is $2 for every male person over 21 and under 70 years of age, is made by the persons authorized by law to appraise the property of the town.

2. Soldiers severely wounded in the Civil War, soldiers of the Civil War honorably discharged having no taxable estate, and persons actually poor are exempt from a poll tax.

3. Real estate used for public, religious, charitable, and educational purposes is for the most part exempt from taxation.

4. United States bonds and certain other stocks and bonds are exempt from taxation; also savings bank deposits to the amount of $1500.

5. Personal property is exempt from taxation to an amount equal to the excess, if any, of the owner's debts over the aggregate amount of his holdings that are exempt according to Note 4; also household goods, farming tools, libraries, etc.

The sum of the poll list and 1% of the taxable real and personal property constitutes what is called the **Grand List** of the town.

The sum of each person's poll tax and 1% of the value of his taxable real and personal property constitutes his grand list.

The state taxes are fixed by the Legislature; ordinary county taxes, by county judges. A town tax is levied by vote of the town, a village tax by vote of the village.

Taxes are levied at a certain number of cents on each dollar of the grand list, or a certain per cent of the grand list.

Thus, the Legislature of 1894 assessed a tax of 12 cents on the dollar for state purposes.

WRITTEN EXERCISES.

1. In the city of Rutland the taxable real estate was $5,531,685, the taxable personal property, $2,135,288, and the taxable polls, 2625. What was the grand list?

SOLUTION.

1% of $5,531,685 = $55,316.85
1% of $2,135,288 =   21,352.88
2625 polls at $2   =   5,250.00
Grand List   = $81,919.73

2. The tax rate for the city of Rutland in 1894 was as follows : for state, 5 cents ; for state schools, 5 cents ; for state roads, 5 cents ; for city highways, 20 cents ; for city schools, 40 cents ; for general city purposes, 65 cents ; for city sinking-fund, 10 cents. What was the tax of a man 50 years of age whose personal property was assessed at $6250, and whose real estate was rated at $21,550?

SOLUTION.

1% of $6250   = $ 62.50
1% of $21,550 =   215.50
Poll tax   =   2.00
His Grand List = $280.00

The sum of the several taxes is 150 cents, therefore the total tax rate is 150% of the grand list, and the man's total tax was

$150% of $280, or $420.

3. The town of Benson raised a town tax of 55%, a state school tax of 12%, and a highway tax of 15% of the grand list. What are the taxes of a man 55 years of age whose real estate is appraised at $4500 and his personal property at $3000?

4. In a certain school district a tax of 15 cents on a dollar of the grand list is to be raised for school purposes. What is the amount of B's school tax who owns a farm valued at $2500?

5. What was the grand list of the town of Lincoln for 1894, if it had 1025 taxable polls, real estate valued at $1,206,175, and personal property worth $835,978? If the town raised $20,295 by taxes, what was the tax upon one dollar of the grand list?

6. What is the tax of a man 72 years old, living in Lincoln, whose real estate is valued at $4225 and personal property at $5000, if in addition to his town tax he pays a state school tax of 10% of his grand list?

ANSWERS.

Page 30. — 2. 2378. **3.** 1892. **4.** 1711. **5.** 3116. **6.** 3328.
7. $29.95. **8.** 3609. **9.** 4007. **10.** $33.72. **11.** $26.00.
12. $24.51. **13.** $30.64. **14.** 27,755. **15.** 36,376. **16.** 36,712.
17. 35,472. **18.** $266.53. **19.** 46,688. **20.** 60,582. **21.** 62,112.
22. $454.49. **23.** $482.40.

Page 31. — 24. 17,070. **25.** 26,273. **26.** $125.99. **27.** $176.64.
28. $97.58. **29.** $44.085. **30.** $252.558. **31.** $50,814. **32.** $96.968.
33. $117.234. **34.** 28,338. **35.** 10,289. **36.** 20,424. **37.** 48,099.
38. 16,803. **39.** 11,377. **40.** 15,247. **41.** 11,773. **42.** 18,604.
43. 14,420. **44.** 8687. **45.** 17,275.

Page 32. — 46. 15,817. **47.** 15,665. **48.** 13,152. **49.** 20,555.
50. 8750. **51.** 8,021,463. **52.** 103,283,772. **53.** 1,028,363,547.
54. 9,101,736,502. **55.** 649,424. **56.** 130,556,589. **57.** 145,770,476.

Page 33. — 58. 723,074,817. **59.** 135,103,556. **60.** 107,823,882.
61. 1,936,123. **62.** 50,451,121. **63.** 146,305,505. **64.** 9089.
65. 6894.

Page 34. — 66. 75,688. **67.** 97,024. **68.** $3200. **69.** $1381.
70. 226,382 shingles ; 106,400 laths. **71.** $5,165,000. **72.** 8774.

Page 35. — 73. 11,240. **74.** 3269. **75.** $41,819. **76.** 55,080.
77. 251,025. **78.** 89,081.

Page 36. — 79. 66,465. **80.** $2353.45, Albany ; $4700.27, New
York ; $7053.72, both. **81.** 11,160. **82.** 14,425, wheat ; 16,740, corn ;
31,165, grain. **83.** 106,618. **84.** $47,492.

Page 37. — 85. 16,201. **86.** 197,680. **87.** 45,050. **88.** 212,482.
89. 91,260 lb. cotton ; 331 hhd. sugar ; 10,550 gal. molasses.

Page 43. — 2. 322. **3.** 144. **4.** 133. **5.** 161. **6.** 122.
7. 4444. **8.** 2222. **9.** 1441. **10.** 1512. **11.** 2721. **12.** $23.52.
13. $34.34. **14.** $32.35. **15.** $31.43. **16.** $32.21.

Page 44. — 17. $31.31. **18.** $10.81. **19.** $14.43. **20.** $32.12.
21. $41.44. **22.** 24,413. **23.** 13,221. **24.** 41,111. **25.** 38,133.
26. 31,155. **27.** 27,312. **28.** 42,253. **29.** 14,542. **30.** 46,112.
31. 24,112. **32.** $220. **33.** $2344. **34.** 1023. **35.** 616.
36. $1113. **37.** 2210. **38.** 3121. **39.** $142.25.

Page 45. — 40. $1123.25. **41.** $333. **42.** 13,211.

Page 47. — 2. 487. **3.** 494. **4.** 283. **5.** 167. **6.** 304. **7.** 119.
8. 416. **9.** 291. **10.** 308.

Page 48. — 11. 276. **12.** 167. **13.** 248. **14.** 482. **15.** 189.
16. 192. **17.** 137. **18.** 324. **19.** 327. **20.** 378. **21.** 189.
22. 426. **23.** 196. **24.** 92. **25.** 343. **26.** 385. **27.** 108.

28. 290. **29**. 220. **30**. 168. **31**. 385. **32**. 7889. **33**. 20,725.
34. 34,724. **35**. 12,827. **36**. 24,298. **37**. 24,588. **38**. 52,583.
39. 10,960. **40**. 21,060. **41**. 17,987. **42**. 40,516. **43**. 34,594.
44. 30,641. **45**. 19,531. **46**. 31,166. **47**. 7200. **48**. 14,207.
49. 28,507. **50**. $122.93. **51**. $195.45. **52**. $196.79. **53**. $21.84.
54. $451.60. **55**. $489.78. **56**. $88.09. **57**. $371.76. **58**. $154.75.
59. $76.98. **60**. $455.79. **61**. $504.28. **62**. $247.74. **63**. $59.72.
64. $60.46. **65**. $264.

Page 49.—**67**. 11,483. **68**. 30,635. **69**. 3907. **70**. 10,261.
71. 14,996. **72**. 11,649. **73**. 26,884. **74**. 53,994. **75**. 751,470.
76. 386,669. **77**. 151,488. **78**. 377,358. **79**. 909,034. **80**. $37,685.17.
81. $29,081.46. **82**. $34,856.97. **83**. $48,169.95. **84**. $38,062.68.
85. $10,764.99. **86**. $25,209.82. **87**. $20,937.06. **88**. 9,115,653.
89. 7,820,961. **90**. 6,642,511. **91**. 5,965,009. **92**. 2,791,654.
93. $2710. **94**. $1890. **95**. 2607. **96**. 1492. **97**. $9175.
Page 50.—**98**. $151. **99**. $683. **100**. 6898. **101**. 6476.
102. $534, gain. **103**. $13,785. **104**. 94,760,000 mi. **105**. $3693.
106. $1895. **107**. $1010.
Page 51.—**108**. $215. **109**. $2390. **110**. $585. **111**. $738, gain.
112. $1350. **113**. $4487. **114**. 45,906. **115**. 303,418. **116**. $9929.
Page 58.—**2**. 1026. **3**. 2064. **4**. 1890. **5**. 1708. **6**. 1629.
7. 3425. **8**. 1137. **9**. 2568. **10**. 1540. **11**. 3095. **12**. 4224.
13. 6324. **14**. 6897. **15**. 7176. **16**. 26,936. **17**. 35,526.
18. 34,020. **19**. 37,709. **20**. 11,824. **21**. 51,258. **22**. 63,328.
23. 31,066. **24**. 39,925. **25**. 59,898. **26**. 62,818. **27**. 103,136.
28. 101,244. **29**. 105,006. **30**. 147,580. **31**. 208,292. **32**. 311,568.
33. 622,242. **34**. 284,235. **35**. 311,632. **36**. 375,201. **37**. 273,875.
38. 691,504. **39**. 547,686. **40**. 494,795. **41**. 358,250. **42**. 733,131.
43. 738,944. **44**. $47.25. **45**. $112.50. **46**. $94.15. **47**. $130.80.
48. $137.55. **49**. $28.75.
Page 59.—**50**. $224.70. **51**. $366. **52**. $69.25. **53**. 31,680.
54. 28,800. **55**. $449.75. **56**. $338.40. **57**. $62.80. **58**. $22.50.
59. $460.25. **60**. $602.80. **61**. 8869 bbl. **62**. 6144. **63**. $4025.
64. $42.75.
Page 61.—**1**. 2740 ; 38,100 ; 9,314,000. **2**. 3860 ; 61,000 ; 8,167,000.
Page 62.—**3**. 4560 ; 90,300 ; 78,300,000. **4**. 3750 ; 85,700 ;
51,690,000. **5**. 3190 ; 31,000 ; 600,800,000. **6**. 4020 ; 41,600 ;
678,500,000. **8**. 7860 ; 244,200 ; 16,690,000. **9**. 14,730 ; 147,800 ;
24,368,000. **10**. 11,360 ; 571,200 ; 20,416,000 **11**. 35,750 ; 396,500 ;
20,514,000. **12**. 29,610 ; 785,600 ; 56,064,000. **13**. 12,640 ; 95,400 ;
53,217,000. **14**. 37,740 ; 256,200 ; 60,718,000. **15**. 15,540 ; 506,700 ;
48,828,000.
Page 63.—**20**. 88,366. **21**. 133,376. **22**. 133,496. **23**. 150,732.
Page 64.—**24**. 148,311. **25**. 375,774. **26**. 201,880. **27**. 282,935.
28. 311,872. **29**. 206,886. **30**. 146,069. **31**. 233,988. **32**. 340,405.
33. 506,785. **34**. 617,064. **35**. 276,250. **36**. 481,663. **37**. 250,098.
38. 489,855. **39**. 619,344. **40**. 591,458. **41**. 11,234,275. **42**. 4,729,104.
43. 19,022,724. **44**. 19,422,156. **45**. 14,424,424. **46**. 11,216,736.
47. 23,103,018. **48**. 13,977,718. **49**. 14,896,404. **50**. 9,765,217.
51. 17,412,096. **52**. 16,571,295. **53**. 39,318,048. **54**. 22,693,488.

55. 221,347,750. **56.** 305,221,392. **57.** 2,026,441,428. **58.** 3,841,167,050.
59. 1,199,528,823. **60.** 1,895,536,280. **61.** 2,361,055,599.
62. $1,833,590.25. **63.** $1,164,998.89. **64.** $2,851,792.00.
65. $2,551,324.02. **66.** $1,533,115.75. **67.** $4,163,565.84.
68. $3,831,397.66. **69.** $2,634,678.20. **70.** $5,574,517.20.
71. $2,155,631.50. **72.** $2,528,601.90. **73.** $1,904,708.16.
74. $1,234,742.52. **75.** $2,853,323.52. **76.** $2,111,073.36.
77. $1,254,133.50. **78.** $1,694,006.08. **79.** $2,842,474.80.

Page 65. —**80.** $361.76. **81.** 1140 mi.; 68,400 mi. **82.** 1287 mi.
83. 256 mi. **84.** $101 gain. **85.** 8073. **86.** 417,872 lb.
87. $470.60. **88.** 134,096. **89.** $517.85.

Page 66. —**90.** $2.80. **91.** $495. **92.** $34. **93.** $11,834.73.
94. $61.20. **95.** $4350. **96.** 545. **97.** $3587.86.

Page 74. —**6.** 906. **7.** 427. **8.** 1284. **9.** 567. **10.** 543.
11. 1066. **12.** 507. **13.** 1221. **14.** 1502. **15.** 1210. **10.** 079.
17. 1065.

Page 75. —**18.** 2646. **19.** 603. **20.** 790. **21.** 1166. **22.** 2292.
23. 1446. **24.** 729. **25.** 947. **26.** 1468. **27.** 490. **28.** $1307\frac{7}{8}$.
29. 603. **30.** 736. **31.** 1704. **32.** 662. **33.** 1496. **34.** 771.
35. 1451. **36.** 923. **37.** 1386. **38.** $692\frac{4}{6}$. **39.** 1245. **40.** 405.
41. 459. **42.** 307. **43.** 451. **44.** 1140. **45.** 1005. **46.** 656.
47. 1058. **48.** 1587. **49.** 661. **50.** 879. **51.** 901. **52.** 837.
53. 793. **54.** 1171. **55.** $522\frac{4}{7}$. **56.** $68,820\frac{1}{5}$. **57.** $70,335\frac{2}{3}$.
58. $97,271\frac{3}{8}$. **59.** 63,804. **60.** $68,598\frac{4}{7}$. **61.** $86.43. **62.** $38.45.
63. $73.47. **64.** $85.40\frac{1}{4}$. **65.** $86.14\frac{3}{5}$. **66.** $85.71\frac{1}{4}$. **67.** $44.17\frac{1}{5}$.
68. $117.04\frac{1}{2}$. **69.** $84.84\frac{4}{5}$. **70.** $34.89\frac{1}{4}$. **71.** $53.70\frac{4}{5}$.
72. $122.45\frac{1}{4}$. **73.** $75.69\frac{3}{5}$. **74.** $43.75\frac{5}{9}$. **75.** $1269\frac{2}{5}$. **76.** 145.
77. 237. **78.** $294.

Page 76. —**79.** 464. **80.** $30.35. **81.** 625. **82.** $5.20.
83. 1142. **84.** $1245. **85.** $2186. **86.** 48. **87.** $13.50.
88. $75.80. **89.** 14,691. **90.** 4087.

Page 77. —**4.** $468\frac{53}{100}$. **5.** $302\frac{78}{100}$. **6.** $385\frac{46}{100}$. **7.** $468\frac{50}{100}$.
8. 317. **9.** $68\frac{543}{1000}$. **10.** $31\frac{927}{1000}$. **11.** $41\frac{687}{1000}$. **12.** $38\frac{125}{1000}$.
13. $41\frac{736}{1000}$. **14.** $54\frac{286}{1000}$. **15.** $3\frac{1854}{10000}$. **16.** $4\frac{8653}{10000}$. **17.** $3\frac{1925}{10000}$.
18. $4\frac{6874}{10000}$. **19.** $7\frac{2840}{10000}$. **20.** $6\frac{1735}{10000}$. **21.** $4\frac{2856}{10000}$.

Page 78. —**23.** $128\frac{5}{10}$. **24.** $123\frac{7}{40}$. **25.** $136\frac{19}{50}$. **26.** $50\frac{9}{18}$.
27. $77\frac{55}{60}$. **28.** $245\frac{357}{500}$. **29.** $116\frac{45}{54}$. **30.** $54\frac{31}{50}$. **31.** $47\frac{213}{50}$.
32. $30\frac{678}{80}$. **33.** $158\frac{857}{2000}$. **34.** $103\frac{3684}{4000}$. **35.** $394\frac{719}{8000}$. **36.** $464\frac{576}{9000}$.
37. $54\frac{4456}{7000}$.

Page 80. —**39.** 313. **40.** 144. **41.** 216. **42.** 384. **43.** 613.
44. 236. **45.** 345. **46.** 435. **47.** 326. **48.** 372. **49.** 856.
50. 756. **51.** 762. **52.** 871. **53.** 453. **54.** 875. **55.** 644.
56. 723. **57.** 834. **58.** 872. **59.** 625. **60.** $576\frac{4}{5}$. **61.** 790.
62. 892. **63.** 785. **64.** 672. **65.** 888. **66.** 916. **67.** 1426.
68. $1274\frac{30}{85}$. **69.** 1347. **70.** 2454. **71.** 3456. **72.** 5834. **73.** 6341.
74. 9850. **75.** 8764. **76.** 7937. **77.** 7777. **78.** 5874. **79.** 7426.
80. 9567. **81.** 56,783. **82.** $53,232\frac{120}{401}$. **83.** $38,507\frac{569}{601}$. **84.** $59,632\frac{25}{510}$.
85. $55,907\frac{258}{610}$. **86.** $72,059\frac{483}{711}$. **87.** $56,311\frac{390}{802}$. **88.** $61,002\frac{327}{608}$.
89. $41,462\frac{53}{518}$. **90.** $60,433\frac{474}{724}$. **91.** $66,801\frac{702}{802}$. **92.** $54,568\frac{563}{631}$.
93. $71,114\frac{424}{911}$. **94.** $73,471\frac{412}{932}$. **95.** $90,639\frac{581}{807}$. **96.** $54,066\frac{521}{717}$.

442 ANSWERS.

97. $75,572\frac{540}{722}$.   98. $73,439\frac{512}{834}$.   99. $79,098\frac{820}{950}$.   100. $50,422\frac{424}{856}$.

101. $68,816\frac{261}{923}$.   102. $79,977\frac{284}{731}$.   103. $82,786\frac{489}{673}$.   104. $72,672\frac{164}{564}$.

Page 81.—105. $30,416\frac{937}{1047}$.   106. $18,388\frac{1146}{3109}$.   107. $16,267\frac{5050}{5138}$.

108. $18,383\frac{3263}{7408}$.   109. $28,956\frac{4606}{8346}$.   110. $39,514\frac{7286}{9215}$.   111. $51,410\frac{5941}{7843}$.

112. $78,428\frac{6336}{9618}$.   113. $36.   114. 217.   115. 342.   116. 72.

117. 3867.   118. 450.   119. 541.   120. $136\frac{360}{365}$.   121. $260\frac{80}{320}$.

122. 31.   123. 450.

Page 82.—124. 625.   125. 25.   126. 200 da.   127. 3520.

128. 190.   129. $4090.   130. 31.   131. 39, and 420 sq. miles over.   132. 5, and 19,930 sq. miles over.

Page 83.—3. 56.   4. 21.   5. 6.   6. 7.   7. 4.   8. 32.   9. 26.

10. 27.   11. 2.   12. 21.   13. 115.   14. 321.   15. 270.   16. 6.   17. 31.

Page 86.—2. 5.   3. $110.50.   4. $1.56.   5. $134.

Page 87.—6. $1493.   7. 70.   8. 115.   9. 74.   10. 327.

11. 96.   12. $125.   13. 463.   14. $11,640.   16. $28,400.

Page 88.—17. $13.75.   18. $384.   19. $88, loss.   20. 264 mi.

21. 549 mi.   22. 40.   23. 975.   24. 13.   25. 10,586 gal.

Page 89.—26. $3985.   27. $361\frac{9}{31}$.   28. 7.   29. 3070.   30. 1704.

31. 1383.   32. 180,604,125.   33. 3007.   34. $626, gain.   35. 10.

36. $3.50.   37. $132.

Page 90.—38. 50.   39. $33.41.   40. $576.15.   41. $5614.   42. 6.

43. $270, horse; $180, buggy.   44. 115.   45. $56.   46. 110.

47. $510\frac{140}{186}$.

Page 95.—2. $3^2, 5$.   3. $2^2, 3, 7$.   4. 5^3.   5. $2, 3, 5, 7$.

6. $3^2, 5, 7$.   7. $2^4, 3^3$.   8. $2, 3, 5, 11$.   9. $2^2, 11^2$.   10. $2^3, 3^2, 5$.

11. $2, 3, 131$.   12. $2^4, 3^2, 13$.   13. $2, 3, 5, 7, 11$.   14. $3^2, 5, 7, 11$.

15. $3^2, 5, 7^2$.   16. $2^2, 3^2, 5^2, 7$.   17. $2^2, 3, 7^2, 13$.   18. $2, 11, 13, 17$.

19. $2, 5, 7, 47$.   20. $2^2, 3, 5, 7, 11$.   21. $2^6, 7^2$.   22. $2^2, 953$.

23. $7^2, 11, 13$.   24. $2, 3, 5^2, 29$.   25. $2^3, 7^2, 29$.   26. $2^{10}, 3, 7$.

27. $2, 5, 7, 11, 13$.   28. $2^6, 5, 101$.   29. $2^{10}, 5^2$.   30. $2^7, 503$.

31. $2, 5, 7, 11, 41$.   32. $2^2, 5^3, 97$.   33. $2^9, 3^5$.

Page 96.—2. 36.   3. 48.   4. 21.   5. $4\frac{1}{4}$.

Page 97.—6. $5\frac{2}{5}$.   7. $13\frac{1}{2}$.   8. $6\frac{7}{8}$.   9. 315.   10. 2.   11. 133.

12. 24.   13. 10.   14. 105.   15. 90.   16. $25\frac{5}{7}$.   17. 444.   18. 84.

19. $197\frac{1}{4}$.   20. 192.   21. $31\frac{1}{2}$.   22. 99.   23. 72.   24. 5440.

25. $257\frac{13}{16}$.   26. $78\frac{1}{4}$.   27. 5700.   28. 45.   29. 27.

Page 98.—30. $4\frac{1}{2}$.   31. 40.   32. $1.20.   33. 19.   34. 306.

35. 50¢.   36. 48.   37. 54.   38. $6\frac{2}{5}$.   39. 36.

Page 103.—2. $\frac{26}{70}$.   3. $\frac{28}{54}$.   4. $\frac{24}{64}$.   5. $\frac{36}{58}$.   6. $\frac{57}{78}$.   7. $\frac{45}{93}$.

8. $\frac{36}{84}$.   9. $\frac{66}{108}$.   10. $\frac{93}{135}$.   11. $\frac{54}{216}$.   12. $\frac{126}{162}$.   13. $\frac{153}{111}$.   14. $\frac{126}{144}$.

15. $\frac{110}{168}$.   16. $\frac{132}{212}$.   17. $\frac{84}{180}$.   18. $\frac{108}{219}$.   19. $\frac{100}{236}$.   20. $\frac{108}{152}$.   21. $\frac{100}{196}$.

22. $\frac{215}{355}$.

Page 104.—2. $\frac{1}{3}$; $\frac{2}{3}$.   3. $\frac{1}{2}$; $\frac{3}{4}$.   4. $\frac{2}{3}$; $\frac{1}{3}$.   5. $\frac{4}{5}$; $\frac{1}{2}$.   6. $\frac{3}{8}$; $\frac{3}{4}$.

7. $\frac{1}{2}$; $\frac{5}{6}$.   8. $\frac{8}{15}$; $\frac{16}{19}$.   9. $\frac{11}{19}$; $\frac{7}{9}$.   10. $\frac{11}{16}$; $\frac{3}{8}$.   11. $\frac{2}{3}$; $\frac{3}{4}$.   12. $\frac{1}{2}$; $\frac{5}{7}$.

13. $\frac{5}{11}$; $\frac{7}{15}$. **14.** $\frac{11}{36}$; $\frac{35}{52}$. **15.** $\frac{5}{7}$; $\frac{2}{3}$. **16.** $\frac{8}{9}$; $\frac{9}{31}$. **17.** $\frac{7}{8}$; $\frac{4}{7}$. **18.** $\frac{5}{9}$; $\frac{4}{5}$.
19. $\frac{3}{5}$; $\frac{7}{9}$. **20.** $\frac{11}{12}$; $\frac{13}{14}$. **21.** $\frac{10}{13}$; $\frac{7}{11}$. **22.** $\frac{1}{3}$; $\frac{5}{8}$. **23.** $\frac{16}{25}$; $\frac{1}{3}$.
24. $\frac{12}{23}$; $\frac{13}{7}$. **25.** $\frac{9}{7}$; $\frac{7}{11}$. **26.** $\frac{3}{4}$; $\frac{1}{4}$. **27.** $\frac{3}{4}$; $\frac{1}{11}$. **28.** $\frac{13}{14}$; $\frac{7}{10}$.
29. $\frac{5}{6}$; $\frac{2}{3}$. **30.** $\frac{7}{11}$; $\frac{5}{8}$. **31.** $\frac{11}{20}$; $\frac{21}{23}$. **32.** $\frac{11}{12}$; $\frac{1}{5}$. **33.** $\frac{3}{5}$; $\frac{7}{11}$.
34. $\frac{8}{9}$; $\frac{9}{10}$. **35.** $\frac{7}{11}$; $\frac{11}{12}$. **36.** $\frac{6}{7}$; $\frac{17}{29}$. **37.** $\frac{1}{3}$; $\frac{11}{34}$. **38.** $\frac{7}{8}$; $\frac{5}{11}$.
39. $\frac{8}{9}$; $\frac{5}{6}$. **40.** $\frac{22}{41}$; $\frac{107}{117}$. **41.** $\frac{13}{14}$; $\frac{41}{61}$.

Page 106. — **2.** $\frac{169}{9}$. **3.** $\frac{197}{8}$. **4.** $\frac{369}{10}$. **5.** $\frac{527}{7}$. **6.** $\frac{701}{13}$. **7.** $\frac{1034}{17}$.
8. $\frac{663}{18}$. **9.** $\frac{929}{19}$. **10.** $\frac{1039}{20}$. **11.** $\frac{1721}{25}$. **12.** $\frac{2691}{37}$. **13.** $\frac{8876}{99}$.
14. $\frac{10117}{24}$. **15.** $\frac{9733}{28}$. **16.** $\frac{17803}{42}$. **17.** $\frac{22095}{49}$. **18.** $\frac{38854}{81}$. **19.** $\frac{35997}{90}$.
20. $\frac{24740}{47}$. **21.** $\frac{15898}{25}$. **22.** $\frac{34451}{72}$. **23.** $\frac{53492}{77}$. **24.** $\frac{64867}{81}$. **25.** $\frac{81541}{100}$.
26. $\frac{120}{5}$; $\frac{104}{8}$; $\frac{315}{7}$; $\frac{444}{12}$; $\frac{555}{15}$; $\frac{408}{17}$; $\frac{900}{25}$; $\frac{1640}{40}$.

Page 107. — **2.** $6\frac{8}{15}$; $2\frac{6}{23}$. **3.** $7\frac{1}{4}$; $3\frac{5}{21}$. **4.** 7; $2\frac{22}{25}$. **5.** $5\frac{1}{7}$; 3.
6. $6\frac{9}{14}$; $2\frac{7}{43}$. **7.** $4\frac{12}{61}$; $1\frac{26}{61}$. **8.** $5\frac{1}{2}$; $3\frac{17}{27}$. **9.** $9\frac{1}{3}$; $5\frac{13}{27}$. **10.** $5\frac{24}{31}$; $6\frac{1}{39}$.
11. $6\frac{5}{11}$; $5\frac{30}{47}$. **12.** $6\frac{9}{57}$; $6\frac{34}{67}$. **13.** $20\frac{14}{25}$; 15. **14.** $12\frac{17}{17}$; $10\frac{61}{69}$.
15. $10\frac{38}{79}$; $8\frac{40}{43}$. **16.** $96\frac{19}{56}$. **17.** $90\frac{4}{55}$. **18.** $93\frac{53}{56}$. **19.** $77\frac{26}{63}$.
20. $81\frac{13}{19}$. **21.** $110\frac{1}{7}$. **22.** 121. **23.** $295\frac{9}{32}$. **24.** $343\frac{7}{15}$. **25.** $392\frac{88}{123}$.
26. $239\frac{32}{75}$. **27.** $170\frac{9}{157}$. **28.** $172\frac{221}{375}$. **29.** $189\frac{41}{200}$.

Page 108. — **2.** $\frac{9}{12}$; $\frac{10}{12}$; $\frac{5}{12}$. **3.** $\frac{6}{8}$; $\frac{4}{8}$; $\frac{5}{8}$. **4.** $\frac{6}{12}$; $\frac{8}{12}$; $\frac{9}{12}$. **5.** $\frac{12}{16}$;
$\frac{10}{16}$; $\frac{7}{16}$. **6.** $\frac{15}{30}$; $\frac{14}{30}$; $\frac{8}{30}$. **7.** $\frac{15}{24}$; $\frac{10}{24}$; $\frac{5}{24}$. **8.** $\frac{20}{24}$; $\frac{15}{24}$; $\frac{10}{24}$. **9.** $\frac{14}{24}$;
$\frac{5}{24}$; $\frac{20}{24}$. **10.** $\frac{15}{20}$; $\frac{8}{20}$; $\frac{6}{20}$. **11.** $\frac{18}{30}$; $\frac{25}{30}$; $\frac{2}{30}$. **12.** $\frac{18}{60}$; $\frac{9}{60}$; $\frac{6}{60}$.
13. $\frac{48}{60}$; $\frac{25}{60}$; $\frac{21}{60}$. **14.** $\frac{25}{45}$; $\frac{15}{45}$; $\frac{27}{45}$. **15.** $\frac{16}{36}$; $\frac{7}{36}$; $\frac{14}{36}$. **16.** $\frac{5}{24}$; $\frac{6}{24}$;
$\frac{14}{24}$. **17.** $1\frac{4}{32}$; $\frac{20}{32}$; $\frac{11}{32}$. **18.** $\frac{6}{24}$; $\frac{8}{24}$; $\frac{2}{24}$. **19.** $\frac{4}{20}$; $\frac{15}{20}$; $\frac{6}{20}$; $\frac{7}{20}$.
20. $\frac{12}{28}$; $\frac{10}{28}$; $\frac{9}{28}$; $\frac{14}{28}$. **21.** $\frac{18}{60}$; $\frac{48}{60}$; $\frac{21}{60}$; $\frac{18}{60}$. **22.** $\frac{66}{88}$; $\frac{32}{88}$; $\frac{20}{88}$; $\frac{33}{88}$.
23. $\frac{18}{42}$; $\frac{14}{42}$; $\frac{36}{42}$; $\frac{15}{42}$. **24.** $\frac{16}{36}$; $\frac{5}{36}$; $\frac{16}{36}$; $\frac{27}{36}$. **25.** $\frac{48}{88}$; $\frac{28}{88}$; $\frac{18}{88}$; $\frac{33}{88}$.

Page 109. — **27.** $\frac{18}{24}$; $\frac{20}{24}$; $\frac{21}{24}$; $\frac{14}{24}$. **28.** $\frac{18}{72}$; $\frac{27}{72}$; $\frac{60}{72}$; $\frac{56}{72}$.
29. $\frac{8}{16}$; $\frac{12}{16}$; $\frac{10}{16}$; $\frac{7}{16}$. **30.** $\frac{12}{30}$; $\frac{25}{30}$; $\frac{14}{30}$; $\frac{11}{30}$. **31.** $\frac{24}{40}$; $\frac{28}{40}$; $\frac{22}{40}$; $\frac{13}{40}$.
32. $\frac{14}{42}$; $\frac{24}{42}$; $\frac{35}{42}$; $\frac{16}{42}$. **33.** $\frac{3}{72}$; $\frac{42}{72}$; $\frac{22}{72}$; $\frac{57}{72}$. **34.** $\frac{80}{120}$; $\frac{24}{120}$; $\frac{105}{120}$; $\frac{100}{120}$.
35. $\frac{18}{60}$; $\frac{28}{60}$; $\frac{27}{60}$; $\frac{26}{60}$. **36.** $\frac{35}{84}$; $\frac{32}{84}$; $\frac{33}{84}$; $\frac{26}{84}$. **37.** $\frac{36}{60}$; $\frac{55}{60}$; $\frac{27}{60}$; $\frac{29}{60}$.
38. $\frac{140}{315}$; $\frac{117}{315}$; $\frac{161}{315}$; $\frac{85}{315}$. **39.** $\frac{77}{99}$; $\frac{45}{99}$; $\frac{88}{99}$; $\frac{27}{99}$. **40.** $\frac{39}{143}$; $\frac{66}{143}$; $\frac{85}{143}$;
$\frac{11}{143}$. **41.** $\frac{54}{90}$; $\frac{45}{90}$; $\frac{70}{90}$; $\frac{24}{90}$. **42.** $\frac{64}{84}$; $\frac{63}{84}$; $\frac{66}{84}$; $\frac{72}{84}$. **43.** $\frac{252}{924}$; $\frac{132}{924}$; $\frac{770}{924}$;
$\frac{231}{924}$. **44.** $\frac{44}{120}$; $\frac{64}{120}$; $\frac{20}{120}$; $\frac{7}{120}$. **45.** $\frac{322}{70}$; $\frac{460}{70}$; $\frac{55}{70}$; $\frac{63}{70}$. **46.** $\frac{476}{63}$; $\frac{594}{63}$;
$\frac{546}{63}$; $\frac{255}{63}$.

Page 112. — **3.** $2\frac{25}{36}$. **4.** $2\frac{1}{4}$. **5.** $1\frac{10}{21}$. **6.** $2\frac{5}{72}$. **7.** $2\frac{23}{28}$. **8.** $2\frac{53}{56}$.
9. $2\frac{19}{36}$. **10.** $2\frac{1}{4}$. **11.** 2. **12.** $1\frac{4}{15}$. **13.** 2. **14.** $1\frac{1}{2}$. **15.** $1\frac{7}{20}$.
16. $2\frac{43}{144}$. **17.** $1\frac{13}{18}$. **18.** $2\frac{47}{72}$. **19.** $1\frac{13}{18}$. **20.** $1\frac{133}{144}$. **21.** $2\frac{31}{2}$.
22. $2\frac{97}{168}$. **23.** $3\frac{19}{70}$. **24.** $3\frac{49}{360}$. **25.** $2\frac{533}{720}$. **26.** $2\frac{7}{18}$. **27.** $1\frac{103}{144}$.
28. $2\frac{71}{18}$. **29.** $22\frac{33}{40}$. **30.** $22\frac{7}{24}$. **31.** $19\frac{8}{35}$. **32.** $22\frac{11}{12}$. **33.** $17\frac{65}{72}$.
34. $16\frac{9}{14}$. **35.** $24\frac{44}{45}$. **36.** $49\frac{13}{45}$. **37.** $61\frac{7}{30}$. **38.** $147\frac{25}{36}$. **39.** $101\frac{157}{210}$.
40. $96\frac{103}{230}$. **41.** $84\frac{23}{42}$.

Page 113. — **42.** $425\frac{13}{24}$ lb. **43.** $2610\frac{51}{60}$ bu. **44.** $157\frac{23}{24}$ yd.
45. $813\frac{9}{16}$ lb. **46.** $\$36\frac{1}{2}$. **47.** $\$273\frac{11}{20}$. **48.** $20\frac{5}{12}$ yr. **49.** $157\frac{25}{112}$ mi.
50. $17\frac{19}{40}$ yd.; $\$68\frac{13}{30}$. **51.** B, $31\frac{1}{4}$; C, $44\frac{3}{4}$; all, $89\frac{1}{2}$ A. **52.** $50\frac{367}{720}$ A.
53. $105\frac{79}{240}$ mi.

Page 115. — **3.** $\frac{11}{40}$. **4.** $\frac{13}{33}$. **5.** $\frac{5}{26}$. **6.** $\frac{13}{30}$. **7.** $\frac{23}{45}$. **8.** $\frac{3}{13}$.

9. $\frac{47}{75}$. **10.** $\frac{28}{117}$. **11.** $\frac{59}{570}$. **12.** $\frac{74}{525}$. **13.** $\frac{11}{40}$. **14.** $\frac{34}{175}$. **15.** $\frac{28}{585}$.
16. $\frac{3}{17}$. **17.** $\frac{83}{330}$. **18.** $\frac{4}{39}$. **19.** $\frac{107}{248}$. **20.** $\frac{51}{80}$. **21.** $\frac{49}{120}$. **22.** $\frac{29}{34}$.
23. $\frac{53}{105}$. **24.** $\frac{17}{150}$. **25.** $\frac{47}{80}$. **26.** $\frac{9}{14}$.

Page 116.—27. $\frac{205}{616}$. **28.** $\frac{59}{90}$. **29.** $\frac{3}{25}$. **30.** $\frac{229}{1190}$. **31.** $\frac{1}{4}$.
32. $\frac{19}{132}$. **33.** $1\frac{11}{12}$. **34.** $2\frac{11}{24}$. **35.** $5\frac{8}{15}$. **36.** $3\frac{19}{21}$. **37.** $4\frac{91}{120}$.
38. $2\frac{173}{210}$. **39.** $4\frac{1}{4}$. **40.** $2\frac{19}{36}$. **41.** $5\frac{47}{50}$. **42.** $1\frac{1}{60}$. **43.** $\frac{281}{420}$.
44. $1\frac{13}{45}$. **45.** $7\frac{1}{4}$. **46.** $\frac{73}{120}$. **47.** $\frac{87}{88}$. **48.** $\frac{19}{60}$. **49.** $1\frac{23}{63}$.
50. $18\frac{39}{60}$. **51.** $15\frac{34}{63}$. **52.** $10\frac{1}{120}$. **53.** $4\frac{1}{5}$. **54.** $6\frac{1}{12}$. **55.** $6\frac{71}{72}$.
56. $15\frac{3}{7}$. **57.** $10\frac{5}{9}$. **58.** $24\frac{1}{24}$ yd. **59.** $\frac{91}{200}$ A. **60.** $23\frac{53}{80}$ yd.
61. $\$.81\frac{1}{2}$. **62.** Increased $\frac{2}{9}$.

Page 118.—2. $\frac{8}{15}$. **3.** $\frac{1}{4}$. **4.** 1. **5.** $\frac{2}{5}$. **6.** $\frac{3}{7}$. **7.** $\frac{5}{12}$.

Page 119.—8. $\frac{3}{5}$. **9.** $\frac{20}{99}$. **10.** $1\frac{1}{8}$. **11.** $\frac{1}{15}$. **12.** $\frac{5}{7}$. **13.** $\frac{9}{50}$.
14. $\frac{45}{256}$. **15.** $\frac{12}{35}$. **16.** $\frac{7}{20}$. **17.** 1. **18.** $\frac{9}{128}$. **19.** $\frac{2}{3}$. **20.** $1\frac{1}{14}$.
21. 3. **22.** 9. **23.** $2\frac{1}{17}$. **24.** $20\frac{2}{5}$. **25.** $4\frac{2}{3}$. **26.** $1\frac{11}{28}$. **27.** 1.
28. $5\frac{2}{5}$. **30.** 189. **31.** 375. **32.** $488\frac{1}{4}$. **33.** $662\frac{2}{3}$. **34.** 1544.
35. 770. **36.** $1693\frac{3}{16}$. **37.** 1263. **38.** $776\frac{2}{3}$. **39.** 998. **40.** $1174\frac{1}{2}$.
41. $891\frac{1}{4}$. **42.** $1045\frac{1}{2}$. **43.** $460\frac{5}{9}$. **44.** $1059\frac{2}{3}$.

Page 120.—46. 95. **47.** 129. **48.** 413. **49.** 539. **50.** 488.
51. 515. **52.** 675. **53.** 366. **54.** $239\frac{1}{5}$. **55.** $510\frac{7}{8}$. **56.** $427\frac{3}{4}$.
57. $202\frac{5}{9}$. **58.** $433\frac{1}{8}$. **59.** $607\frac{4}{8}$. **60.** 87. **61.** $199\frac{1}{2}$. **62.** 175.
63. $238\frac{1}{8}$. **64.** $171\frac{3}{8}$. **65.** $170\frac{4}{5}$. **66.** 244. **67.** 248. **68.** $172\frac{2}{7}$.
69. $249\frac{2}{3}$. **70.** $248\frac{1}{12}$. **71.** $273\frac{22}{25}$. **72.** 790. **73.** $507\frac{13}{15}$. **74.** $407\frac{13}{18}$.
75. $337\frac{1}{2}$. **76.** $1026\frac{2}{3}$. **77.** $582\frac{2}{3}$. **78.** 629. **79.** 912. **80.** $1432\frac{7}{8}$.
81. $1414\frac{7}{8}$. **82.** 2937. **83.** $1633\frac{88}{117}$. **84.** $634\frac{2}{3}$. **85.** 1406.
86. $1712\frac{3}{8}$. **87.** $2244\frac{3}{4}$. **88.** $\$5\frac{2}{25}$. **89.** $\$45$. **90.** $\$25$.
91. $\$27\frac{11}{32}$. **92.** $\$116\frac{33}{50}$.

Page 121.—93. $\$611\frac{1}{4}$. **94.** $\$2\frac{17}{20}$. **95.** $\$105\frac{5}{9}$. **96.** $\$16\frac{3}{8}$.
97. $\$121\frac{1}{2}$. **98.** $\$62\frac{1}{8}$. **99.** $\$10,455$. **100.** $235\frac{3}{8}$ lb. **101.** $\$11\frac{11}{15}$.
102. $508\frac{1}{2}$ mi. **103.** $\$129\frac{1}{5}$. **104.** A, $\$33\frac{1}{3}$; B, $\$41\frac{2}{3}$. **105.** $382\frac{1}{2}$ ft.
106. $\$35\frac{1}{4}$. **107.** $278\frac{1}{2}$ mi.

Page 123.—2. $\frac{5}{7}$. **3.** $\frac{2}{5}$. **4.** $\frac{10}{27}$. **5.** $1\frac{1}{4}$. **6.** $\frac{5}{7}$. **7.** $\frac{14}{25}$. **8.** $\frac{34}{75}$.
9. $\frac{30}{47}$. **10.** $1\frac{1}{27}$. **11.** $2\frac{6}{29}$. **12.** $\frac{5}{6}$. **13.** $\frac{20}{23}$. **14.** $\frac{6}{7}$. **15.** $\frac{133}{338}$. **16.** $\frac{27}{55}$.
17. $2\frac{2}{3}$. **18.** $17\frac{1}{2}$. **19.** $14\frac{2}{3}$. **20.** $10\frac{2}{3}$. **21.** $12\frac{3}{5}$. **22.** $10\frac{2}{7}$. **23.** $11\frac{3}{8}$.
24. $5\frac{1}{4}$. **25.** $3\frac{3}{8}$. **26.** $1\frac{2}{3}$. **27.** $6\frac{1}{3}$. **28.** 10. **29.** 8. **30.** $3\frac{1}{3}$. **31.** $2\frac{26}{63}$.
32. $1\frac{2}{5}$. **33.** $2\frac{2}{13}$. **34.** 4. **35.** $5\frac{11}{15}$. **36.** $4\frac{2}{5}$. **37.** $5\frac{1}{3}$. **38.** $5\frac{1}{30}$.
39. $\frac{1}{14}$. **40.** $\frac{3}{46}$. **41.** $\frac{4}{133}$. **42.** $\frac{1}{26}$. **43.** $\frac{27}{70}$. **44.** $\frac{1}{46}$. **45.** $\frac{2}{99}$.

Page 124.—46. $\frac{45}{3136}$. **47.** $\frac{1}{8}$. **48.** $\frac{5}{8}$. **49.** $\frac{10}{49}$. **50.** $\frac{2}{21}$. **51.** $\frac{665}{2013}$.
52. $\frac{9}{184}$. **53.** $\frac{1}{99}$. **54.** $1\frac{43}{128}$. **55.** $2\frac{1}{5}$. **56.** $11\frac{319}{1539}$. **57.** $129\frac{16}{81}$.
58. $11\frac{37}{45}$. **59.** $\frac{904}{1125}$. **60.** $1\frac{463}{572}$. **61.** $\frac{861}{968}$. **62.** $\frac{6}{575}$. **63.** $\frac{5760}{33761}$.
64. $2\frac{767}{1944}$. **65.** $\frac{4216}{30375}$. **66.** $\frac{1001}{2784}$. **67.** $\frac{1805}{5832}$. **69.** $\frac{7}{24}$. **70.** $4\frac{4463}{35328}$.
71. $\frac{5681}{34020}$. **72.** $\frac{455}{19584}$. **73.** $17\frac{333}{13312}$. **74.** $\frac{1701}{490100}$. **75.** $6\frac{14923}{119952}$.
76. $1\frac{2729}{7911}$.

Page 125.—78. $4\frac{23}{30}$. **79.** $4\frac{29}{72}$. **80.** $8\frac{40}{49}$. **81.** $10\frac{23}{40}$. **82.** $5\frac{5}{32}$.
83. $5\frac{21}{64}$. **84.** $5\frac{3}{5}$. **85.** $4\frac{2}{27}$. **86.** $4\frac{23}{30}$. **87.** $4\frac{1}{49}$. **88.** $3\frac{29}{56}$.

89. $6\frac{13}{23}$. **90.** $6\frac{16}{21}$. **91.** $5\frac{9}{40}$. **92.** $8\frac{7}{18}$. **94.** $7\frac{1}{2}$. **95.** $12\frac{6}{17}$.
96. $5\frac{9}{13}$. **97.** $6\frac{3}{14}$. **98.** $10\frac{22}{41}$. **99.** $7\frac{19}{23}$. **100.** $6\frac{18}{51}$. **101.** $5\frac{20}{31}$.
102. 6. **103.** $2\frac{31}{34}$. **104.** $8\frac{16}{21}$. **105.** $3\frac{1}{13}$. **106.** $7\frac{1}{22}$ yd. **107.** 11 bbl.
108. $8\frac{16}{17}$ hr.

Page 126.—**109.** $10\frac{16}{19}$ da. **110.** $1\frac{73}{90}$. **111.** 10 children.
112. 80 pairs. **113.** $4\frac{2}{5}$. **114.** $74\frac{2}{7}$ yd. **115.** $147\frac{37}{84}$ lb. **116.** $25\frac{47}{84}$ bu.
117. 2112 steps. **118.** $202\frac{13}{25}$ A. **119.** 63¢, or $\$\frac{63}{100}$. **120.** $23\frac{1}{5}$ bu.
121. $\$1081\frac{13}{18}$. **122.** $\$11\frac{2}{3}$. **123.** $\$5\frac{17}{55}$.

Page 127.—**2.** $\frac{13}{21}$. **3.** $\frac{10}{27}$. **4.** $1\frac{4}{5}$. **5.** $1\frac{1}{2}$. **6.** $1\frac{5}{13}$. **7.** 10.
8. 27. **9.** $\frac{7}{12}$. **10.** 80. **11.** $67\frac{1}{2}$. **12.** $2\frac{3}{8}$. **13.** $16\frac{1}{4}$. **14.** $3\frac{7}{27}$.
15. $3\frac{95}{144}$. **16.** $68\frac{3}{4}$. **17.** $2\frac{67}{75}$. **18.** $2\frac{13}{16}$. **19.** $1\frac{179}{900}$. **20.** $1\frac{935}{1592}$.
21. $1\frac{107}{441}$.

Page 128.—**10.** $\frac{8}{25}$. **11.** $1\frac{3}{48}$. **12.** $\frac{3}{10}$. **13.** $1\frac{1}{52}$. **14.** $\frac{1}{24}$.
15. $\frac{4}{75}$. **16.** $\frac{1}{49}$. **17.** $1\frac{3}{175}$. **19.** $\frac{4}{9}$. **20.** $\frac{25}{52}$. **21.** $1\frac{6}{57}$. **22.** $\frac{20}{31}$.
23. $\frac{3}{8}$. **24.** $\frac{9}{15}$. **25.** $1\frac{4}{8}$. **26.** $\frac{3}{4}$. **27.** $\frac{30}{43}$. **28.** $\frac{4}{57}$. **29.** $\frac{42}{73}$.
30. $\frac{64}{73}$. **31.** 20 times. **32.** 10 times. **33.** $11\frac{7}{8}$ times. **34.** $10\frac{2}{7}$ times.
36. $\frac{4}{8}$. **37.** $\frac{45}{32}$. **38.** $\frac{2}{3}$. **39.** $\frac{65}{124}$. **40.** $\frac{4}{3}$. **41.** $1\frac{3}{25}$. **42.** $\frac{17}{37}$.
43. $\frac{33}{76}$. **44.** $\frac{65}{124}$. **45.** $\frac{41}{54}$. **46.** $\frac{77}{108}$. **47.** $1\frac{117}{175}$. **48.** $\frac{8}{9}$. **49.** $\frac{21}{20}$.
50. $\frac{55}{48}$. **51.** $\frac{27}{20}$.

Page 129.—**2.** 240. **3.** 240. **4.** 220. **5.** 216. **6.** 320. **7.** 280.
8. 288. **9.** 495. **10.** 360. **11.** 312. **12.** 608. **13.** 882. **14.** 913.
15. 1027. **16.** 1065. **17.** 600. **18.** 1050. **19.** 930. **20.** 1044.
21. 800. **22.** $810. **23.** $3360. **24.** $3237\frac{7}{9}$. **25.** $132.30.
26. $34.64. **27.** 2212 books.

Page 130.—**28.** 2464 bu. **29.** $4308. **30.** 1820 bu. **31.** $452.04.
32. $2288. **33.** $47,500. **34.** 5280 ft. **35.** $42,000. **36.** Mr. B.,
$56. **37.** $2322. **38.** $5080.

Page 135.—**1.** $155\frac{17}{120}$. **2.** $\$8\frac{7}{8}$. **3.** $11\frac{23}{24}$ hr.

Page 136.—**4.** $\$14.58\frac{1}{3}$. **5.** $9065\frac{3}{8}$. **6.** $289\frac{3}{8}$ A. **7.** $33\frac{7}{121}$ sq. rd.
8. $8873. **9.** Increased $\frac{4}{45}$. **10.** Diminished $\frac{4}{9}$. **11.** $46. **12.** 800
lb. **13.** $1\frac{23}{280}$. **14.** $\frac{9}{112}$. **15.** $27\frac{1}{5}$ gal. **16.** $20\frac{500}{747}$¢.

Page 137.—**17.** $75\frac{2}{3}$. **18.** A, $1704 ; B, $1597\frac{1}{2}$; C, $958\frac{1}{2}$.
19. $1\frac{23}{33}$. **20.** 24 bu. **21.** $128\frac{4}{6}$¢. **22.** $1\frac{79}{81}$. **23.** $9\frac{123843}{218448}$.
24. 6. **25.** $44\frac{7}{10}$. **26.** $6.25. **27.** $3\frac{3}{4}$ T.

Page 138.—**28.** A, $\frac{607}{1200}$ mi. **29.** $825. **30.** $19,312\frac{1}{2}$. **31.** $1440.
33. $\frac{91}{1920}$. **34.** Corn, 48 ; wheat, $21\frac{1}{3}$; oats, $10\frac{2}{3}$. **35.** $2.55\frac{3}{4}$.

Page 139.—**36.** $7466\frac{2}{3}$. **37.** $1662\frac{5}{56}$. **38.** $8\frac{3}{4}$. **39.** $1252 ;
$2921\frac{1}{3}$. **40.** $31\frac{7}{10}$. **41.** $11\frac{57}{100}$. **42.** 36 da. **43.** $64. **44.** $12\frac{4}{5}$.
45. $76\frac{7}{10}$. **46.** $.84\frac{19}{64}$.

Page 140.—**47.** A, $6.20 ; B, $9.30. **48.** 1st, $10\frac{10}{17}$; 2d, $9\frac{7}{17}$.
49. B, by $\frac{10}{11}$ hr. **50.** 36 hr. **51.** $34\frac{4}{5}$. **52.** A, $4500 ; B, $5000.
53. 8 children. **54.** R, $1260 ; Q, $896 ; W, $1204 ; cost of drove,
$3360. **55.** $3\frac{700}{1020}$. **56.** $1\frac{144}{409}$. **57.** $2000

Page 141.—**58.** $31,733\frac{1}{3}$. **59.** $1558\frac{12}{32}$. **60.** $1125. **61.** $286\frac{13}{32}$.

62. 74 121/150 yd. 63. $14,875. 64. The 1st, 2 1/3 gal. more per min.
65. Gain $56. 66. 2 17/84. 67. $1520.

Page 142. — 68. 1st, $961 4661/6649; 2d, $768 3643/6649; 3d, $619 4994/6649.
69. 1st, $50 199/2095; 2d, $18 1896/2095. 70. $106 3/4. 71. 5 3/5 bu. 72. $3 7457/9706.
73. Value of estate, $105,495; elder brother, $40,575; younger, $31,648 1/2; sister, $33,271 1/2. 74. 263/2000. 75. 62 475/1081 da.

Page 143. — 76. 16 2/3 hr. 77. $1 1/8. 78. 1st, $35; 2d, $40.
79. $45,937 1/2. 80. 3 61/132. 81. A, 28 days; B, 21 days. 82. $9468.
83. 9 1/3 hr.

Page 148. — 2. 1/4. 3. 3/4. 4. 13/20. 5. 13/25. 6. 19/50. 7. 16/25. 8. 3/8. 9. 7/8.

Page 149. — 10. 87/200. 11. 71/125. 12. 81/200. 13. 127/200. 14. 3/80.
15. 43/2000. 16. 227/2000. 17. 1/400. 18. 439/625. 19. 19/400. 20. 9/160.
21. 687/20000. 22. 1033/20000. 23. 247/20000. 24. 1651/4000. 25. 3/20000. 27. 1/8.
28. 3/16. 29. 3/8. 30. 393/800. 31. 5/8. 32. 81/75. 33. 1 23/500. 34. 3 41/...
35. 5/12. 36. 3/800. 37. 753/10000. 38. 3219/5000. 39. 17/12000. 40. 12 153/1600.
41. 22 43/60. 42. 43 437/500.

Page 150. — 8. .6. 9. .25. 10. .375. 11. .8. 12. .75. 13. .15.
14. .56. 15. .4. 16. .333 1/3. 17. .555 5/9. 18. .24. 19. .57 1/7.
20. .923 1/13. 21. .533 1/3. 22. .2916 2/3. 23. 1.5. 24. .055 5/9. 25. .12.
26. .1875. 27. .735 5/17. 28. .545 5/11. 29. .204. 30. .056. 31. .35.
32. .45. 33. .16666+. 34. .25. 35. .42857+. 36. .8169+.
37. .98666+. 38. 1.45454+. 39. 12.5. 40. 18.75. 41. 24.6.
42. .25. 43. .04761+. 44. 37.5. 45. .4525. 46. 16.4444+.
47. 48.53. 48. .23625. 49. 60.08. 50. .0001733+. 51. 513.00666+.
52. 75.0005.

Page 151. — 2. 52.234. 3. 95.7953. 4. 42.2717. 5. 9.88.
6. 9.5824. 7. 54.4174. 8. 138.8875. 9. 109.185. 10. 294.534.
11. 247.59. 12. 126.7814. 13. 535.12112. 14. 260.6319605.
15. $234.15. 16. $343.10. 17. $205.56 1/4. 18. $2020.78 3/4.
19. 2.775 tons.

Page 152. — 20. $38.50. 21. 39.385 cords. 22. 120115.054048.
23. $102.50. 24. 2301.9779. 25. $11.58. 26. 65.09895. 27. $32,653.21.
28. $11,218.03.

Page 153. — 2. .219. 3. .1682. 4. 2.3038. 5. 2.2215. 6. 12.2124.
7. 305.09746. 8. 16.763807. 9. 106.1226. 10. 18.332. 11. 11.079.
12. 230.25. 13. 158.846. 14. 665.8794. 15. 646.63. 16. 999.999.
17. $25.915. 18. $27.17. 19. $35.67. 20. $25.60. 21. $86.25.
22. $58.25. 23. $9.96. 24. $99.62 1/2. 25. $181.84 1/4. 26. $50.22 1/4.
27. $221.59 1/4. 28. 1433.525 T.

Page 154. — 29. $58.88. 30. 484.006651. 31. $2.17. 32. $10.13.
33. $2566.74. 34. 147.875 bbl. 35. .621. 36. $4.10 1/2. 37. $274,741.89.
38. $3,395.03.

Page 155. — 2. .08. 3. 2.304. 4. 4.410. 5. .2795.

Page 156. — 6. 160.08. 7. .23328. 8. 25.752. 9. 1.152. 10. .4.
11. 3.8. 12. 10.692. 13. .1785. 14. 58.05. 15. 386.4. 16. 74.375.
17. .024288. 18. 1199. 19. 21.528. 20. 29.495. 21. .3136.
22. 46.875. 23. 197.775. 24. 2.25225. 25. 151.75836. 26. 272.80767.
27. 393.225. 28. 27. 29. .825. 30. 2.048. 31. .7272. 32. 1.15.

33. 24.869. **34.** 1714.0102. **35.** 76.327. **36.** 19,135.97504. **37.** .00001032. **38.** 5.251. **39.** 429.66. **40.** 30,574.45. **41.** 1331.34945. **42.** 732.09636. **43.** .0063612. **45.** 583.6. **46.** 1683.4. **47.** 95,817. **48.** 373,186. **49.** 77.12. **50.** 148.11. **51.** 2963.5. **52.** 35,682. **53.** 128,509.2. **54.** 3,505,692. **55.** 4,579,880. **56.** 4880.556.

Page 157. — **57.** $\$30.81\frac{1}{4}$. **58.** $\$22.343\frac{3}{4}$. **59.** \$8238.75. **60.** 818.75 yd. **61.** 13,599.1 tons. **62.** \$19.295. **63.** $\$3.26\frac{1}{4}$. **64.** \$305.50. **65.** \$27.595. **66.** \$31.155.

Page 159. — **2.** 1.39. **3.** 21.5434+. **4.** .25. **5.** .25. **6.** 42.8. **7.** .0005. **8.** 16.89513+. **9.** 87.5. **10.** .00365. **11.** .763. **12.** 356.11111+. **13.** 30.2. **14.** 2.13. **15.** 12.24. **16.** 1485.60159+. **17.** .15. **18.** 3650. **19.** 73.21. **20.** 27,500. **21.** .475. **22.** 2643.6923+. **23.** .21. **24.** .916. **25.** 12310.7. **26.** .027. **27.** 790. **28.** .0066. **29.** .01. **30.** 100. **31.** .00005. **32.** 6000. **33.** 360. **34.** 7580. **35.** .0000561.

Page 160. — **37.** 3.3. **38.** 2.4125. **39.** 1.91238. **40.** 2.4187. **41.** .0993405. **42.** .01529. **43.** .0023719. **44.** 5.322. **45.** 711.25. **46.** .072345. **47.** 2.31206. **48.** .00017216. **49.** .1073035. **50.** .206288. **51.** \$12. **52.** 5.557 + T. **53.** 17 harrows. **54.** 45 bbl. **55.** 128 doz. **56.** \$8.50. **57.** $88\frac{1}{2}$ bbl. **58.** 50 bu. **59.** 27 bureaus. **60.** 9 T.

Page 161. — **2.** 3,947,625. **3.** 2,382,999. **4.** 1,451,870. **5.** 42,117,840. **6.** 74,703,294. **7.** 40,844,133. **8.** 34,439,944. **9.** 50,320,032. **10.** 672,544,296. **11.** 860,796,984.

2. 215,334. **3.** 373,116. **4.** 1,585,557. **5.** 493,416. **6.** 1,670,559. **7.** 1,620,402. **8.** 723,114. **9.** 2,190,832.

Page 162. — **10.** 837,408. **11.** 2,149,888. **12.** 4,323,228. **13.** 8,049,776.

2. 95,600. **3.** 210,900. **4.** 114,900. **5.** 224,700. **6.** 146,600. **7.** 107,400. **8.** 81,550. **9.** 538,200. **10.** 2,448,500. **11.** 2,366,300. **12.** 321,000. **13.** 431,600. **14.** 515,500. **15.** 798,000. **16.** 315,000.

Page 163. — **2.** $\$26.73\frac{3}{4}$. **3.** $\$78.42\frac{1}{4}$. **4.** $\$5.77\frac{1}{2}$. **5.** \$69.60625 **6.** $\$45.93\frac{3}{4}$. **7.** $\$164.62\frac{1}{2}$. **8.** \$5.97. **9.** \$89.99375. **10.** $\$84.81\frac{1}{4}$. **11.** \$32.721. **12.** \$278.73. **13.** $\$47.81\frac{1}{4}$. **14.** \$52.32.

Page 165. — **2.** \$6.23. **3.** \$44.90. **4.** \$23.35. **5.** \$4.36. **6.** \$74.25. **7.** \$94.855. **8.** \$115.50. **9.** \$76.525.

Page 166. — **10.** \$130.075. **11.** \$34.50. **12.** $\$595.27\frac{1}{2}$. **13.** $\$574.86\frac{3}{8}$. **14.** \$446.93. **15.** \$37.70. **16.** $\$76.95\frac{5}{8}$.

1. 21 lb. **2.** 26 shovels. **3.** 58,317.798 gr.

Page 167. — **4.** 150 bu. **5.** \$10.626. **6.** $\$19.76\frac{1}{4}$. **7.** 21,504,200 cu. in. **8.** A, 135 A.; B, 225 A. **9.** 200 bu. **10.** .00144. **11.** 1,000,000. **12.** .001. **13.** 18 da. **14.** $148\frac{27}{35}$ bu. **15.** 315.75 mi. **16.** \$87. **17.** \$2268.895. **18.** \$11,377.

Page 168. — **19.** 578.31+. **20.** .33075. **21.** 5372.136 ft. **22.** 139.91 mi. **23.** .17899+. **24.** \$39.25. **25.** \$75. **26.** $\$19.86\frac{1}{4}$. **27.** \$3598.56. **28.** 1045.769 A. **29.** \$4.50 gain.

Page 169. — **30.** 102.722. **31.** \$5.375+. **32.** .677857+. **33.** .05903+. **34.** $69\frac{1}{8}$ C.; $\$293.78\frac{1}{8}$. **35.** \$14,061.921+. **36.** \$195.85 gain. **37.** $.053\frac{1}{7}$. **38.** \$110.10. **39.** $\$30.52\frac{1}{2}$.

Page 172. — **2.** 74 ft. **3.** 109 ft. **4.** $96\frac{1}{2}$ ft. **5.** $231\frac{1}{2}$ ft. **6.** 501 ft. **7.** $10,815\frac{1}{2}$ ft. **8.** $16,264\frac{1}{2}$ ft. **9.** 28,065 ft. **10.** 98 in. **11.** 124 in.

12. 210 in.　**13.** 5098 in.　**14.** 198,103 in.　**15.** 326,920 in.　**17.** 2 yd. 7$\frac{1}{5}$ in.　**18.** 2 yd. 2$\frac{1}{4}$ in.　**19.** 3 yd. 2 ft. 9$\frac{3}{7}$ in.　**20.** 4 yd. 2 ft. 10$\frac{1}{5}$ in. **21.** 106 rd. 3 yd. 2 ft.　**22.** 137 rd. 2 ft. 4$\frac{2}{7}$ in.　**23.** 177 rd. 4 yd. 10 in.　**24.** 186 rd. 3 yd. 2 ft.

Page 173.—26. 2 ft. 3 in.　**27.** 2 ft. 10$\frac{1}{5}$ in.　**28.** 1 ft. 10$\frac{1}{2}$ in. **29.** 2 ft. 7$\frac{1}{2}$ in.　**30.** 2 yd. 2$\frac{1}{4}$ in.　**31.** 3 yd. 1 ft. 7.71 in.　**32.** 232 rd. **33.** 312 rd.

Page 174.—2. 6 rd. 3 yd. 2 ft.　**3.** 21 rd. 2 yd. 2 ft.　**4.** 1 mi. 138 rd. 1 yd.　**5.** 9 mi. 190 rd. 5 yd.　**6.** 24 mi. 58 rd. 1 yd.　**7.** 1 mi. 128 rd. 2 yd. 1 ft. 4 in.　**8.** 1 mi. 167 rd. 2 ft.　**9.** 14 mi. 106 rd. 3 yd. 2 ft.　**10.** 55 mi. 123 rd. 3 yd. 1 ft. 6 in.　**11.** 18 mi. 225 rd. 3 yd. 2 ft. 6 in.　**12.** 56 mi. 261 rd. 3 yd. 1 ft. 6 in.　**13.** 6 mi. 229 rd. 3 yd. 2 ft. 10 in.　**14.** 9 mi. 80 rd. 1 ft. 8 in.　**15.** 14 mi. 176 rd. 5 yd. 1 ft. **16.** 13 mi. 266 rd. 1 yd. 1 ft. 4 in.　**18.** $\frac{1}{22}$ rd.　**19.** $\frac{5}{132}$ rd.　**20.** $\frac{127}{3300}$ rd. **21.** $\frac{1}{216}$ rd.　**22.** $\frac{7}{3564}$ rd.　**23.** $\frac{1}{528}$ rd.　**24.** $\frac{1}{360}$ mi.　**25.** $\frac{1}{4864}$ mi. **26.** $\frac{11}{8000}$ mi.　**27.** $\frac{1}{14080}$ mi.　**28.** $\frac{1}{19800}$ mi.　**29.** $\frac{7}{105600}$ mi.

Page 175.—31. .7070707+ rd.　**32.** .81818+ rd.　**33.** .510101+ rd.　**34.** 4.631313+ rd.　**35.** 8.3484848+ rd.

Page 177.—1. 5904 sq. in.　**2.** 12,096 sq. in.　**3.** 26,496 sq. in. **4.** 318,816 sq. in.　**5.** 471,456 sq. in.　**6.** 4,704,600 sq. in.　**7.** 31,389,120 sq. in.　**8.** 51,945,300 sq. in.　**9.** 188,375,220 sq. in.　**10.** 8,032,115,520 sq. in.　**11.** 5 sq. yd. 6 sq. ft. 116 sq. in.　**12.** 5 sq. yd. 1 sq. ft. 96 sq. in. **13.** 6 sq. yd. 1 sq. ft. 80 sq. in.　**14.** 45 sq. rd. 9 sq. yd. 7 sq. ft. 108 sq. in.　**15.** 1 A. 90 sq. rd. 17 sq. yd. 4 sq. ft. 72 sq. in.　**16.** 1 A. 159 sq. rd. 28 sq. yd. 2 sq. ft. 36 sq. in.　**17.** 1 sq. mi.　**18.** 3 sq. mi. 503 A. 10 sq. rd.　**19.** 91 A. 16 sq. rd. 18 sq. yd. 1 sq. ft.　**20.** 18 sq. yd. 8 sq. ft. 22$\frac{1}{2}$ sq. in.　**21.** 100 sq. rd.　**22.** 25 sq. yd. 8 sq. ft. 51$\frac{3}{7}$ sq. in.　**23.** 16 sq. yd. 4 sq. ft. 54.18 sq. in.　**24.** 5 sq. ft. 36 sq. in. **25.** 126 sq. in.　**26.** 7 sq. yd. 2 sq. ft. 48$\frac{24}{25}$ sq. in.　**27.** 79 sq. rd. 6 sq. yd. 64$\frac{1}{5}$ sq. in.　**29.** $\frac{10}{3267}$ sq. rd.　**30.** $\frac{1}{1458}$ sq. yd.　**31.** $\frac{13}{96800}$ A. **32.** .632716+ sq. yd.

Page 179.—1. 26,040 cu. in.　**2.** 55,410 cu. in.　**3.** 1,897,344 cu. in. **4.** 2,842,560 cu. in.　**5.** 3,760,128 cu. in.　**6.** 456,192 cu. in.　**7.** 1,128,384 cu. in.　**8.** 27,035 cu. in.　**9.** 3 cu. yd. 5 cu. ft. 152 cu. in.　**10.** 2 cu. yd. 2 cu. ft. 12 cu. in.　**11.** 1 cu. yd. 13 cu. ft. 755 cu. in.　**12.** 15 cu. yd. 14 cu. ft. 538 cu. in.　**13.** 9 cu. yd. 3 cu. ft. 1702 cu. in.　**14.** 129 cu. yd. 11 cu. ft. 228 cu. in.　**15.** 23 cu. ft. 1080 cu. in.　**16.** 1440 cu. in.　**17.** 20 cu. ft. 432 cu. in.　**18.** 1166.4 cu. in.　**19.** $\frac{1}{45}$ cu. yd. **20.** .30144 cu. yd.　**21.** $17.65.

Page 180.—1. 1015 l.　**2.** 87$\frac{1}{2}$ l.　**3.** 140 l.　**4.** 764 l.　**5.** 2595 l. **6.** 4060 l.　**7.** 7575 l.　**8.** 97,620 l.　**9.** 1 rd. 12 l. 3.96 in.　**10.** 57 ch. 14 l. 2.26 in.　**11.** 15 l.　**12.** 3 rd. 5 l.　**13.** 54 ch. 14. 2 rd. 9 l. 3.96 in.　**15.** 1 ch.　**16.** 8 ch. 3 rd. 1 l.　**17.** 76 ch. 3 rd. 10 l.　**18.** 1 mi. 4 ch. 1 rd. 11 l.　**19.** 1 mi. 16 ch. 2 rd. 7 l. 5.56 in.　**20.** 1 mi. 75 ch. 3 rd. 12 l. 6.96 in.　**21.** $\frac{3}{640}$ mi.　**22.** 71$\frac{3}{4}$ l.　**23.** $\frac{7}{25}$ ch.

Page 181.—1. 50,000 sq. l.　**2.** 448 sq. rd.　**3.** 2 rd. 12 l. 3.96 in. **4.** 24,150,000 sq. l.　**5.** 310,320 sq. rd.　**6.** 6 sq. ch. 7 sq. rd. 125 sq. l. **7.** 89 A.　**8.** 6 A.　**9.** 3 sq. rd.　**10.** 192 A.　**11.** 3 sq. rd. 555 sq. l. **12.** 300 A.　**13.** 5 sq. rd. 250 sq. l.　**14.** 46 A. 8 sq. ch. 12 sq. rd. **15.** 13 sq. rd. 515 sq. l.

1. 828 gi. **2.** 884 gi. **3.** 986 gi. **4.** 1 qt. 1 pt. **5.** 510 gi. **6.** 1463 gi. **7.** 1 qt. 1 pt. **8.** 2 qt. 1 pt. $2\frac{6}{7}$ gi.

Page 182. — **9.** 24 gal. 2 qt. **10.** 13 gal. 1 qt. 1 pt. **11.** 5 bbl. 12 gal. 2 qt. **12.** 1 bbl. 30 gal. 1 qt. 1 pt. **13.** 10 bbl. 6 gal. 2 qt. **14.** 6 bbl. 17 gal. **15.** 14 bbl. 15 gal. 3 qt. 1 pt. **16.** 61 bbl. 4 gal. 2 qt. **17.** 25 bbl. 12 gal. 2 qt. **18.** $\frac{7}{80}$ gal. **19.** $\frac{3}{256}$ gal. **20.** .1875 gal.

1. 61 pt. **2.** 91 pt. **3.** 314 pt. **4.** $38\frac{2}{5}$ pt. **5.** 187 pt. **6.** 423 pt. **7.** $967\frac{1}{2}$ pt. **8.** 10 pt. **9.** 67 bu. **10.** 105 bu. **11.** 171 bu. 3 pk. 4 qt. **12.** 72 bu. 2 pk. **13.** 58 bu. 3 pk. **14.** 150 bu. **15.** 15 bu. 1 pk. 3 qt. 2 gi. **16.** 122 bu. 3 pk. 7 qt. **17.** 31 bu. 1 pk. **18.** $\frac{3}{640}$ bu. **19.** $\frac{5}{224}$ bu. **20.** .96875 bu.

Page 183. — **1.** 6812 oz. **2.** 6024 oz. **3.** 3497 oz. **4.** 12,000 oz. **5.** 11,460 oz. **6.** 120,130 oz. **7.** 176,392 oz. **8.** 67 lb. 8 oz. **9.** 87 lb. 8 oz. **10.** 66 lb. **11.** 1 cwt. 30 lb. **12.** 2 T. 2 cwt. 60 lb. **13.** 3 T. 15 cwt. 25 lb. **14.** 4 T. 1 cwt. 23 lb. **15.** 9 cwt. 24 lb. **16.** 18 T. 4 cwt. 50 lb. **17.** 30 T. 17 cwt. 31 lb. **18.** $\frac{1}{2240}$ cwt. **19.** $\frac{1}{2250}$ T. **20.** .00275 T. **21.** $\frac{29}{80000}$ T.

Page 184. — **1.** 1892 gr. **2.** 3658 gr. **3.** 5196 gr. **4.** 7 oz. 4 pwt. **5.** 50,778 gr. **6.** 262,887 gr. **7.** 10 oz. 10 pwt. **8.** 14 pwt. $6\frac{6}{7}$ gr. **9.** 4 oz. 20 gr. **10.** 5 oz. 6 pwt. 16 gr. **11.** 5 lb. 3 oz. 16 pwt. **12.** 18 lb. 7 oz. **13.** 2 lb. 6 oz. 5 pwt. **14.** 102 lb. 9 oz. 16 pwt. **15.** 658 lb. **16.** 40 lb. 3 oz. 18 pwt. **17.** 6 lb. **18.** $\frac{1}{640}$ lb. **19.** $\frac{79}{96000}$ oz. **20.** .27083+ lb.

Page 185. — **1.** 475 gr. **2.** 3220 gr. **3.** 89,000 gr. **4.** 141,255 gr. **5.** 12 ℔. 10 oz. 7 dr. **6.** 14 ℔. 9 oz. 4 dr. **7.** 38 ℔. **8.** 28 ℔. 8 oz. 1 dr. 1 sc. **9.** 2 ℔. 2 oz. 1 dr. 1 sc. **10.** 16 ℔. 3 dr. 1 sc. 15 gr.

1. $\$32.91\frac{2}{3}$. **2.** $\$26.66\frac{2}{3}$. **3.** $\frac{144}{175}$. **4.** $\$2.12\frac{4}{11}$.

Page 186. — **1.** 18,912 sec. **2.** 23,258. **3.** 469 hr. **4.** 17 hr. 8 min. $34\frac{4}{7}$ sec. **5.** 720 hr. **6.** 348 hr. **7.** 994 hr. **8.** 18 hr. 50 min. 24 sec. **9.** 1 da. 20 min. **10.** 21 wk. 5 da. **11.** 44 wk. 1 da. 16 hr. **12.** 47 wk. 4 da. 8 hr. **13.** 71 wk. 3 da. **14.** 6 wk. 3 da. 11 hr. **15.** 5 da. 15 hr. 15 min. 50 sec. **16.** 1 wk. 3 da. 1 hr. 4 min. 56 sec. **17.** 1 wk. 6 da. 8 hr. 30 min. **18.** $\frac{1}{2400}$ da.

Page 187. — **4.** 123,163″. **5.** 130° 9′ 20″. **6.** 1 S. 24° 20′. **7.** 128,478″; 67,034″. **8.** 136°. **9.** 105° 56′ 40″. **10.** 68° 58′ 20″. **11.** 88° 43′ 20″. **12.** 135° 5′. **13.** 108° 13′ 20″.

1. 2424 far. **2.** 12,743 far. **3.** 13,749 far. **4.** 19,803 far. **5.** 33,921 far. **6.** 43,383 far. **7.** 72,000 far. **8.** 7*s.* 6*d.* **9.** 13*s.* **10.** 9*s.*

Page 188. — **11.** £ 36 1*d.* 3 far. **12.** £ 89 18*s.* 10*d.* **13.** £ 4 1*d.* 2 far. **14.** £ 37 9*s.* 4*d.* **15.** £ 68 15*s.* **16.** £ 197 8*s.* 8*d.* **17.** £ 50 12*s.* 5*d.* **18.** £ 145 4*s.* 8*d.* **19.** £ 50. **20.** £ .175. **21.** £ $.283\frac{1}{3}$. **22.** £ 3.3208+. **23.** £ $5.41\frac{2}{3}$. **25.** $\$152.422+$. **26.** $\$118.803+$. **27.** $\$144.90+$. **28.** $\$249.651+$. **29.** $\$172.436+$. **30.** $\$89.868+$. **31.** $\$50.226+$. **32.** $\$172.314+$. **33.** $\$74.781+$. **34.** £ 81 4*s.* 3.9+ far. **35.** £ 50 14*s.* 9*d.* 3.1+ far. **36.** £ 117 15*s.* 10*d.* 3.3+ far. **37.** £ 126 11*s.* .8+ far. **38.** £ 48 14*s.* 7*d.* 3.8+ far. **39.** £ 87 14*s.* 7*d.* 3.1+ far. **40.** £ 66 12*s.* 6*d.* 3.8+ far. **41.** £ 205 9*s.* 8*d.* 3+ far.

Page 189. — **2.** 83 lb. 10 oz. 3 pwt. 3 gr. **3.** 186 bu. 2 pk. 4 qt. 1 pt. **4.** 80 T. 17 cwt. 6 lb. 5 oz.

Page 190. — **5.** 89 gal. 1 pt. 1 gi. **6.** 126 lb. 7 ℥ 6 ʒ 2 ℈ 8 gr.

7. 92 mi. 162 rd. 1 yd. 2 ft. 8 in. **8.** 145 sq. rd. 25 sq. yd. 2 sq. ft. 58 sq. in. **9.** £320 13*s.* 10*d.* 1 far. **10.** 1222 cu. yd. 2 cu. ft. 149 cu. in. **11.** 76° 23′. **13.** 23 wk. 6 da. 8 hr. 42 min. 40 sec. **14.** £9 13*s.* **15.** 13 cwt. 78 lb. $8\frac{4}{9}$ oz.

Page 191. — **2.** 3 lb. 10 oz. 19 pwt. 3 gr. **3.** £4 15*s.* 2*d.* **4.** 1 lb. 8℥ 2ʒ 1℈ 5 gr. **5.** 22 gal. 3 qt. 1 pt. **6.** 1 mi. 306 rd. 10 in. **7.** 9 gal. 1 qt. 1 pt. 2 gi. **8.** 3 hr. 40 min.

Page 192. — **10.** 2*s.* 1*d.* 1 far. **11.** 21 rd. 3 yd. 5.3 in. **12.** 5 da. 20 hr. 36 min. **13.** 14 bu. 2 pk. 5.232 qt. **14.** 167 rd. 2 ft. 6 in. **15.** 45° 49′ 15″. **17.** 32 yr. 2 mo. 15 da. **19.** 5 yr. 5 mo. 28 da. **20.** 36 yr. 16 da. old.

Page 193. — **2.** 102 bu. 2 pk. 4 qt. **3.** 115 lb. 11 oz. 16 pwt. 6 gr. **4.** £22 2*s.* 6*d.* **5.** 37 cwt. 26 lb. 12 oz. **6.** 389 gal. 1 qt. 1 pt. **7.** 35 bu. 2 pk. 7 qt. **8.** 7304 da. 20 hr. 16 min. 34 sec. **9.** 3 lb. 6 oz. 7 pwt. 12 gr. **10.** 404 bu. 3 pk. 5 qt. **11.** 103 cu. yd. 25 cu. ft. 432 cu. in.

Page 194. — **2.** 11 lb. 9 oz. 15 pwt. 18 gr. **3.** 16 T. 2 cwt. 38 lb. **4.** 13 hhd. 3 gal. 2 qt. 1 pt. $3\frac{7}{9}$ gi. **5.** 13 mi. 319 rd. 2 yd. 1 ft. **6.** 10 C. 39 cu. ft. 1100 cu. in. **7.** 2 lb. 7 oz. 15 pwt. $17\frac{3}{5}$ gr. **8.** 7 rd. 1 yd. 2 ft. **9.** 12 mi. 139 rd. **10.** 9 cwt. 42 lb. **11.** 2° 14′ 27″.

Page 195. — **13.** 7. **14.** 6. **15.** 15.083+. **16.** 25 da. **17.** 20 sacks. **18.** 9 bales. **19.** 78 hr. 18 min. 33.2+ sec. **20.** $60.85. **21.** 100 pickets. **22.** 187 medals. **23.** 160 ft.

Page 196. — **1.** $$\!.83\frac{3}{4}$. **2.** $2.28. **3.** 93 boxes. **4.** $3.70. **5.** $7\frac{2}{3}$ bu. **6.** 500 sq. yd. **7.** 30 ft. **8.** 41,775,360 ft. **9.** 5 ft. **10.** 271.32 rd. **11.** 47,322 in. **12.** 80 rd. **13.** 90 sq. ft. **14.** $35.20. **15.** $54.88.

Page 197. — **16.** 48 bars. **17.** $4281\frac{3}{37}$. **18.** 66 yr. 10 mo. 29 da. **19.** 35 C. 4 cu. ft. **20.** 179 A. 130 sq. rd. 2 sq. yd. 5 sq. ft. 36 sq. in. **21.** $6\frac{2}{5}$ qt. **22.** $\frac{5}{2016}$ lb. **23.** 43 sq. rd. 19 sq. yd. 2 sq. ft. 36 sq. in. **24.** 792. **25.** .01015625 bu. **26.** 84. **27.** $27\frac{73}{235}$ bbl. **28.** $\frac{3}{416}$ yr. **29.** $\frac{19}{47}$. **30.** .17708+ da. **31.** .005765625 gal. **32.** $\frac{1}{9}$. **33.** 2 oz. 5 pwt. **34.** 102 rd. 4 yd. 1 ft. 8 in.

Page 198. — **35.** $188.73. **36.** 47 cups. **37.** $53\frac{1}{2}$ bags. **38.** Lead, 1240 gr. **39.** Silver, $42\frac{1}{2}$ gr. **40.** 139 lb. 9 oz. 1 pwt. 16 gr. **41.** 1760 rails. **42.** $35\frac{5}{41}$ mi. **43.** $19,406.25. **44.** 280 rd. 2 yd. 4 in. **45.** $\frac{59}{4320}$ mi. **46.** $282.135. **47.** 25 bu. 3 pk. 4 qt. 1.92+ pt. **48.** $15.739+. **49.** $2680.

Page 199. — **50.** $56\frac{16}{19}$ mi. **51.** 31.858+ lb. **52.** 3° 17′ 55″. **53.** 76° 20′ 25″. **54.** $$\!259.87\frac{1}{2}$. **55.** 18 bu. 2 pk. $7\frac{1}{5}$ qt. **56.** 30.03+ ch. **57.** $16\frac{2}{3}$ da. **58.** $20.85. **59.** 4.447+ bbl. **60.** $1.43+. **61.** 34 spoons. **62.** 13,040; $74.98.

Page 200. — **63.** $$\!.39\frac{3}{8}$. **64.** $193. **65.** $$\!14.17\frac{1}{2}$. **66.** $2050.06. **67.** $12.87. **68.** 20 powders. **69.** 92 pills. **70.** $$\!.83\frac{53}{84}$. **71.** 4.528+ bbl. **72.** $54.85. **73.** 140 coins. **74.** 49 bags.

Page 202. — **2.** 3 hr. 5 min. 2 sec. **3.** 5 hr. 8 min. $11\frac{1}{5}$ sec.

Page 203. — **4.** 54 min. $31\frac{4}{5}$ sec. **5.** 50 min. 55 sec. after 8 o'clock. **6.** 23 min. $57\frac{1}{5}$ sec. before twelve. **7.** 1 hr. 17 min. $20\frac{2}{15}$ sec. **8.** 6 hr. 31 min. $18\frac{13}{15}$ sec. **9.** 9 min. $21\frac{7}{15}$ sec. slow. **10.** 53 min. 50 sec. after noon Jan. 1.

Page 204. — **2.** 49° 5′ 45″. **3.** 19° 3′ 30″. **4.** 15° 35′. **5.** 22° 30′. **6.** 10° 53′. **7.** 73° 54′ 25″. **8.** 122° 24′ 15″ west. **9.** 76° 50′ west. **10.** East 23° 45′. **11.** 2° 20′ east.

Page 206. — **1.** 1 A. 20 sq. rd. **2.** 5 A. 64 sq. rd. **3.** 180 sq. yd.
4. $3555\frac{5}{9}$ sq. yd. **5.** $311\frac{1}{4}$ sq. yd. **6.** 10 sq. ft. $72\frac{1}{25}$ sq. in. **7.** 8294.4
sq. ft. **8.** 4319.84 sq. mi. **9.** 2236 sq. ft. **10.** $\frac{9}{10}$ A. **11.** $308.25.
12. 40 A. **13.** 120 A. **14.** $11,900. **15.** 24 yd. **16.** 40 rd. **17.** 5 ft.
18. 60 yd. **19.** 200 rd.

Page 207. — **1.** 460 sq. ft. **2.** 624 sq. ft. **3.** 705 sq. ft. **4.** 31,535
sq. ft. **5.** 48,500 sq. ft. **6.** $14,437\frac{1}{2}$ sq. ft. **7.** 2970 sq. yd. **8.** 46,750
sq. rd. **9.** 22 ft. **10.** 92 ft. **11.** $13\frac{1}{3}$ rd. **12.** 7 rd. **13.** 160 rd.

Page 208. — **1.** 180 sq. ft. **2.** 675 sq. ft. **3.** 518 sq. ft. **4.** 1161 sq. ft.
5. $1842\frac{1}{2}$ sq. ft. **6.** 500 sq. ft. **7.** $7\frac{151}{242}$ A. **8.** $677.30+. **9.** 364 sq. ft.

Page 209. — **1.** 130 sq. ft. **2.** 180 sq. ft. **3.** 342 sq. ft. **4.** $637\frac{1}{2}$
sq. ft. **5.** 2139 sq. ft. **6.** $9\frac{1}{5}$ A. **7.** $13\frac{3}{4}$ A. **8.** 336 A. **9.** $114\frac{3}{4}$ A.
10. $82\frac{1}{2}$ A. **11.** 80 sq. ft.

Page 210. — **1.** 110 ft. **2.** 242 ft. **3.** 198 ft. **4.** 154 ft. **5.** 264 ft.
6. 176 ft. **7.** 308 ft. **8.** 330 ft. **9.** 396 ft. **10.** 528 ft. **11.** 47.124 ft.
12. 62.832 ft. **13.** 75.3984 ft. **14.** 59.6904 ft. **15.** 91.1064 ft. **16.** 109.956
ft. **17.** 50.2656 ft. **18.** 78.54 ft. **19.** 97.3896 ft. **20.** 141.372 ft.

Page 211. — **22.** 4.8818+ ft. **23.** 52.2026+ ft. **24.** 101.2223+
ft. **25.** 135.5996+ ft. **26.** 213.2671+ ft. **27.** 304.1443 rd.
28. 381.9709+ rd. **29.** 533.4861 rd.

1. $198.937\frac{1}{2}$ sq. ft. **2.** 286.47 sq. ft. **3.** 113.0976 sq. ft. **4.** 7854
sq. ft. **5.** 32,592 sq. ft. **6.** 60093.66+ sq. rd. **7.** 42174.68+ sq. rd.
8. 45239.04 sq. rd. **9.** 12271.875 sq. rd. **10.** 104062.3584 sq. rd.
11. 8148.48 sq. rd. **12.** 94.5457+ A.

Page 212. — **1.** $42.93. **2.** 19.67\frac{1}{2}$. **3.** $27.77. **4.** $21.68.
5. $23.84. **6.** 8.82\frac{1}{2}$. **7.** $57.545.

Page 213. — **1.** $61.20. **2.** $72. **3.** 48 yd. **4.** $84 ; $88.08.
5. $48 ; $50.40. **6.** $49\frac{3}{5}$ yd.; $91.76. **7.** $64.59.

Page 214. — **8.** 22.12\frac{1}{5}$. **1.** 14 rolls. **2.** 7 double rolls.
3. 8 double rolls, 1 single roll.

Page 215. — **4.** 8 double rolls. **5.** 7 double rolls, 1 single roll.
6. $24.40.

1. $50. **2.** $29.70. **3.** $44. **4.** $117.

Page 216. — **1.** 2640 bricks. **2.** $62.524. **3.** $51\frac{13}{33}$ perches.
4. $86.88+. **5.** $708.48. **6.** $830.39.

1. $3\frac{3}{8}$ C. **2.** $3\frac{15}{64}$ C. **3.** $3\frac{7}{16}$ C. **4.** $4\frac{13}{128}$ C.

Page 217. — **5.** $4.49. **6.** 14.94\frac{3}{8}$. **7.** $14.355+. **8.** $12\frac{31}{64}$ C.
9. 60 C.

1. 15 ft. **2.** $17\frac{1}{2}$ ft. **3.** 24 ft. **4.** 15 ft.

Page 218. — **5.** 150 ft. **6.** 196 ft. **7.** 162 ft. **8.** $35. **9.** $21.60.
10. 1.18\frac{3}{4}$.

1. 12.053+ bu. **2.** 24.106+ bu. **3.** 52.231+ bu. **4.** 84.374+ bu.
5. 4.977+ bu. **6.** 77.343+ bu.

1. 14 bbl. 7.8 gal. **2.** 13 bbl. 9.4 gal.

Page 219. — **3.** 24 bbl. 18.2337+ gal. **4.** 49 bbl. 12.448 gal.
5. 1496.1038+ gal. **6.** 53.716+ bbl. **7.** 190.99+ bbl.

1. 48 bu. **2.** 70 gal. **3.** $68\frac{4}{7}$ bbl. **4.** $6\frac{3}{5}$ T. **5.** $6\frac{6}{11}$ T.
6. $16\frac{16}{23}$ T.; $16\frac{16}{35}$ T.; 16 T.

Page 224. — **1.** 158.33\frac{1}{3}$. **2.** 14 da. **3.** $213. **4.** 665 mi.
5. 3360 bu. **6.** 60 A. **7.** $83.16. **8.** 10 men.

Page 225. — **9.** $13.32. **10.** $6461.53. **11.** $108\frac{1}{3}$ A. **12.** $162.71. **13.** 52 wk. **14.** 14 kegs. **15.** $68.57. **16.** $50,575; $57,800. **17.** $97.849+. **18.** $51\frac{1}{2}$ lb. **19.** $22\frac{9}{35}$ T. **20.** $90\frac{2}{3}$ A. **21.** E, 13,910 A.; F, 12,840 A. **22.** A, 40,327 lb.; B, 51,849 lb.; C, 5761 lb.

Page 226. — **23.** $440\frac{1}{2}$; $482\frac{9}{12}$. **24.** $\frac{93}{328}$; $\frac{221}{328}$. **25.** $10,165, 1st; $10,326, 2d. **26.** $2300. **27.** 3726. **28.** 1771. **29.** $892.50. **30.** 160 rd. **31.** 40.287 bbl. **32.** $74.81\frac{1}{4}$. **33.** $98. **34.** $15. **35.** 2 cwt. 63 lb. $2\frac{15}{16}$ oz.

Page 227. — **36.** A, $12; B, $28. **37.** N, $140; M, $180. **38.** $28\frac{1}{3}$ da. **39.** $400; $500. **40.** H, $203; K, $290. **41.** 5 da. **42.** $146.40. **43.** $27.379; $47.621. **44.** $1.80 per day; $64.80, 1st; $73.80, 2d; $81, 3d. **45.** $3000.

Page 228. — **46.** $186.205. **47.** 24.674 A. **48.** A, $149\frac{1}{3}$ bu.; B, $186\frac{2}{3}$ bu.; C, 224 bu. **49.** $.7109+; $341.232+. **50.** $9000. **51.** A, $420; B, $547\frac{1}{2}$; C, $832\frac{1}{2}$. **52.** 833; 816. **53.** $10, sheep; $30, cow; $90, horse. **54.** A, $1166\frac{2}{3}$; B, $875; C, $1458\frac{1}{3}$. **55.** $840. **56.** $632.478+, A; $666.66\frac{2}{3}$, B; $700.854+, C.

Page 229. — **57.** $21.87\frac{1}{2}$. **58.** $7\frac{13}{16}$; $5\frac{5}{96}$. **59.** 60 sheep. **60.** $.60728+; $455.46+; $497.97+; $546.55+. **61.** $230.77; $369.23. **62.** $5433\frac{1}{3}$, 1st; $5033\frac{1}{3}$, 2d; $4533\frac{1}{3}$, 3d. **63.** $42.336; 7056 slates. **64.** $.8179+. **65.** $2952, D; $738, E; $246, F. **66.** $9856, cheaper.

Page 230. — **67.** $601.875; $802.50; $1003.125; $5.57 per day. **68.** $222\frac{2}{3}$ panels. **69.** $288.64; $335.87; $419.84; $519.55. **70.** 35 ft.; 11.1408+ ft. **71.** 12 men. **72.** 81 ft. 9.2+ in. **73.** 272 sq. ft. **74.** $400. **75.** $605, C; $670, D. **76.** $2400, daughter; $5600, son.

Page 232. — **19.** .0075. **20.** .006. **21.** .007. **22.** .0045. **23.** .00625. **24.** .0084.

19. $\frac{1}{160}$. **20.** $\frac{3}{400}$. **21.** $\frac{7}{1000}$. **22.** $\frac{11}{2000}$. **23.** $\frac{17}{2500}$. **24.** $\frac{49}{5000}$.

Page 234. — **2.** $146.31. **3.** $429.25. **4.** $2.882. **5.** $472.50. **6.** $2330. **7.** $44.10. **8.** 140 cows. **9.** 250 A. **10.** 2900 bbl. **11.** 207 sheep. **12.** $607.50.

Page 235. — **13.** 825 A. **14.** 250 boys. **15.** 39.37\frac{1}{2} T. **16.** $3966.25. **17.** 2.31 yd. **18.** $168.75. **19.** $9585. **20.** $708, expenses; $1092, saved. **21.** $12,857.14\frac{2}{7}$.

Page 236. — **2.** 50%. **3.** $33\frac{1}{3}$%. **4.** 25%. **5.** $16\frac{2}{3}$%. **6.** $38\frac{8}{9}$%. **7.** $66\frac{2}{3}$%. **8.** 75%. **9.** $66\frac{2}{3}$%. **10.** $33\frac{1}{3}$%. **11.** 30%. **12.** 150%. **13.** 40%. **14.** 25%.

Page 237. — **15.** 94%. **16.** $14\frac{6}{11}$%. **17.** 74%. **18.** $87\frac{1}{2}$%. **19.** $53\frac{1}{3}$%. **20.** $31\frac{1}{4}$%. **21.** $3\frac{1}{3}$%. **22.** $5\frac{5}{11}$%. **23.** $80\frac{439}{475}$%. **24.** $37\frac{11}{20}$%.

Page 239. — **2.** 425. **3.** 2400. **4.** 330. **5.** 430. **6.** 2394. **7.** 800. **8.** 1090. **9.** 1000. **10.** 1416. **11.** 4300. **12.** 192. **13.** 62. **14.** 464. **15.** 625. **16.** 519. **17.** 3000. **18.** $28\frac{1}{8}$. **19.** $9\frac{1}{2}\frac{1}{7}$. **20.** 4800. **21.** 11,000. **22.** 300. **23.** 1048 bu. **24.** $26,600. **25.** $4000. **26.** 1050 bu. **27.** 1475. **28.** $1200. **29.** $250. **30.** 1700 T. **31.** 116 mi.

Page 240. — **32.** $2610. **33.** $55\frac{1}{4}$ gal. **34.** $1485.60. **35.** 1984 bu. **Page 241.** — **2.** 500. **3.** 600. **4.** 600. **5.** 700. **6.** 400. **7.** 600.

8. 800. **9.** 1350. **10.** 496. **11.** 898. **12.** 310 sheep. **13.** $913.043.
14. 500 bu.

Page 242. — **15.** $27.36. **16.** $3801.23. **17.** $1480. **18.** $7400.
19. 558 bu. **20.** 7216. **21.** 3.63\frac{7}{11}$. **22.** $6300.

Page 243. — **2.** 360. **3.** 650. **4.** 610. **5.** 640. **6.** 126. **7.** 400.

Page 244. — **8.** $16.48. **9.** $1100. **10.** 400 bu. **11.** $39.
12. $76.25. **13.** $211. **14.** $5675. **15.** 980 men. **16.** $11,250.
17. 4760 rails. **18.** $424.

Page 247. — **1.** $7.3395. **2.** $420. **3.** $615. **4.** $374. **5.** $301.
6. $315. **7.** $4248. **8.** 2906\frac{2}{3}$. **9.** $100,625. **10.** $58.905.
11. $2382.125.

Page 248. — **13.** 10 %. **14.** 15 %. **15.** 25%. **16.** 20 %. **17.** 33$\frac{1}{3}$ %.
18. 50 %. **19.** 33$\frac{1}{3}$ %. **20.** 25 %. **21.** 15 %. **23.** $50. **24.** $18.

Page 249. — **25.** $1.12. **26.** $2000. **27.** $.25. **28.** $75.
29. $3228. **30.** $4375. **31.** $4400. **32.** $18,250. **35.** $35.60.

Page 250. — **36.** $1125. **37.** $212.669+. **38.** $113.70. **39.** $380.
40. $1089.20. **41.** $6790.50. **42.** $4740.932+. **43.** 14$\frac{2}{7}$ %.
44. $83,375. **45.** $1 per yd. **46.** $480 loss. **47.** 12 %.

Page 252. — **3.** $44.10. **4.** $18.70. **5.** $3277.50. **6.** $7500.
7. 8552 bu. 1 pk. 7.3 qt. **8.** 2698.31\frac{1}{4}$.

Page 253. **9.** $4506.341+. **10.** 16,000 bu. **11.** $1793.60.
12. $3450. **13.** 3$\frac{1}{2}$ %.

Page 254. — **1.** $324. **2.** $516.80. **3.** $598.50. **4.** $570.96.
5. 7.08\frac{3}{4}$. **6.** $3.876. **7.** $208.25. **8.** $273.52. **9.** $203.853+.
10. $397.80. **11.** $9.60. **12.** $38.304. **13.** $301.53. **14.** 283.93\frac{7}{8}$.
15. $12.793+. **16.** $269.325. **17.** $289.80 ; 19$\frac{1}{2}$ %.

Page 257. — **3.** $47.4538. **4.** $105.8565. **5.** $58.49. **6.** $110.15685.
7. .0055. **8.** $185.835. **9.** .0065. **10.** $20.475, A ; $27.30, B ;
$36.3675, C. **11.** $6420.

Page 258. — **1.** $183.75. **2.** $59.85. **3.** $1161.207. **4.** $12.41.
5. $207.48. **6.** $1890. **7.** $16.65. **8.** $1848. **9.** $28.50.
10. $580.50. **11.** $852.

Page 260. — **1.** $233.75. **2.** $54. **3.** $525. **4.** $710.50.
5. 1$\frac{11}{84}$ %. **6.** $1271.605. **7.** $57.40. **8.** $30,000. **9.** $5.225.

Page 261. — **1.** $102.80. **2.** $191.75. **3.** $2011.95. **4.** $35.
5. $3739.20. **6.** $4208. **7.** $34.30.

Page 263. — **2.** $198.736. **3.** $109.06. **4.** $162.528. **5.** $423.572.
6. $60.12. **7.** $210.364. **8.** $161.245. **9.** $417.294. **11.** $144.343.
12. $133.3864. **13.** $117.607. **14.** $118.813. **15.** $210.0564.
16. $208.227.

Page 264. — **17.** $380.298. **18.** $150.191. **19.** $22.527. **20.**
$31.425. **21.** $45.143. **22.** $94.43. **23.** $119.028. **24.** $154.677.
25. $268.315. **26.** $541.477. **28.** $42.32 ; $355.82. **29.** $223.80 ;
$1159.55.

Page 265. — **30.** $35.18 ; $304.68. **31.** $47.85 ; $516.60.
32. $42.71 ; $316.79. **33.** $49.61 ; $414.11. **34.** $78.83 ; $364.92.
35. $95.72 ; $464.47. **36.** $100.14 ; $468.32. **37.** $265.66 ;
$846.56. **38.** $24.69 ; $300.29. **39.** $73.44 ; $541.69. **40.** $303.69 ;
$1118.96. **41.** $14.85 ; $140.65. **42.** $17.96 ; $202.46. **43.** $135.08 ;
$695.33. **44.** $62.93 ; $439.40. **45.** $254.92; $1254.92.

46. $1091.80 ; $5211.80. **47.** $366.05 ; $3546.05. **48.** $856.27 ; $3731.27, **50.** $462.03. **51.** $356.87. **52.** $442.19. **53.** $703.16. **54.** $736.61.

Page 266.—2. $75.38. **3.** $88.24. **4.** $58.92. **5.** $65.51. **6.** $121.11. **7.** $72.95. **8.** $191.94. **9.** $132.89.

Page 267.—10. $62.89. **11.** $142.14. **12.** $182.98. **13.** $417.03. **14.** $221.39.

2. $9.10. **3.** $11.24. **4.** $19.63. **5.** $22.52. **6.** $22.195. **7.** $19.60. **8.** $12.51. **9.** $109.50.

Page 268.—2. $22.89. **3.** $48.36. **4.** $43.14. **5.** $297.69. **6.** $54.04. **7.** $38.46. **8.** $66.30. **9.** $175.39.

1. $6.52. **2.** $7.49. **3.** $10.47. **4.** $12.41. **5.** $59.61. **6.** $260.69. **Page 269.— 2.** $1457.28. **3.** $1844.30. **4.** $2668.15. **5.** $2427.63. **6.** $3002.63. **7.** $3565.00. **8.** $5208.56. **9.** $5015.325. **10.** $7173.07. **11.** $13088.54. **12.** $10189.18.

Page 270.—2. $37.08. **3.** $83.055. **4.** $53.32.

Page 271.— 5. $113.205. **6.** $139.51. **7.** $140.72. **8.** $41.41. **9.** $84.28. **11.** $126.39. **12.** $76.21. **13.** $230.61. **14.** $351.50. **15.** $96.69. **16.** 373.525. **17.** $520.855. **18.** $645.19. **19.** $204.80. **20.** $125.05. **21.** $1467.43. **22.** $1417.96. **23.** $21.74. **24.** $362.65. **25.** $236.40. **26.** $254.68. **27.** $1898.369.

Page 275.— 8. $18.725. **9.** $27.23. **10.** $43.38. **11.** $52.08. **Page 276.— 1.** $251.54. **2.** $300.20. **3.** $1665.31. **4.** $433.54. **Page 278.— 2.** $366.02. **3.** $495.83. **4.** $452.41. **5.** $261.15. **6.** $520.81. **7.** $581.85. **8.** $1210.26. **9.** $1307.14.

Page 279.—2. 4%. **3.** 6%. **4.** 7%. **5.** 6%. **6.** $2\frac{11}{26}$%. **7.** 6%. **8.** $6\frac{1}{2}$%. **9.** 6%. **10.** 5%.

Page 280.— 2. 2 yr. 6 mo. **3.** 5 yr. 1 mo. 27 da. **4.** 2 yr. 2 mo. 18 da. **5.** 7 yr. 8 mo. **6.** 5 yr. 9 mo. **7.** 3 yr. 8 mo. **8.** 3 yr. 8 mo. 16 da. **9.** $14\frac{2}{3}$ yr. **10.** 12 yr. 6 mo. **11.** 3 yr. 6 mo. **12.** $18\frac{2}{11}$ yr. **13.** Oct. 1, 1891. **14.** June 24, 1875.

Page 281.—2. $255. **3.** $250. **4.** $219.30. **5.** $1292.21. **6.** $1279.32. **7.** $538.95. **8.** $3392.59. **9.** $2098.72. **10.** $297.19. **11.** $2273.39. **12.** $1693.33. **13.** $13,769.23.

Page 283.— 2. $551.91 ; $24.84. **3.** $730.42 ; $30.43. **4.** $395.93 ; $41.57. **5.** $584.32 ; $64.28. **6.** $1108.03, $91.97 ; $1122.37, $77.63. **7.** $1455.93, $152.07 , $1491.19, $116.81. **8.** $2488.42, $86.58 ; $2499.63, $75.37. **9.** $1331.23, $26.62 ; $1332.86, $24.99. **10.** $2822.20, $358.30. **11.** $148.65. **12.** $9.71. **13.** $440.47. **14.** $4.13.

	Time.	Term of dis.	Discount.	Proceeds.
Page 286.— 3.	May 4	55 days	$7.01	$757.74.
4.	Aug. 14	81 days	7.26	530.19.
5.	Dec. 5	34 days	4.82	845.68.
6.	May 8	26 days	1.02	234.66.
7.	Sept. 2	96 days	8.82	463.66.
Page 287.— 8.	Oct. $^{24}/_{27}$	47 days	6.53	993.47.
9.	Oct. $^{5}/_{8}$	64 days	11.92	1105.13.
10.	July $^{2}/_{5}$	46 days	1.05	135.87.
11.	June $^{16}/_{19}$	76 days	9.65	643.46.
12.	Nov. $^{1}/_{4}$	63 days	16.80	1183.20.

Page 288.—2. $600. **3.** $340. **4.** $1882.68. **5.** $1010.61.
6. $909.14.

Page 292.—2. $13,368.75. **3.** $7761.50. **4.** $2480.625.

Page 293.—5. $4065. **6.** $6502.50. **7.** $14,203.125. **8.** $1305.
9. $7766.875. **10.** $42,328.125. **11.** $14,562.50. **12.** $422.50.
14. 120 shares. **15.** 112 shares. **16.** 160 shares.

Page 294.—18. $300. **19.** $280. **20.** $1090. **21.** The
latter $20. **22.** $720.

Page 295.—24. $12,195. **25.** $22,740. **26.** $27,309.375.
27. $19,125. **29.** 8%. **30.** $6\frac{2}{3}$%. **32.** $142\frac{6}{7}$%. **33.** 150%.

Page 298.—1. 48,600. **2.** $4896. **3.** $5600. **4.** $17,500.
5. $61\frac{1}{5}$%. **6.** $3041.25. **7.** $28\frac{1}{13}$%. **8.** $12\frac{1}{2}$%.

Page 299.—9. 10%. **10.** $12,000; $180. **11.** $1302.40. **12.** $7855.
13. $2\frac{1}{4}$%. **14.** $15,000. **15.** $12,580.15. **16.** .004 rate. **17.** $951.
18. $292.50. **19.** $185.79. **20.** $21,016.67.

Page 300.—21. $378.48. **22.** $180.78. **23.** $281.25. **24.** $10.96.
25. $167.05. **26.** $273.85. **27.** 8.33\frac{1}{3}$. **28.** $5715. **29.** $360.
30. $18\frac{2}{30}$%. **31.** Increased $120.

Page 304.—3. $1209. **4.** $1494.375. **5.** $805. **6.** $1581.60.
7. $472.98.

Page 305.—8. $588.45. **9.** $890.10. **10.** $1165.20. **11.** $551.42.
12. $1696.48. **15.** $2779.16. **16.** $1244.44.

Page 306.—17. $1811.32. **18.** $1991.04. **19.** $648.70.
20. $1027.57.

Page 307.—3. $2073.83. **4.** $1557.09. **5.** £400 13s. 8+d.
6. £589 18s. 1+d. **7.** £822 3s. 11+d. **8.** $968.99. **9.** $1518.34.
10. $1269.20.

Page 309.—2. A, $1600; B, $900; C, $700. **3.** A, $765.96;
B, $919.15; C, $714.89. **4.** A, $3490.91; B, $5585.45; C, $3723.64.

Page 310.—5. A, $1631.25; B, $1522.50; C, $2066.25; D, $1740.
6. A, 1833\frac{1}{3}$; B, 2166\frac{2}{3}$. **7.** A, $7507.50; B, $8872.50. **8.** E,
$1080; F, $1260; G, $1440; H, $1620. **9.** A, $1250; B, $1875;
C, $3125.

Page 311.—11. A, $840; B, $1152; C, $960. **12.** A, $1040;
B, $540. **13.** A, $19.20; B, $32; C, $76.80. **14.** A, $10,270; B,
$10,270; C, $5135. **15.** D, $218.18, E, $174.55; F, $87.27. **16.** A,
$990; B, $1485; C, $1155. **17.** A, $1242.69; B, $1257.31.

Page 318.—3. $200. **4.** $407.22. **5.** 12$\frac{6}{7}$ da. **6.** 67,200 ft.
7. 135 ft. **8.** $3.15. **9.** $175. **10.** 16$\frac{7}{8}$ bu. **11.** 65 bbl. **12.** 520 bu.

Page 319.—13. $56.59. **14.** 31$\frac{1}{2}$ yd. **15.** 10 men. **16.** 58$\frac{5}{6}$ ft.
17. 40 revolutions. **18.** 22$\frac{1}{2}$ da. **19.** 45$\frac{5}{6}$ da. **20.** 125. **21.** 20 da.
22. 20 h. 41.44 min. **23.** 2711$\frac{1}{4}$ bu. **24.** 214$\frac{7}{16}$ mi.

Page 321.—2. 9 men. **3.** 18 days. **4.** 216 men. **5.** $880.
6. 19,800 lb. **7.** 289$\frac{7}{9}$ bu. **8.** $685.71.

Page 322.—9. 21$\frac{3}{5}$ da. **10.** 8$\frac{1}{10}$ da. **11.** 750 lb. **12.** 21$\frac{3}{32}$ da.
13. 158$\frac{4}{5}$ da. **14.** 419$\frac{2}{21}$ yd. **15.** 27,600 lb. **16.** 18,750 lb. **17.** 21$\frac{1}{8}$ T.

Page 323.—3. 60; 150; 210. **4.** 50; 100; 150; 200; 250. **5.** 216;
144; 108. **6.** $480; $540; $576. **7.** $8400; $8750; $9000. **8.** Wife,
$60,344.82; each son, $43,103.45; each daughter, $34,482.76.

Page 325.—2. 169; 324; 441; 1296. **3.** 729; 3375; 13,824; 74,088.

456 ANSWERS.

4. 625 ; 1024 ; 2304 ; 4356. **5.** 10,648 ; 15,625 ; 157,464 ; 357,911. **6.** 256, 1296 ; 20,736 ; 130,321. **7.** 12,167 ; 27,000 ; 79,507 ; 421,875. **8.** 2025 ; 4761 ; 7396 ; 8836. **9.** $\frac{4}{9}$; $\frac{16}{25}$; $\frac{36}{49}$; $\frac{25}{81}$. **10.** $\frac{1}{8}$; $\frac{8}{27}$; $\frac{27}{64}$; $\frac{64}{125}$. **11.** 7225. **12.** 117,649. **13.** 1600. **14.** 125,000. **15.** 10,404. **16.** 42.25. **17.** .5625. **18.** .000125. **19.** .000016. **20.** 9.3025. **21.** $1\frac{44}{169}$. **22.** $\frac{625}{1225}$. **23.** $1\frac{681}{3721}$. **24.** $\frac{512}{729}$. **25.** $\frac{4913}{9261}$. **26.** $56\frac{1}{4}$. **27.** $413\frac{4}{9}$. **28.** $16.40\frac{1}{4}$. **29.** $12.2850\frac{1}{4}$. **30.** $25.2255\frac{1}{8}$.

Page 327.—**2.** 15 ; 36 ; 49. **3.** 105 ; 120 ; 216. **4.** 7 ; 12 ; 25. **5.** 27 ; 32 ; 42. **6.** 16 ; 12. **7.** 24 ; 12.

Page 331.—**4.** 55. **5.** 74. **6.** 98. **7.** 109. **8.** 115. **9.** 121. **10.** 145. **11.** 153. **12.** 204. **13.** 229. **14.** 278. **15.** 416. **16.** 43.6. **17.** .717. **18.** 9.89. **19.** .035. **20.** 9.469. **21.** 50.405. **22.** 531,441. **23.** $4\frac{2}{53}$. **24.** $2\frac{16}{343}$. **25.** $5\frac{12}{625}$. **26.** 49.5. **27.** $221\frac{5}{8}$. **28.** $2\frac{35}{886}$. **29.** 4.24264. **30.** 5.91607. **31.** 6.85565. **32.** 9.53939. **33.** 11.26942. **34.** 15.65247. **35.** 19.23538. **36.** 28.51315. **37.** 2.69258. **38.** .72525. **39.** .17606. **40.** 6.54980. **41.** 3.56195. **42.** 5.00749. **43.** .06831. **44.** .02108.

Page 332.— **1.** 85 rd. **2.** 80 rd.; 160 rd. **3.** 88 men. **4.** 972 yd. **5.** $40.50.

Page 333.— **7.** 41.56+ ft. **8.** 123.59+ ft. **9.** $210. **10.** 339.41 rd. **11.** 56 ft. **12.** 32.31+ ft. **13.** 142.13 ft.

Page 334.— **2.** 16 ft. **3.** 53.66 rd.; 40.24 rd. **4.** 18.178 rd. **5.** 480 gal. **6.** 9 : 36.

Page 340.— **5.** 38. **6.** 56. **7.** 74. **8.** 95. **9.** 145. **10.** 352. **11.** 507. **12.** 1231. **13.** 1596. **14.** 4567. **15.** 7894. **16.** 23.7. **17.** 3.04. **18.** .055. **19.** .0125. **20.** 1.2599. **21.** 1.81712. **22.** .7631 ; $\frac{18}{27}$; $\frac{54}{327}$.

Page 341.— **1.** 38 in. **2.** 14 ft. **3.** 3249 sq. in. **4.** 4 ft. **5.** 11 ft. 5.16 in. **6.** 11 ft. 10.77 in. **7.** $27.52. **8.** 13.55 ft. **9.** Rectangle, 169.616 sq. ft. greater.

Page 342.— **2.** 64. **3.** $32\frac{11}{27}$ lb. **4.** 803.52 bu. **5.** 2.38 ft. **6.** 3.76 in. **7.** $181\frac{100}{1331}$ lb. **8.** 5.73 in. **9.** 26 ft. **10.** Depth, 5.039 in.; diam., 11.654 in.

Page 350.— **1.** 15,378. **2.** 202,700. **3.** .00230728. **4.** .00413+. **5.** $1\frac{1}{4}$. **6.** $25.20. **7.** $143.38. **8.** A, $54 ; B, $36. **9.** $15\frac{7}{12}$ yd. **10.** $11.635. **11.** $4.38. **12.** $500. **13.** Girl, $1.00 ; boy, $.75.

Page 351.— **14.** 8 hr. 48 min. **15.** $4\frac{3}{37}$ da. **16.** $14.78. **17.** 150 oranges. **18.** $22,200. **19.** Wheat, 120 bu.; oats, 160 bu.; corn, 200 bu. **20.** 694 A. 74.78 sq. rd. **21.** $12\frac{1}{2}$ cords. **22.** $28,400. **23.** $26\frac{2}{23}$ ft. **24.** $50\frac{5}{7}$ oz. **25.** 1584. **26.** 690.

Page 352.— **27.** $12,480. **28.** $24,527.16. **29.** 44 ft. per sec. **30.** A, $55 ; B, $48 ; C, $52. **31.** $80.05. **32.** $1500. **33.** $13\frac{1}{3}$ oz. **34.** $51\frac{9}{41}$ da. **35.** $4.70. **36.** $147.06.

Page 353. — **37.** $40.33\frac{1}{3}$ loss. **38.** 165 ft. **39.** $.314. **40.** $180.29. **41.** 810 rev. **42.** 252 A. **43.** $1057.268. **44.** 24,897.6 mi. **45.** $2500.

Page 354.— **46.** 1734 sq. in. **47.** 19 horses. **48.** Wheat, $1.50 ; corn, $.40. **49.** $31.35. **50.** $21.60. **51.** $152.36. **52.** $46.20. **53.** $882.46. **54.** 3750 sq. ft. **55.** $106\frac{2}{3}$ acres. **56.** $16\frac{2}{3}$ yr. **57.** 30 ft.

Page 355.— **58.** $152. **59.** $106\frac{2}{3}$. **60.** 72.32 bu. **61.** Nothing. **62.** All, $18\frac{299}{300}$ da. ; A, $58\frac{87}{89}$ da. ; B, $70\frac{11}{89}$ da. ; C, $46\frac{74}{125}$ da. **63.** $19\frac{22}{49}$ bbl. **64.** $776.53\frac{1}{4}. **65.** 120 da. **66.** 30 min. **67.** $400 lost. **68.** 81 shares. **69.** $73.75.

Page 356.—**70.** $23\frac{1}{2}$ mi. **71.** $177.10. **72.** 24 min. **73.** 10° Centigrade. **74.** $9975. **75.** $1203. **76.** $454.20. **77.** 25.09 ft. **78.** A, $437 ; B, $414.

Page 357.—**79.** 12 oz. **80.** $20.003\frac{1}{3}$. **81.** $7210. **82.** 457.5736 acres. **83.** $.557. **84.** 32 oz. **85.** 299.025 A. **86.** 27 balls. **87.** 53 da. **88.** $2964.71.

Page 358.—**89.** 1st, $11,200 ; 2d, $11,025 ; 3d, $10,300. **90.** $$208\frac{1}{3}$. **91.** $61.60. **92.** $1775. **93.** $1148.35. **94.** $935.55. **95.** 1st, $68\frac{4}{7}$ da. ; 2d, $53\frac{1}{3}$ da. **96.** $2875. **97.** A, $432 ; B, $405 ; C, $459.

Page 359.—**98.** $312. **99.** 120.68 ft. **100.** $390. **101.** 46 min. ; 5 times. **102.** Daughter, $813.38 ; son, $686.62. **103.** A, $450 ; C, $750. **104.** Lot, $1650 ; store, $2200 ; house, $7150.

Page 360.—**105.** $3435.255. **106.** 150 lb. **107.** 25 rd. **108.** 40 rd. **109.** Horse, $240 ; carriage, $270. **110.** $$66\frac{2}{3}$. **111.** 10%. **112.** $$3.66\frac{2}{3}$. **113.** 3 mo. **114.** 45.48 ft.

Page 361.—**115.** 1st, 162 ; 2d, 144 ; 3d, 128. **116.** 9.801 da. **117.** 24 ft. **118.** $320.185. **119.** 3 yr. 5 mo. 7 da. **120.** 6%. **121.** A, $1344 ; B, $1008 ; C, $840. **122.** D, $126 ; E, $120 ; F, $135. **123.** A, $7500 ; B, $6000 ; C, $5100. **124.** $15\frac{3}{5}$%.

Page 362.—**125.** 20 ft. **126.** 15.6 oz. **127.** 62. **128.** 57,330. **129.** A, $1425 ; B, $1900 ; C, $1425. **130.** $2600. **131.** Lost, $40 ; $6\frac{1}{4}$%. **132.** 4 hr. 56 min. 12 sec. **133.** 5 hr. 5 min. 32 sec. **134.** Gold, $42\frac{1}{2}$ gr. **135.** $.006\frac{1}{4}$. **136.** $500.

Page 363.—**137.** 27.64 ft. **138.** $233.99. **139.** $9.228. **140.** $64,931. **141.** 13.775 A. **142.** John, 81 da. ; Charles, $101\frac{1}{4}$ da. **143.** A, $3 ; B, $21. **144.** A, 50 da. ; B, 60 da. **145.** $74.07. **146.** $5000.

Page 364.—**147.** $361.07. **148.** .131 in. **149.** 50 min. **150.** $37\frac{1}{2}$%. **151.** 8 oz. 18 pwt. $14\frac{1}{3}$ gr. **152.** $550. **153.** $46,710. **154.** $22.22. **155.** $14.

Page 365.—**156.** $700. **157.** 21. **158.** $3206.63. **159.** Wheat, $2000 ; barley, $3000 ; oats, $4000. **160.** $557.244. **161.** Lost, $10. **162.** 150 lb. ; 90 lb. **163.** $600.

Page 366.—**164.** Better, $4650 ; other, $3100. **165.** $25.40. **166.** Former, $\frac{1}{3}$%. **167.** $25,000. **168.** $54\frac{22}{57}$%. **169.** 266,951.87 yd. **170.** A, $1200 ; B, $1600 ; C, $800. **171.** A, $7200 ; B, $6000 ; C, $5040.

Page 367.—**172.** 200 shares. **173.** Former, $\frac{25}{126}$%. **174.** Yes, $6\frac{2}{3}$%. **175.** $3827.96. **176.** Horse, $391.72 ; carriage, $195.86. **177.** $22.26. **178.** 4448 slates ; $211.28. **179.** $15. **180.** 1st, 3.68 in. ; 2d, 4.78 in. ; 3d, 11.54 in.

Page 369.—**2.** 2 mo. 29 da. **3.** 2 mo. 18 da. **4.** 1 mo. 12 da. **5.** 2 mo. 10 da. **6.** $3\frac{1}{4}$ mo.

Page 370.—**2.** June 20, 1887.

Page 371.—**3.** May 1, 1892. **4.** Jan. 24, 1892. **5.** Dec. 22, 1891. **6.** April 23, 1892. **7.** June 7, 1892. **8.** Aug. 16, 1892. **9.** $5\frac{1}{2}$ months.

Page 373.—**2.** June 20, 1892. **3.** June 15, 1892. **4.** July 6, 1892. **5.** $1198.80.

Page 375.—**2.** $329.90. **3.** $177.94.

Page 377.—**2.** $1.72. **3.** $209\frac{1}{12}$ ft. **4.** 5070.

Page 378.—**5.** 55. **6.** 198. **8.** 3775. **9.** 505. **10.** 330 mi. **11.** 78. **12.** $3360. **13.** $1287\frac{1}{2}$.

Page 379.—2. 2430. 3. 10,240. 4. $984.15. 5. $133.82. 6. $696.85.

Page 380.—8. 1364. 9. $4\frac{8}{27}$. 10. 4. 11. $\frac{382433}{20480}$. 12. $20,971.51.

Page 381.—2. $5304.387. 3. $3638.85. 4. $2046.58 ; $3022.35.

Page 382.—2. 6%. 3. 4%. 4. 7%. 5. 8%.

2. 15 yr. 8 mo. 18 da. 3. 14 yr. 2 mo. 12 da. 4. 10 yr. 10 mo. 3 da. 5. 11 yr. 2 mo. 18 da. 6. 10 yr. 4 mo., nearly.

Page 384.—3. $3488. 4. $8486.40. 5. $9810.81. 6. $30,780. 7. $1173.91.

Page 385.—2. $1609.49. 3. $3447.39. 4. $9710.35. 5. $17,465.74. 6. $1839.28. 7. $4060.55. 8. $4024.24. 9. $5827.34.

Page 388.—2. 28. 3. 17. 4. 72. 5. 63. 6. 28. 7. 544. 8. 73. 9. 15. 10. 42. 11. $\frac{3}{7}$. 12. $2\frac{3}{43}$. 13. $1\frac{2}{12}$. 14. $\frac{3}{4}$. 15. $\frac{4}{7}$. 16. $\frac{7}{12}$. 17. $\frac{3}{10}$. 18. $\frac{108}{269}$. 19. $\frac{31}{38}$. 20. $\frac{3}{47}$. 21. $\frac{39}{47}$. 22. $\frac{224}{225}$. 23. 48.

Page 391.—17. 1260. 18. 3584. 19. 6160. 20. 33,228. 21. 5616. 22. 156,240. 23. 7770. 24. 34,650. 25. 27,720. 26. 60 qt. 27. 270 in. 28. 180 min. 29. 60 yd.

Page 392.—1. $\frac{1}{24}$. 2. $\frac{5}{588}$. 3. $\frac{3}{175}$. 4. $\frac{4}{35}$. 5. $\frac{11}{75}$. 6. $\frac{7}{12}$. 7. 413 rails.

Page 393.—1. $\frac{105}{4}$. 2. $\frac{245}{12}$. 3. 231. 4. $\frac{64}{3}$. 5. $\frac{1008}{25}$. 6. 100. 7. $95\frac{1}{4}$ sec.

Page 396.—14. $\frac{149}{300}$. 15. $\frac{77}{300}$. 16. $\frac{59}{180}$. 17. $\frac{5579}{9900}$. 18. $\frac{9}{44}$. 19. $\frac{393}{1100}$. 20. $\frac{163}{1998}$. 21. $\frac{5617}{9990}$. 22. $\frac{125}{396}$. 23. $\frac{263}{2750}$. 24. $\frac{299}{30300}$. 25. $\frac{385277}{999900}$.

Page 399.—2. 110,244 ; 141,421 ; 110,333. 3. 21,024 ; 25,643 ; 15,316. 4. 331,223 ; 1,110,333 ; 330,032. 5. 3701 ; $4t63$; $403t$.

2. 4354 ; 731 ; 4858 ; 12,884. 3. 492 ; 33,511 ; 2714 ; 5534. 4. 3549 ; 76,295 ; 8831 ; 53,123.

1. $30,333_5$. 2. $30,314_7$. 3. $27,564_9$. 4. $24,564_7$. 5. $31,650_8$. 6. $2,034,431_5$.

Page 405.—1. 31.416 sq. ft. 2. 40 sq. ft. 3. 144 sq. ft. 4. 37.6992 sq. ft.

Page 406.—1. 540 sq. ft. 2. 376.992 sq. ft. 3. 628.32 sq. ft. 4. $64. 5. 89.5356 sq. ft. 6. 400 sq. ft. 7. 75.3984 sq. ft. 8. 157.08 sq. ft.

Page 407.—1. 251.328 sq. ft. 2. 3000 sq. ft. 3. $5.654. 4. 340 sq. ft. 5. $33.68.

1. 4.908 sq. ft. 2. 1.396 sq. ft. 3. 26.50+ sq. in. 4. 45.836 sq. ft.

Page 408.—1. 2 cu. ft. 2. 7.0686 cu. ft. 3. $9.00. 4. 462.852+ bu. 5. 2632.089+ gal. 6. $4013.80+.

Page 409.—1. 84.8232 cu. ft. 2. 18,000 cu. ft. 3. 12,440.736 lb. 4. 7296 lb. 1. $4666\frac{2}{3}$ cu. ft. 2. 236.405+ cu. ft.

Page 410.—3. 136.136 cu. ft. 4. 6415.718 gal.

1. 65.45 cu. ft. 2. 268.0832 cu. ft. 3. 14.1372 cu. ft. 4. 795.217+ lb. 5. 8.181 cu. ft. 6. 8181.25 cu. ft. 7. 29.4674+ lb.

Page 414.—1. .15675 Km. 2. 75.60 a. 3. 67.34 l.; .6734 Hl. 4. 43.628 g.; .043628 Kg. 5. 750 l.; 7.5 Hl. 6. .087637 sq. m.; .00087637 a. 7. 230.5 g. 8. 4500 Dg. 9. 1300 Kg. 10. 1000 Kg.; 1000 l. 11. 65.75075 cu. m.; 65,750.75 Kg. 12. 810 Kg.

Page 415.—13. 7210 g. 14. 920 Kg. 15. Former 17 ¢ per m. 16. 27.032 a. 17. 22.26 m. 18. 3120 l. 19. .90225 m. 20. 88.9042 Kg. 21. 225 Hl. 22. 337.5 g. 23. 10,944 l. 24. 30.8965 hr. 25. 292.948 Kg. 26. $32.266. 27. 6.592 cu. yd. 28. $29.918.

Page 416. — **29.** $243.036. **30.** 2.583 Kg. **31.** $27.215+.
32. 92.986+ Hg. **33.** 364.544+ revolutions. **34.** 21 Dl. is
12.476 gal. greater. **35.** 2.204+ lb. Avoir., 2.679+ lb. Troy.
36. 3785.37 g. **37.** $.997 per bu. **38.** .0929 sq. m. **39.** 9.29+ ca.
40. 95.9+ lb. **41.** 28.327 Kg. **42.** 3423.451+ m. **43.** 63.4+ gal.
44. $.949+ per lb. **45.** 4755.15 gal. **46.** $2.326— per bu. **47.** 88 Hg.
Page 417. — **48.** 580.598+ Kg. **49.** 2.5 sp. g. **50.** 30184 Dg.
51. $.171+ per qt. **52.** 26.729+ g. **53.** .245 m̄m. **54.** $1.92.
55. 13,500,000 g. **56.** 118.371+ g. **57.** .83½ m. **58.** $1.261872
per yd. **59.** 1.0416+ lb. **60.** 30.283— francs per gal. **61.** $1680.
62. 2.2046 lb.
Page 433. — **2.** $1685.66.
Page 434. — **3.** $952.64. **4.** $696.61. **5.** $399.59. **6.** $687.79.
7. $842.87. **8.** $2114.64.
Page 435. — **2.** $1881.38. **3.** $3884.60.
Page 437. — **2.** $267.32. **3.** $242.799.
Page 438. — **3.** $63.14. **4.** $4.05. **5.** $22,471.53 grand list, $.90.
6. $99.05.

Elementary English

LONG'S NEW LANGUAGE EXERCISES. Part I. . . 20 cents
LONG'S NEW LANGUAGE EXERCISES. Part II. . . 25 cents
LONG'S LESSONS IN ENGLISH (Grammar and Composition) 35 cents

A popular and carefully graded series, based on actual schoolroom work. Part I. for first and second years. Part II. for third and fourth year grades. The "Lessons in English" occupies the place of a primary Grammar and Composition.

LYTE'S ELEMENTARY ENGLISH . . . . . 35 cents

For primary and lower grammar grades. Divided into three parts, each representing a year's work.

MAXWELL'S FIRST BOOK IN ENGLISH . . . . 40 cents

Provides instruction for a three years' course in Language and Composition. Includes lessons, practice, and instruction in the elementary principles of the English language.

METCALF AND BRIGHT'S LANGUAGE LESSONS. Part I. 35 cents
METCALF AND BRIGHT'S LANGUAGE LESSONS. Part II. 55 cents

A graded series of lessons intended to cover the course in language in primary and intermediate grades. A study of literary examples is a marked feature of the second book.

SWINTON'S LANGUAGE PRIMER . . . . . 28 cents
SWINTON'S LANGUAGE LESSONS . . . . . 38 cents

The Primer, or Beginner's Lessons in Speaking and Writing, is designed for use in primary grades. The Language Lessons furnishes material for elementary instruction in Grammar and Composition.

Language Tablets and Blanks

NATIONAL LANGUAGE TABLETS . . . Per dozen, 90 cents

PATTERSON'S COMPOSITION BOOKS

No. 1.	Flexible.	36 pages .	.	.	.	Per dozen,	96 cents
No. 2.	Boards.	60 pages .	.	.	.	Per dozen,	$1.80
No. 3.	Cloth.	84 pages .	.	.	.	Per dozen,	2.70
No. 4.	Extra.	108 pages .	.	.	.	Per dozen,	3.60

WARD'S GRAMMAR BLANKS. 2 Nos. . . Per dozen, 90 cents

Copies sent, prepaid, to any address on receipt of price.

American Book Company

New York • Cincinnati • — Chicago
(82)

Carpenter's Geographical Readers

By Frank G. Carpenter

These new Geographical Readers are by far the most attractive and instructive books of their kind ever published. They are not mere compilations of other books or stories of imaginary travels, but they are the results of the author's actual journeys through the different countries, with personal observations of their native peoples, just as they are found to-day in their homes and at their work. These journeys and visits are described in such simple and engaging manner as to make the books as entertaining as stories, while conveying in this attractive way, useful knowledge and information. While they are written in easy familiar style, and in language not above the comprehension of children, they are strictly accurate in every detail and statement.

The books are well supplied with colored maps and illustrations, the latter mostly reproductions from original photographs taken by the author on the ground. They combine studies in geography with stories of travel and observation in a manner at once attractive and instructive. Their use in connection with the regular text-books on geography and history will impart a fresh and living interest to their lessons.

Copies of Carpenter's Geographical Readers will be sent, prepaid, to any address on receipt of the price by the Publishers :

American Book Company

New York • Cincinnati • Chicago

General History

COLBY'S OUTLINES OF GENERAL HISTORY

By FRANK MOORE COLBY, M.A. $1.50

This General History possesses certain features and advantages which distinguish it from all other text-books of its class. It gives in brief compass a comprehensive outline of the history of the whole world, but a larger proportional space is given to mediaeval and modern history than in most other text-books, in recognition of the relation of these later periods to the present status of the world's history. Written in a fascinating style it is not a mere collection of dates and names, but a vivid picture of the progress of civilization.

FISHER'S BRIEF HISTORY OF THE NATIONS

By GEORGE PARK FISHER, LL.D. $1.50

This is an entirely new work, especially prepared to meet the needs of high school students and general readers. It presents in compact form a graphic and impressive delineation of the world's progress in civilization from the earliest historical period down to the present time. It is by far the most attractive, impartial, and trustworthy text-book on the subject ever written.

BARNES'S BRIEF GENERAL HISTORY OF THE WORLD

By J. DORMAN STEELE and ESTHER B. STEELE. . . $1.60

A complete history of ancient, mediaeval, and modern peoples, as interesting to the general reader as it is valuable as a text-book. Whether considered for its choice of material, its teaching quality, its charm of style or its richness of illustration, this book stands preëminent as a manual for the class room or for the general reader. It is one of the best known and most widely used text-books on the subject.

SWINTON'S OUTLINES OF THE WORLD'S HISTORY

By WM. SWINTON. Revised Edition. $1.44

This is a work on ancient, mediaeval, and modern history, with special reference to the history of civilization and the progress of mankind. Its use will stimulate the student to wider historical reading and research.

THALHEIMER'S GENERAL HISTORY

By M. E. THALHEIMER. Revised Edition. . . . $1.20

These outlines of General History aim to combine brevity with a clear and simple narrative. The large number of sketch and colored maps and apposite illustrations constitute an important feature of the book, greatly adding to its value as a text-book or for reference.

Copies of any of these books will be sent, prepaid, to any address, on receipt of the price, by the Publishers:

American Book Company

New York   ◆   Cincinnati   ◆   Chicago

ELEMENTARY NATURE STUDY

Abbott's A Boy on a Farm . . . . **45 cents**
Two stories by Jacob Abbott, revised, and in new and attractive form. They are admirably suited for young readers. The illustrations are numerous and pleasing.

Bartlett's Animals at Home . . . . **45 cents**
The object of these stories is to arouse the interest of children in certain representative individual animals, and by so doing to awaken a love for Natural History in general. The illustrations are attractive and true to life.

Bradish's Stories of Country Life . . . **40 cents**
These recollections of a childhood spent on a northwestern farm aim to emphasize the attractiveness of life in the country, and to add to its charm by awakening an intelligent interest in its many activities.

Dana's Plants and Their Children . . . **65 cents**
A series of easy lessons on the wonders of Plant Life, as entertaining for children as stories. These studies in nature are not only interesting and instructive in themselves, but they teach the child to see, to think, and to observe for himself.

Holder's Stories of Animal Life . . . **60 cents**
This book is intended to serve either as a first book on Zoölogy or as a supplementary reader. The author has aimed to create in young students an enthusiastic interest in Nature Study by presenting some of the most remarkable phases of animal life.

Kelly's Short Stories of Our Shy Neighbors . **50 cents**
This book furnishes children with entertaining and instructive reading in the field of Natural History. It tells about the living creatures that dwell near us and yet are oftentimes strangers. It does this in the form of stories, written in a pleasing and attractive style, and copiously illustrated.

Monteith's Some Useful Animals . . . **50 cents**
The subjects here treated assist both in Nature Study and in learning to read. The moral lessons derived from the actions of animals are vivid and engaging, and much useful and interesting information is imparted.

Needham's Outdoor Studies . . . . **40 cents**
This book is suitable for pupils in the intermediate or grammar grades. May be used as a guide for field work as well as a reader in Nature Study, and it will pave the way for more advanced text-book study and for laboratory work in the higher grades.

Pyle's Stories of Humble Friends . . . **50 cents**
These stories are about animals and birds familiar to the children. They are simple in style and sympathetic in treatment. The many pictures, drawn by the author, are vividly illustrative of the incidents described.

Stokes s Ten Common Trees . . . **40 cents**
A series of simple nature lessons for young children, familiarly treating and giving a few definite impressions of what trees are and how they live.

AMERICAN BOOK COMPANY